(Courtesy *Astronautical Sciences Review*.)
An Astronomical Telescope in Space (See page 270).

ATOMS
TO GALAXIES

AN INTRODUCTION
TO MODERN ASTRONOMY

JAMES STOKLEY
MICHIGAN STATE UNIVERSITY

THE RONALD PRESS COMPANY , NEW YORK

Library of Congress Catalog Card Number: 61:6144

PRINTED IN THE UNITED STATES OF AMERICA

To Don
Whose generation
will begin to explore
the universe

Preface

Only a few years ago astronomy was largely regarded as something far removed from the lives of most people. To many, indeed, that was its great attraction. From Earth, with all its conflicts and disappointments, we could look into the skies where the stars and the planets moved serenely indifferent to us and our problems, distant and unapproachable.

Now man has taken his first halting steps into space, and will soon go much farther. He has extended his reach to the Moon and has put artificial planets into orbit around the Sun. He is listening for radio signals that might be sent by intelligent beings on planets of distant suns. New instruments, detecting both light and radio waves, are probing far out in the universe. Man has even been able to duplicate (unfortunately, for purposes of destruction) the process whereby the Sun keeps itself fueled. He seems well on the way to applying a similar method to produce power for his own use in virtually unlimited amounts.

The story is long—and one that will never be completed—but in these pages I have tried to give a few of the highlights as we see them today. Starting with the atom, nuclear energy, and radiation, we study the modern instruments—telescopes, spectroscopes, and radio telescopes—of astronomical research, the process the Sun uses to produce heat and light, and the movement of the planets of our solar system. We examine the Earth's structure, oceans, and atmosphere, and then "visit" the Moon, each of the other planets, and the Sun.

A study of the possible means of space exploration—some quite startling, but all under serious consideration by scientists—is followed by a discussion of our present knowledge of the stars, the space between stars, and the galaxies. After reviewing the various theories of the universe, from the one which placed the earth at the center to the one which postulates the continuous creation of matter, we speculate on the existence of life elsewhere in the universe and on the future of the Sun and Earth. Thus the horizon of the known universe is reached, a horizon that is ever receding as the power of astronomical instruments increases.

In writing this book I have had the cordial assistance of many people. In particular, I wish to express my gratitude to my former associate, Dr. I. M. Levitt, director of the Fels Planetarium of the Franklin Institute, for many helpful suggestions. Some of the figures have been reproduced from other books, with the kind permission of the publishers credited in the captions. The quotations in the text are gratefully acknowledged on the pages on which they occur.

JAMES STOKLEY

East Lansing, Michigan
    January, 1961

Contents

ATOMS
TO GALAXIES

1

The Universal Atom

Curious as it now seems, there was a time—only a generation or two ago—when the atom did not arouse fear in a large part of the population; when it was not a major concern of governments; when no international conferences were called to discuss the problems which arose from it. You heard about it in chemistry courses, but to most people it did not seem particularly to concern their future. But now, many wonder if it will allow us to have a future!

Yet the atom has always been important, for it is the building block of which everything is made. You are made of atoms, so am I. So is the Earth itself; so are the Moon and the Sun and the other more distant stars.

Atomic power stations are already in operation; splitting atoms of uranium provides energy which generates electricity to light homes and factories. In the future we will become increasingly dependent on such sources—or perhaps on another process whereby very light atoms fuse together into heavier ones and yield energy in the fusion process.

Terrestrial power stations deriving energy from such atomic processes are something new, but atomic power is not. Indeed, the world has never used anything but atomic power, although from a plant 93,000,000 miles away. This is the Sun—the ultimate source of energy behind all our conventional supplies of power: water power and the burning of wood, coal, or oil.

In view of this, it is small wonder that scientists have long conducted an intensive study of the atom. Such studies have already enabled them to reproduce the solar process on Earth. Eventually, as supplies of coal and oil are exhausted, we shall have to depend more and more on atomic energy.

Laboratory research, aided by huge accelerators or "atom smashers," has revealed much about the inner structure of atoms, but in many distant parts of the universe—in the stars and between them—matter is subjected to conditions that we cannot hope to duplicate here. Astronomers analyze the light and other radiations that come from stars to learn more of their nature and to apply the knowledge gained by the atomic physicists. But the exchange goes both ways. As the physicists correlate the information supplied by the astronomers with what physics has previously discovered, physicists too gain in understanding their problems.

Of course, atoms are important in more immediately practical areas. In theory, steel beams could be made many times stronger than the best yet produced by metallurgical science, if only we knew how to put the atoms together in the right way. For their action, drugs, too, depend on the way these building blocks are grouped into the larger units called molecules. Often a slight structural variation turns a useless or even a poisonous compound into a valuable cure for disease or into an essential component of our diet.

It is hardly too much to say that all science depends basically on the atom, a microcosm far smaller than anything that can be seen in the most potent microscopes. And if we are to understand the workings of the universe—the macrocosm in which we live—we need to understand the inner workings of the atom.

THE NON-SPLITTABLE ATOM

"Atom splitting" is really a contradiction, for the very word "atom" means something that cannot be cut. If it can be split, it's not an atom! Moreover, it cannot have any structure, for an atom, according to the original idea, is the simplest thing that can exist. If it has a structure, there must be something still simpler.

Philosophers of ancient times argued about what would happen if a thing were cut in half, then one of the pieces were cut in half, then one of these pieces were cut in half, and so on. If the knife were sufficiently sharp, one group supposed, this process could go on indefinitely.

But another group, the atomists, exemplified by Democritus, Leucippus, and others who lived in Greece some five centuries before Christ, had other ideas. They thought that, even if the knife were sharp enough, there would be a limit, with two pieces incapable of any further division. And because they couldn't be cut, they called them "atoms." According to the Roman philosopher Lucretius, who wrote about atoms in his poem of the first century B.C., "On the Nature of Things," they were "parts which themselves are partless."

However, Aristotle (384-322 B.C.) did not approve of atoms, and the idea lay fallow for many centuries. But in the sixteenth and seventeenth centuries the work of such famous scientists as Galileo, Descartes, Francis Bacon, Boyle, and Newton led to a rather general belief that atoms might exist after all. Then, in 1808, John Dalton gathered together these loose ends and introduced the basis of modern chemistry. He listed the elements, as he knew them, and showed that compounds are made of atoms of these elements, combined in simple proportions. Water, for example, contains two atoms of hydrogen and one of oxygen; thus the familiar formula, H_2O. But even to Dalton, atoms seemed devoid of structure, and this idea prevailed until the closing decade of the nineteenth century.

Since about 1890, however, a new concept of the atom has emerged. Even though its diameter is about a hundredth of a millionth of an inch, it is very complex, and the complexity increases with the results of additional research. Just as matter is constructed of the building blocks called atoms, so atoms are composed of still smaller units.

Basically, our modern atom is the one proposed by Ernest Rutherford in England and elaborated upon by the Dane, Niels Bohr. According to this idea, which has been modified in a number of important respects, the atom is built like the solar system. At the center, corresponding to the Sun, is the nucleus. Revolving around it, like planets, are one or more of the particles called *electrons*. These were discovered in 1898 by an English physicist, Sir Joseph Thomson. The electron is the unit of negative electricity. In fact, an electric current flowing along a copper wire is in reality a drift of loosely attached electrons from one copper atom to another.

At the heart of the atom—the "sun" around which the "planets" revolve—is the nucleus, which has a positive electrical charge; see Fig. 1. This neutralizes the negative charge of the planetary electrons, so the atom as a whole is electrically neutral. The nucleus must be a very tiny thing, as Rutherford showed in 1914, about a ten-thousandth of the diameter of the entire atom. Yet in this nucleus is concentrated the greater part of the atomic mass.

Rutherford also discovered the principal particle of which the nucleus is made, which he called the *proton*. This has a positive

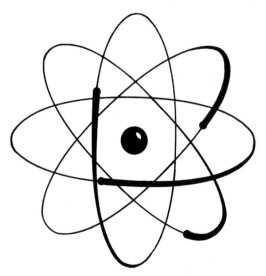

Fig. 1. The atom as usually pictured. This shows a small nucleus with electrons revolving in elliptical orbits. Actually there are no definite orbits; they are merely regions where there is a certain probability that an electron will be.

charge exactly balancing the negative charge on the electron. But in mass (or weight) the two particles are very different, for the proton is 1,837 times as massive as the electron.

The simplest possible atom, according to this concept, is one which has a single proton, as the nucleus, with a single electron moving around the proton. This is hydrogen, the most abundant element in the universe and probably the unit from which more complicated elements have been constructed.

ATOMIC BUILDING BLOCKS

Hydrogen can be built up. Add another proton to a hydrogen nucleus and there is a magical change. It is no longer hydrogen but has turned into helium, the light gas used to fill balloons. Add another proton to the helium atom's nucleus; now it is lithium, a light metal. Add one more and it becomes another metal, called beryllium. With additional protons, it successively becomes boron, carbon, nitrogen, and oxygen.

Of course, as soon as the second proton is added to make helium, there is twice as much positive electrical charge; so you would have to put on another negative charge, in the form of an electron, to neutralize the proton. In any normal atom there are just as many electrons as there are protons in the nucleus. And it is the number of protons that determines what element the atom is. Any atom with one proton in the nucleus must be hydrogen, any with two is helium, any with six is carbon, and any with 92 is uranium, the heaviest that occurs in nature. Still heavier are the man-made trans-Uranium elements, of which nobelium, with 102 protons, is the heaviest thus far.

But this isn't the whole story. Since the time of Dalton, chemists have been busily weighing atoms. The uranium atom doesn't weigh 92 times as much as one of hydrogen; it weighs about 238 times as much. So there must be something else in these atomic nuclei; some sort of "ballast," which gives added weight without affecting the charge.

Physicists at one time thought that additional protons in the nucleus accounted for the extra weight. For each proton above the number needed to make an atom the element that it was, there was an electron in the nucleus which neutralized the proton. Experiments showed that electrons could be emitted from the nucleus, which lent support to the idea that they had been there already.

But, with further study, some very good reasons were advanced to show that there was no place in the nucleus for electrons. And if there wasn't, there couldn't be any extra protons. So what, then, was the ballast?

Ernest Rutherford thought it might be a new particle without any electrical charge. He tentatively called this particle a *neutron*. In 1930 he and Sir James Chadwick searched for it, in vain. But two years later Chadwick, now on his own, did discover it—and won the Nobel prize in physics as a result. No longer were electrons needed in the nucleus. Now we believe that the nucleus contains the same number of protons as the atomic number (designated by the letter Z) of the element. In all nuclei, except that of ordinary hydrogen, there are also neutrons. These add weight without increasing the charge.

Thus there are two important data that we wish to know about an atomic nucleus. One is the atomic number (Z), the number of protons; the other is the mass number (A), the total number of particles, both protons and neutrons. Any atom with the same Z must be the same element. If Z is 6, the atom must be carbon; 26 must be iron; 50 must be tin; and 92 must be uranium.

Even with Z the same, A may vary. All nuclei of tin atoms have 50 protons. But, in addition, there may be as few as 62 neutrons, or as many as 74. Actually there are ten varieties of tin nuclei—or ten *isotopes*—with masses ranging from 112 to 124. Ordinary tin consists of about a third of the 120 isotope, along with smaller amounts of the others, down to about a third of one per cent of tin 115.

Ordinary iron consists of four isotopes. About 92 per cent is iron 56. Similarly, most natural elements combine several isotopes in varying proportions.

So we have, indeed, gotten far away from the old idea of a structureless atom, the ultimate particle, incapable of division. And it turns out that the atom can be split after all, thus contradicting the original meaning of the word.

RADIOACTIVITY

Around the beginning of the twentieth century, physicists found that some atoms break down spontaneously in the process called *radioactivity*. The original discovery was that of a French scientist, Antoine Henri Becquerel, who found that uranium yielded rays capable of passing through an opaque screen and making an image on a photographic plate in much the same manner as the X-rays which Roentgen had discovered in Germany shortly before.

Pierre Curie and his wife Marie, who were working in Becquerel's laboratory, then discovered radium, which is even more active than uranium. Still other radioactive elements were found: thorium and polonium. And when radium was left by itself, sealed in a glass tube, a new radioactive gas appeared.

In 1902, Rutherford and Frederick Soddy proposed the radical idea that atoms were not necessarily permanent. Somehow, they said, radium changes into another element, called *radium emanation* or *radon,* which was the radioactive gas that had been observed earlier. Both of these elements are steps in a series which starts with uranium and ends—after 15 stages—with an isotope of lead.

This isotope is of mass number 206; it constitutes a minute proportion of ordinary lead.

Despite strong opposition from conservative scientists, who didn't believe that atoms could change, the idea of radioactive disintegration finally prevailed. But it wasn't until much later, after Rutherford had discovered the proton, that physicists found what happens in the process.

Radium is a metal, something like barium and calcium, while radon is a gas belonging to the same group of elements as helium and neon. The atomic number of radium is 88 and of radon 86. Its mass number, however, is 4 units less than radium; 222, instead of 226. This means that when radium changes into its emanation, two protons and two neutrons must be removed.

The earlier work on the radioactive process had demonstrated that in many steps in the series, including that from radium to radon, an *alpha particle* was emitted. This proved to be the nucleus of a helium atom, and it does consist of two protons and two neutrons.

Proton and neutron emission is not the only way in which one element can change to another. Consider the beginning of the radium series. In the first stage, uranium changes into an isotope of thorium by emitting an alpha particle. Then the thorium isotope gives off a beta ray, which is really an electron. This ray, of course, comes from the nucleus without involving the orbital electrons of the atom, since all these changes are nuclear. Where, then, does this electron come from? Didn't we just say that after Chadwick discovered the neutron, the idea of electrons in the nucleus was abandoned?

Neutrons occur not only in the atomic nucleus; they can occur alone. But alone, they are not stable. In a short time, a neutron spontaneously turns into a proton and an electron, and apparently the same thing can happen to a neutron in the nucleus. The electron comes off, the proton stays behind. With one more proton than there was before, the atomic number has increased, although the mass hasn't changed appreciably. It has become an atom of the next element up the list.

This, then, is what happens in the change from the second to the third stage in the radium series: Thorium has an atomic number of 90, and the particular isotope involved here has a mass number of 234. The emission of a beta ray (an electron) causes the loss of one negative charge, which is the same as the addition of a positive charge, or a proton. Thus stage three, which is an element called *protactinium,* has an atomic number of 91, although the mass is still 234.

GAMMA RADIATION

In addition to alpha particles and beta rays, there is a third kind of radiation which is emitted at certain steps in the series. This radiation consists of gamma rays, which are highly penetrating, like X-rays of very high energy. Gamma rays are not as directly involved in the nuclear alterations as the other two rays but are a secondary effect. The radon nucleus, when first formed, is in a highly excited state. As the particles in the nucleus settle down, gamma radiation occurs.

The time required for such changes varies greatly. A particular uranium nucleus may change into thorium in the next second—or it may not do so for millions of years. It's like predicting a person's death. He may die today, or he may live to a hundred. However, insurance companies have tables which show accurately what proportion of a population of a certain age will die this year or next, and this enables the companies to set their premiums.

Similarly with radioactive atoms: we do not know when one uranium nucleus is going to change, but we do know that in the next second about one two-hundred quadrillionth of the nuclei in a lump of the element will make the alteration. At this rate, after 4,500 million years, just half of any given amount of uranium 238 will have changed to thorium.

This 4,500-million-year period is called the *half-life* of uranium, and it is one of the longest of any of the radioactive elements. For radium it is 1,690 years, and for radon 3.82 days. Polonium 214, the eleventh stage in this series, has a half-life of less than a five-thousandth of a second.

In addition to the one headed by uranium, there are three other radioactive series. Two of these still exist naturally. The other probably occurred in nature at an earlier stage in the Earth's history, but its half-lives are so short that practically all of the elements have reached the end of the series. Some of these elements, however, can be made artificially, and with them physicists have been able to study the series.

After radioactivity was discovered, scientists tried in many ways to slow down the process—or to speed it up. But nothing they could do seemed to affect it, nor could they produce nuclear changes artificially—not until 1919. Again we meet Ernest Rutherford, for in that year, in his laboratory at Cambridge University, he produced the first "man-made" change of one element into another.

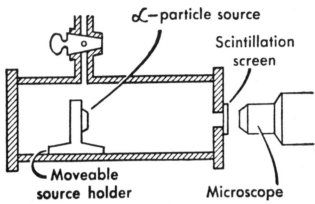

Fig. 2. Rutherford's experiment. A source of alpha particles (such as radium) was placed too far away from the scintillation screen for the particles to reach it, yet scintillations were observed. The alpha particles had hit nuclei of nitrogen (which the tube contained), changing them to nuclei of oxygen and liberating protons, or hydrogen nuclei. These caused the scintillations. (By permission from *First Principles of Atomic Physics*, by R. F. Humphreys and Robert Berings. Copyright, 1950, Harper & Bros., New York.)

He bombarded nitrogen with alpha particles from radium. Occasionally one of the protons in the particle would stick to a nitrogen nucleus, increasing its atomic number from 7 to 8; in other words, changing nitrogen to oxygen; see Fig. 2. Transmutation of elements, which the medieval alchemists had sought to accomplish when they tried to change lead into gold, had finally been achieved.

Actually, however, this was not artificial transmutation, because the bullets he used to fire at the nitrogen atoms were alpha particles, produced from the natural disintegration of radium. No doubt it often happened, in nature, that such an alpha particle hit a nitrogen atom in the air, and turned the atom to oxygen. What Rutherford did was to perform the experiment in the laboratory where he could observe it.

TRANSMUTATION ACHIEVED

But in 1932, in the same Cambridge University laboratory, Sir John D. Cockroft and E. T. S. Walton accelerated protons artificially, to energies of 600,000 volts, and fired them at lithium. This element has an atomic number of 3 and a mass number of 7. When a proton hit and remained with the nucleus, these numbers increased to 4 and 8, respectively, creating a very unstable isotope of beryllium. The nucleus would immediately split into two equal parts, each with two protons and two neutrons, which are alpha particles—helium nuclei. Thus, by truly artificial means, they had transmuted lithium to helium.

The energies of such particles, used in "atom-smashing" experiments, are generally measured in *electron volts*. One electron volt is the energy gained by an electron which has passed through a potential difference of 1 volt. It is abbreviated ev. Kev (for kilo electron volt) equals 1,000 ev, while Mev is used for *million electron volt* and, in the United States, Bev for *billion electron volt*. In England, where a billion is not a thousand million but a million million, they use "Gev" for 1,000 million ev. The letter G stands for *gigas,* meaning giant.

The Cockroft-Walton experiment had another important aspect, in addition to being the first successful effort to change atoms by artificial means. Some years before, as part of the theory of relativity, Albert Einstein had stated that mass and energy are equivalent; that one could be converted into the other. The relation could be expressed, he said, by the formula $E = mc^2$. E is the energy, in the units called *ergs;* m the mass, in grams; and c the velocity of light, which is about 30 billion centimeters (186,000 miles) per second. Expressing it in more familiar units, this means that a pound of matter, of any kind, would yield nearly 11 million kilowatt-hours of energy, if the complete conversion could be made.

This was verified, for the first time, in the Cockroft-Walton experiment. With a later and improved form of their apparatus, they could determine the energies of the alpha particles they produced and also the masses. They knew the mass of the proton bullet and of the original lithium nucleus. Their total mass, when added together, was slightly more than that of the two alpha particles into which they had been changed; so a little mass had been lost in the process. When this loss proved equal to the increased energy of the alpha particles, as calculated by Einstein's formula, the theory had been verified.

BOMBARDING THE ATOMIC ISLAND

One writer has compared the atomic nucleus to a little island with a high wall around it. If you want to find out something about the island, you might throw stones over the wall and see what happens. Because the wall is so high, you have to throw the stones with high speed. Some might be tossed back; from the way they are ejected, you might form some estimate of the intelligence of the inhabitants. And if the stones that come back are not the same as those you throw in, you might infer something about the kinds of rocks they have on the island.

This is the way we study the nucleus of the atom. But we cannot see a nucleus, even with the most powerful microscope; and we cannot aim our particles at it. It's as if it were pitch dark, with the island invisible. We would have to throw our stones at random; occasionally some would hit. Similarly, in nuclear research, the physicist has to shoot lots of particles at his target, on the chance that some few will make a bull's-eye.

The wall around our nuclear island is produced by the combined positive charges of the protons it contains. A fountain pen is given a negative charge when you rub it on your coat sleeve because extra electrons become attached to some of the pen's atoms. It will pick up positively charged bits of paper because unlike charges attract each other. But similar charges repel each other. Thus the positive charge around the nucleus repels the protons or alpha particles which the physicist may fire at it, as these particles are positively charged. The deuteron, the nucleus of heavy hydrogen, consists of a proton and a neutron and is also positively charged.

There is one puzzling feature of the atomic nucleus which has not yet been fully explained. The nucleus contains only positively charged particles and particles with no charge at all. And since positive charges push against other positive charges, why don't the protons push on each other? In other words, how does the nucleus hold itself together? Much modern research in nuclear physics is concerned with the "binding forces" that tie up the protons, along with the neutrons, into a tight little package. Evidently these are very short-range forces that cause attraction only at very short distances, such as inside a nucleus.

Now the physicist's arsenal includes a whole range of artillery —so-called atom smashers—that produce the bullets he shoots at nuclei. There is the linear accelerator, where particles go down a long tube and are given an additional kick every time they pass from one section to the next. There are the cyclotron, the betatron, and the synchrotron, in which particles are whirled around, slingshot fashion, between the poles of a powerful electromagnet. The largest yet built is a synchrotron which accelerates protons to energies of 35 billion volts at the Brookhaven National Laboratory on Long Island. Still more potent accelerators are in the planning stage.

With these huge devices, scientists in many laboratories are conducting a fascinating game, taking nuclei apart and building up new ones. For many years uranium, with 92 protons, was listed as the heaviest of the elements, but now scientists have created others still heavier, up to nobelium, which has 102 protons in its nucleus. Among familiar elements, scientists produce different isotopes, which behave chemically the same as the ordinary forms but give off various types of radiation, which can be detected with appropriate instruments. These isotopes have provided science with valuable "tracers." A radioactive isotope of phosphorus, for example, may be added, in minute proportions, to fertilizers containing phosphorus in its more common form. Then, when the fertilizer is fed to plants, scientists can find just how rapidly, and by what routes, it goes to the plant tissues. Such studies have given plant physiologists an entirely new understanding of how fertilizers work.

But even the most powerful atom smashers that men have made are puny in comparison with the stars and galaxies, where natural forces transmute atoms and even whirl around their nuclei to produce radiations which sometimes reach the Earth. Our study of the atom, indeed, gives us knowledge to interpret what we observe happening in distant parts of the universe.

2

Radiation

In a few years man will be able to travel to the Moon; some day to other planets in the solar system; and eventually, perhaps, to planets in far-distant systems. But it is hardly likely that space travelers will ever be able to approach closely to the Sun or to other stars; they are so hot that the astronaut and his spaceship would be completely vaporized.

Up to now our knowledge of celestial bodies has come solely by the messages they send us in their radiations. For many of these bodies, it seems, this will continue to be the case. And since radiation forms our sole contact with the stars, let us find just what radiation is and where it comes from.

We see the Moon, like the planets, by the sunlight it reflects to us; the Sun and stars send us light, along with other and invisible radiations, that originates within them. And it is only with the development of modern atomic theory that science has found a satisfactory explanation of the process. Indeed, it was largely to explain radiation that Bohr developed his theory of the atom.

As we have already learned, the atom is considered to be a nucleus of protons and neutrons with electrons revolving around. (Actually, the orbits of the electrons are not now believed to be as precisely defined as those of the planets around the Sun; rather they are regions where there is a certain probability of an electron being located.) The real planets remain in their orbits, but an electron can jump from one orbit to another or even leave the atom completely. When an electron has left, we say the atom is positively ionized. Without the normal quota of negative electrons, the positive charges predominate.

15

Normally an electron moves in the innermost of several possible orbits. But sometimes it absorbs energy and shifts to an orbit farther from the nucleus. This leaves the atom temporarily in an "excited" state. Then the electron drops back to its basic orbit

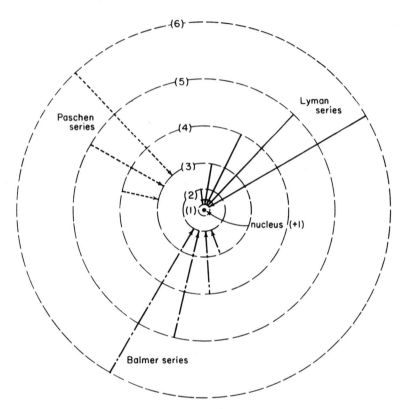

Fig. 3. Bohr's concept of the hydrogen atom. The electron may be displaced from its usual orbit to "allowed" orbits farther away from the nucleus. Then it falls back to an inner orbit, giving rise to spectral lines in what are known as the Lyman, Balmer, and Paschen series. (By permission from *Matter, Energy and Radiation,* by J. R. Dunning and H. C. Paxton. Copyright, 1941, McGraw-Hill Book Co., Inc., New York.)

(perhaps in two or more steps) and, as it does so, it gives up the energy it previously gained. The energy is sent out as a pulse, or quantum, of radiation.

It's much as if you carried a baseball upstairs, and then let it fall down the steps. It might fall step by step, or it might pass several steps at a time. In any event, it could only fall in discrete jumps, from one step to another. The ball couldn't go three-fourths of the distance between two steps. Moreover, in falling, it would give up the energy it had gained when you lifted it to the upper story.

Fig. 3 is a diagram of the hydrogen atom, simplest of all, and the various steps down which the electron can fall. Orbit *1* is the floor at the bottom of the stairs, *2* is the first step, *3* the next, and so on. The electron can drop from any orbit to the inner-most, to the second from any of those orbits above, or to the third from any orbit above *3*. Different amounts of energy are involved for each such shift. This is measured in volts, actually in electron volts, abbreviated *ev*. We have already seen that 1 electron volt is the amount of energy acquired by an electron in dropping through a potential difference of 1 volt.

In the hydrogen atom, energy amounting to 10.2 ev must be applied to an electron in the first orbit to shift it to the second, but an additional 1.9 ev will take it to the third, while 0.65 ev will take it to the fourth. Still smaller additions of energy will get it to orbits farther out, while a total of 13.6 ev will remove it completely from association with the nucleus. This leaves the atom ionized, i.e., denuded of its electron.

SHIFTING ELECTRONS

There are various possible ways to give an electron energy to enable it to make such a shift. It may be hit by another electron or by a positive ion, the proton remaining from a hydrogen atom which has lost the electron, or by a *photon,* a quantum of radiation. Ordinarily the atom doesn't remain very long in a higher energy state. The electron soon falls back, perhaps to its original orbit, or possibly to an intermediate position, from which it will return later to the ground floor.

As the electron falls back (this is a most important point), it gives off the energy it gained originally. It gives off this energy in the form of radiation—a photon. However, not all photons are alike, as they too vary in energy. Differences in energy are mani-fested as differences in frequency—the rate at which photons vibrate.

This brings us to the spectrum and the spectroscope—the tool that has brought us a vast amount of knowledge of the universe.

Long ago, men noticed the colors that appeared when white light passed through a piece of glass in the shape of a prism. Sir Isaac Newton made fundamental observations of this effect, which he described in a letter to the Royal Society in 1671. Through a small hole in a window shutter, a narrow beam of sunlight came into his house. He let it fall on a sheet of paper, and there was a spot of white light.

But then he held a prism over the hole and the beam passed through the prism. Instead of a white spot, there was a *spectrum*— a band of seven colors. At least Newton counted seven; red, orange, yellow, green, blue, indigo, and violet. Now we consider that there are six; indigo is no longer regarded as a separate color.

The spectrum produced in this manner is not a pure one, for one color overlaps on another. But, if you first pass the light beam through a narrow slit, and use appropriate lenses in conjunction with the prism, you get a pure spectrum. And if this is done with light from the Sun, or many other sources, a number of dark lines are seen crossing the spectrum. These are called the *Fraunhofer lines,* after a nineteenth-century German scientist who charted the more prominent ones in the solar spectrum and designated them by letters.

Some years later, in 1859, two other German physicists, Gustav Kirchhoff and Robert Bunsen, showed that these lines are caused by the absorption of certain colors by gases in the atmosphere of the Sun and other stars.

The effect is shown in Fig. 4. A beam of light shines from an electric incandescent lamp. Passing the light through the spectroscope would form a continuous spectrum—one with no dark lines. But here is a lamp burning alcohol, to which a pinch of salt has been added. The sodium in the salt gives the normally pale-blue alcohol flame an intense yellow color. If the light from the flame were analyzed with the spectroscope, it would show two yellow lines very close together. But when we place the alcohol lamp in such a position that the beam from the electric lamp passes through the flame before reaching the spectroscope, we find that the spectrum shows two dark lines—in exactly the same position as the bright yellow lines from the sodium light alone.

What happens is this: Sodium is vaporized by the heat of the flame, and shifts of electrons in the sodium atoms cause them to give off the yellow light. But if a whole range of color, like that of which white light consists, passes through this sodium vapor cloud, the cloud acts as a filter, removing this yellow color from the white light. Thus the dark lines appear in the spectrum. And when we see two dark lines in the Sun's spectrum in this same position, we know that the solar atmosphere contains sodium, which absorbs certain colors from the white light shining from the lower levels of the Sun. Other lines indicate other elements; thus we can tell what the Sun's atmosphere is made of.

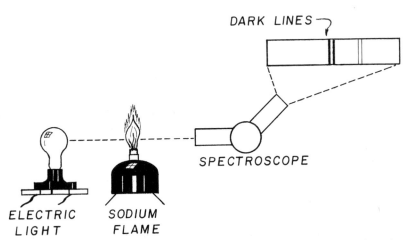

Fig. 4. Absorption spectrum. When the light from a flame to which sodium has been added is analyzed with the spectroscope, there are two bright yellow lines, while the light from an electric lamp shows a complete spectrum from red to violet. But if the electric light is passed through the sodium flame, some yellow rays are absorbed. The spectrum shows two dark lines where the bright yellow lines were located in the flame spectrum.

CONFIRMED AT ECLIPSE

The flash spectrum, which appears at a total solar eclipse, when the Moon passes in front of the Sun, hiding the solar disk, shows a similar effect. Just before and just after the Sun's globe is completely covered, there is an instant when we receive only the light from the solar atmosphere. If you are watching through a spectroscope at such a time, the normal solar spectrum, with all its dark lines, suddenly changes to one of bright lines.

Many of the lines in the solar spectrum are caused by hydrogen. In the early 1880's a Swiss scientist named Balmer noticed that these lines are not scattered at random, but form a regular series.

First comes a line in the red. It is called *H alpha*. There is a considerable space to the next, in the green, termed *H beta*. The third, *H gamma,* in the blue part of the spectrum, follows after a shorter gap. Then come others, in the ultraviolet part of the spectrum. We cannot see these but can photograph them; and, in each case, the distance to the next is shorter than it was from the previous line. Finally they are all squeezed so closely together that they cannot be separated. Balmer devised a mathematical formula which gives the position of these lines with considerable precision.

Later four other series of lines were found, and named after the physicists who discovered them: Lyman, Paschen, Brackett, and Pfund. All the lines of the Lyman series are in the ultraviolet, while those of the other three series are in the infrared—the part beyond the red end of the spectrum, and which is also invisible. Lines of the Balmer and Paschen series have been found in spectra of light from the stars. Doubtless the others are present also; but they cannot be observed from Earth because these radiations cannot penetrate our atmosphere.

Bohr's concept of the atom provided an explanation for these series. Look back again at Fig. 3. When an electron falls from the second orbit to the first, the energy of 10.2 ev that is released appears as a photon. Its quota of energy determines the part of the spectrum in which it appears, that is, its *wave length*. For light has a split personality. Sometimes it acts as if it were a particle; sometimes as if it were a wave motion.

The spectrum can be explained by the latter concept. If the wave length, measured from the crest of one wave to the crest of the next, is 1/40,000 inch, the light is deep red, while a wave length of 1/70,000 inch makes violet light. Intermediate wave lengths make the other colors of the visible spectrum. Waves shorter than violet form the invisible ultraviolet part of the spectrum, while beyond red are the longer infrared waves. The infrared spectrum also makes no impression on the eye.

Although you cannot see infrared waves, sometimes you can feel them. If you slowly heat a piece of iron, you will find that you can feel the heat, radiated from the metal, on your face or hands. This is due to the infrared waves the metal emits, even at a temperature of only a few hundred degrees Fahrenheit. By the time iron gets to 900°F., it glows a dull red. As it absorbs additional energy and becomes hotter still, it shines with a bright red light, then orange. Hotter yet, it gives off the shorter waves of blue light which, combined with the other colors also being radiated, gives the effect of white heat. With still higher temperatures it will even give off ultraviolet waves in large amounts.

Thus there is a definite relation between wave length and energy. Radiation of 10.2 ev, released when an electron falls from the second to the innermost orbit of the hydrogen atom, corresponds to ultraviolet waves about 1/220,000 inch long, less than a third the wave length of the visible violet. This is the position of the first line of the Lyman series, Lyman alpha. The second line, Lyman beta, comes from a longer drop, from orbit three to orbit one. With more energy, the wave length is even shorter. And so on, with gamma, delta, and the rest. But each added increment of energy is less than before, so the distances between the lines in the spectrum become smaller, ending when the energy is sufficient to detach the electron completely from the atom.

All of the Lyman lines are in the far ultraviolet, but the Balmer series, as we have noted, comes in the visible range and originates in a similar way. The drop from orbit three to two produces the first of the Lyman lines; then come the rest, at successively smaller intervals. The Paschen series is formed by electrons falling back to the third orbit, and all these lines are in the infrared. Still farther into the infrared, so that they are difficult to observe, are the Brackett series and the Pfund series, formed by falls to orbits four and five, respectively.

OTHER SPECTRA MORE COMPLEX

For elements with additional electrons, the spectra are far more complicated, although their atoms radiate in fundamentally the same way: an electron drops back to its normal orbit from an outer position. Some of these transitions are "allowed"; others are "forbidden," which means merely that they are highly improbable here on Earth. But vastly different conditions, regarding temperature, pressure, etc., prevail in stars and nebulae. In these objects, such forbidden transitions account for some very prominent lines.

Then there is the process of *fluorescence,* an important source of illumination in our homes and offices, which occurs as well in astronomical objects.

The familiar fluorescent lamp contains mercury in vapor form. An electric current passes through and shifts some of the electrons,

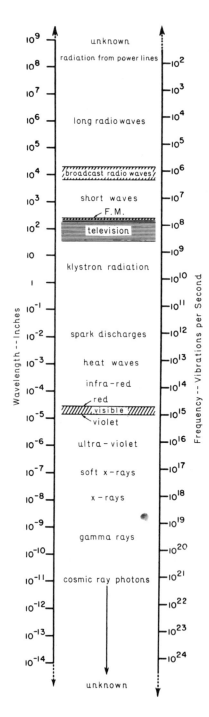

attached to mercury atoms, to excited states. They fall back and emit ultraviolet radiation. This hits the solid phosphor with which the tube is lined; electrons in its atoms are shifted; as they fall back into place, light is radiated. Sometimes their return to the normal orbit is delayed, and the light may continue to be radiated, even after the current has been turned off. This effect is called *phosphorescence.*

While the eye is the most important of all detectors of radiation, its range is severely limited. It's like an ordinary home radio receiver, sensitive only to waves in the broadcast band, that is, between about 655 and 1,790 feet in length. The radio will not detect the shorter or longer waves used for other forms of communication.

Similarly, the eye cannot detect waves shorter than those that produce the sensation of

Fig. 5. The complete electromagnetic spectrum. The spectrum ranges from the very short-wave high-frequency radiations associated with cosmic rays, at one end, to long radio waves and the waves emitted from electric power lines, at the other. The spectrum of visible light occupies a narrow band in the middle. (By permission from *Matter, Energy and Radiation,* by J. R. Dunning and H. C. Paxton. Copyright, 1941, McGraw-Hill Book Co., Inc., New York.)

violet or longer than those of red light. Those longer than red—the infrared—extend on and overlap the shortest radio waves. The long radio waves extend upward to those produced by electric power lines carrying 60-cycle alternating current, which have wave lengths that may be counted in thousands of miles.

Even shorter than ultraviolet waves, but basically the same in other respects, are X-rays. Shorter yet are the gamma rays produced by radioactive materials as their atomic nuclei rearrange themselves. Still shorter, down to trillionths of an inch or even less, are the photons associated with cosmic radiation from space— radiation of many billions of electron volts in energy.

This range of radiation is shown in Fig. 5, with the wave lengths on the left. But there is another way of designating them: by their frequencies, as shown on the right. The frequency is simply the number of vibrations a wave makes each second. On this diagram, these numbers, like the wave lengths, are expressed in what may be an unfamiliar system—the use of exponents—so let us digress a moment to explain this system.

HOW TO WRITE BIG NUMBERS

Numbers such as 10, 100, 1,000, etc., are all powers of 10. Multiply 10 by 10; the product is 100. The mathematician says this is 10 to the second power, or 10 squared, and expresses it as 10^2. The little number above and to the right is called the exponent; in this case it shows that two 10's were multiplied together to get the result. Similarly 10^3 (10 to the third power or 10 cubed) shows that you use three 10's to get the product: 10 times 10 times 10, which equals 1,000. When you mutiply this by another 10 you have 10 to the fourth power, or 10^4, which is 10,000. And so on: $10^5 = 100,000$; $10^6 = 1,000,000$; etc. But notice that, in each case, the exponent is equal to the number of zeroes after the number one.

This makes it easy to express very large numbers. A sextillion, for example, is 1,000,000,000,000,000,000,000. How much easier it is to write 10^{21}, which shows at once that the number is a one followed by 21 ciphers. Or perhaps you want to express a value of eight sextillion. Then you write 8×10^{21}, that is, 8 multiplied by 1 followed by 21 ciphers. Similarly, $5 \times 10^6 = 5,000,000$ and $3.2 \times 10^4 = 32,000$.

You may use the same system to express fractional values by using negative exponents. Thus, $10^1 = 10$; $10^0 = 1$; $10^{-1} = 0.1$; $10^{-2} = 0.01$; $10^{-3} = 0.001$; etc. That is, the number of decimal places is the same as the exponent. Or you may think of it in another way: with a negative exponent the value is 1 over the value without the minus sign. That is, $10^4 = 10,000$ while the expression $10^{-4} = 1/10,000$.

The frequency of red light, then, is 4.71×10^{14}, and that of violet light is 7×10^{14}. If you multiply either of these by the wave length of the radiation in decimals of an inch (and using more precise values than the approximations given here), you will find that in each case the result is about 12 billion, which is the number of inches that the radiation travels in a second, or about 186,000 miles per second. This is true for any of these radiations, from radio waves to the cosmic-ray photons. Multiplying any frequency by the corresponding wave length, you get the same result, which means that all radiation travels at the same speed: sufficient to take it completely around the Earth about seven times in a second.

It wasn't always known that light has a definite speed. Early attempts were made to clock it. Two men with covered lanterns were stationed out of doors at night, perhaps several miles apart. One would uncover his lantern, and as soon as the other saw it, he would uncover his. Then the first man would measure the time until he saw the other light. As far as they could tell, with such crude methods, light didn't take any time to travel; as soon as it left the first lantern it arrived at the second.

THE SPEED OF LIGHT

But, in 1676, a Danish astronomer named Roemer showed that light does take time to travel, even though it goes at a very high speed. His method used the four bright moons of Jupiter, which can be seen even with a small telescope. Periodically, they are eclipsed as they pass into the shadow of Jupiter. This cuts off the Sun's light, which ordinarily illuminates them; therefore, they disappear from view. Astronomers had computed the time it took these satellites to make one trip around the planet, and it seemed that the astronomers could accurately predict when the eclipses would happen. Sometimes, however, the eclipses came several minutes early; and sometimes they were several minutes late.

Roemer found that the eclipses were early when Jupiter was nearest Earth, that is, when both planets were on the same side of the Sun. But when Jupiter was on the opposite side of the Sun, *and many millions of miles farther away,* the eclipses came late. The eclipses occurred as expected, he concluded, but the predictions had not allowed for the extra time required for light to travel the

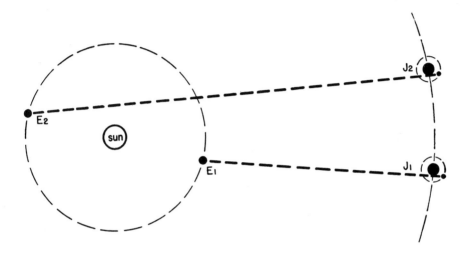

Fig. 6. Measuring the speed of light. Roemer determined the speed of light from eclipses of Jupiter's moons behind that planet. Sometimes they seemed to occur ahead of schedule and sometimes they were late. This shows why. With Earth and Jupiter on the same side of the Sun (E1) the light had a shorter path to travel than when the Earth was on the far side of the Sun, as at E2. Knowing the diameter of the Earth's orbit (about 186,000,000 miles) he was able to calculate how long light took to travel this distance. (By permission from *Matter, Energy and Radiation,* by J. R. Dunning and H. C. Paxton. Copyright, 1941, McGraw-Hill Book Co., Inc., New York.)

added distance. Once this correction was made, the predictions were accurate; see Fig. 6.

Since then, many laboratory methods have been devised to measure, with high precision, the speed of light and other radiations. The speed is about 186,100 miles per second, and it has been determined within an error of less than 10 miles a second.

In one year, light, or any other electromagnetic radiation, will travel 6×10^9 miles. This is called the *light-year* and is widely used in expressing astronomical distances, where it would be as inconvenient to use miles as it would be to use inches in telling how far San Francisco is from New York.

Scientists and philosophers over the ages have discussed the nature of light. For a long time they thought that a luminous body emitted streams of particles. When these particles entered the eye, they produced the sensation of light. But then it was found that, under some conditions, the combination of two beams of light could produce darkness.

This could hardly happen with two streams of particles, for with twice as many particles the intensity should be doubled. But waves can behave this way. Imagine two sets of waves in water coming together. If two waves are in step, with the crests coinciding, one will be piled on top of the other, making a new wave twice as high. But if they are out of step, the crest of one will fill in the trough of the other; each will cancel the other, and there will be smooth water. Similar *interference* occurs when two beams of light are combined in the proper manner, making alternate bands of light and dark, depending whether they are in or out of step. This seemed to prove the wave theory, and it was accepted for many years.

However, as we mentioned earlier, light seems to have a split personality. Much of the time it behaves like a wave, but some effects have been observed that the wave theory cannot explain.

THE QUANTUM THEORY

A great advance in physics was made in 1900 when Max Planck introduced the quantum theory. According to him, light consists of a series of little packets of wave energy, which he called *quanta*.

Each quantum, also called a photon, has energy proportional to its frequency, as we noted before. This energy is equal to the frequency multiplied by 6.624×10^{-27}, a value known as Planck's constant, and designated by the letter h. (It is expressed in units called erg-seconds.)

Mention the name of Albert Einstein, and most people, even physicists, think of the theory of relativity. But when Einstein was awarded the Nobel Prize in physics in 1921, it was not for relativity, but for his explanation of the photoelectric effect. He showed that the quantum theory was not merely a convenient mathematical expression, but a real expression of what happens.

Experimenters had found that, when light falls on various metals, such as potassium or cesium, electrons are knocked out of the surface. This effect is applied in the photoelectric cell to convert light changes into a varying electric current, and the effect makes possible television, sound movies, and many devices used in science and industry.

But scientists had found a curious fact about the photoelectric effect. It appeared that the stronger the light, the more electrons were emitted, provided any were emitted at all. But if the frequency of the light was below a certain value, characteristic for each metal, electrons would not be given off no matter how intense the light!

For potassium this threshold is at the energy corresponding to the frequency of yellow light. Green, blue, or violet (all higher in frequency) will therefore knock electrons out of potassium. But red, orange, and infrared (all of lower frequency) have less than the minimum energy needed. For cesium the threshold is lower, in the deep red, so practically any visible light can eject photoelectrons from this metal, while infrared rays cannot.

According to Einstein's explanation an electron in an atom is held to the nucleus with a certain force. To break it loose, there must be at least enough energy to overcome that force. No quantum of orange light has enough energy to pull an electron loose from a potassium atom, one of yellow light has barely enough to do so, while a violet quantum has more than enough. The excess energy is added to the ejected electron and gives it additional speed.

The photoelectric effect cannot be explained by the wave concept; on the other hand, it is hard to explain interference on the basis of quanta. Evidently light has characteristics both of waves and particles (someone has suggested calling them "wavicles"!), and we must use one concept or the other at different times. However, for most of the usual properties of light the wave theory is quite adequate.

THE DOPPLER EFFECT

The wave theory will, for example, explain the *Doppler effect*. Perhaps you have stood near a railroad track as a locomotive rushed past, its whistle blowing. Just as it goes by, the sound seems to drop in pitch; the sound is deeper when the locomotive is going away than when it is approaching. The reason is that sound consists of waves in the air, and the pitch is determined by the wave length. Middle C has a frequency of 261.63 vibrations per second and each wave is about 4.37 feet long. As with light, the frequency multiplied by the wave length gives the speed, 1,100 feet per second in air at ordinary temperatures. For a sound of higher pitch the frequency is greater and the wave length less, while a lower-pitched sound has longer waves.

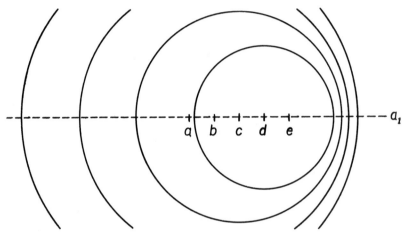

Fig. 7. The Doppler effect. a, b, c, d, and e represent successive positions of a source of sound, such as a whistle, which is rapidly approaching an observer at a_1. Sound waves leave the whistle at regular intervals but, because of its motion, they are squeezed together in the forward direction. Thus the observer hears them at more frequent intervals and they sound higher in pitch than if the whistle were stationary. To an observer in the opposite direction, the waves would be stretched out and their pitch would be lower. A similar effect happens with light.

If the distance between the source and the listener is decreasing (i.e., if one is approaching the other), the sound waves are squeezed together and become shorter—or so it seems to the listener. Thus, the pitch seems higher, and this is what happened with the locomotive whistle as it rushed toward you. As it goes away (or as the listener moves away from the source), the waves are stretched out and the pitch it lowered; see Fig. 7.

The same thing happens with light. If a star is approaching Earth, the light waves increase in frequency, or "pitch." It is lowered if the star's distance is increasing. Either change is shown by the lines in the star's spectrum; the astronomer compares their positions with those of similar lines in the spectrum of a laboratory light source. An approach causes lines in the stellar spectrum to shift to the blue end of the spectrum; when the star is receding, the lines are shifted toward the red.

Light and other radiations from the stars are broadcast in all directions. Imagine a light source, such as a 100-watt electric bulb, inside a room with a window. If the window is covered with a sheet of white paper, the light falling on the paper has a certain intensity. But now move the paper outside the house until it is twice as far from the bulb. The light is spreading, so now it covers an area twice as wide and twice as high, with the total area four times as great. Since the light is spread more thinly, the intensity at twice the distance is not half, but a quarter of the intensity at the window. Four times as far, the intensity would be reduced by the square of 4, or 16. Thus, the intensity gets smaller as the square of the distance increases. This is usually expressed by saying that light intensity, like that of other radiations, varies inversely with the square of the distance.

Even though the stars are very bright, by the time their light has traveled the vast distance to the Earth, the light is very feeble. Only an exceedingly minute proportion of the light from a star can enter a human eye through the pupil, which is about $\frac{1}{4}$ inch in diameter. If the pupil were larger, more could get in. In effect, a telescope makes it larger. Suppose the telescope has a lens 10 inches in diameter, 40 times that of the pupil. The lens covers 40×40, or 1,600, times the area of the opening of the eye, so that an increased proportion of light energy is collected.

The main telescope lens collects the light waves, brings them to a focus, and forms an image of the real object at which the telescope is pointed. A second lens or, usually, a system of lenses (the eyepiece) is right in front of the observer's eye. With the eyepiece he examines the image of the main lens. The result is that the 10-inch cylinder of light, which bore the original view of the object, is squeezed to a quarter-inch diameter and funneled into the eye. Without the eyepiece, only the quarter-inch light cylinder that could enter the pupil would be used. If the light were very feeble, it would, perhaps, not be able to affect the sensitive nerve endings on the retina—the sensitive film of the eye.

Thus, with the telescope, we can see stars many times fainter than the faintest star that the naked eye can detect. And there is magnification in the process; the object is apparently made larger and brought nearer. This is particularly important in observing the planets and other bodies that are relatively close. The stars are all so far away that, even if magnified a thousand diameters, they still do not look big enough to appear as more than a point of light. The telescope of the present day makes them appear brighter, but no bigger.

If the Moon is magnified the same thousand diameters, it appears to be brought to a thousandth of its actual distance. Since the Moon is about 240,000 miles away, this would enable us to see it as if we were only 240 miles above its surface.

In referring to magnification, astronomers speak of so many *diameters* rather than so many *times*. This also applies to magnifications of minute objects seen through a microscope. If a disk of a certain diameter is viewed through a telescope and it seems to have a diameter ten times as large as it does to the unaided eye, the telescope is said to magnify "10 diameters." However, seen through such a telescope, the object would seem to have an *area* 10 × 10, or 100, times as large as when seen with unaided vision. Thus, a magnifying power of 100 *times* would be equal to 10 *diameters*, which means that the object then appears at one tenth the distance.

The image of a star formed by a lens is not actually a point of light, as the star itself appears in the sky. Instead, it is a small bright disk, around which are a series of fainter and fainter rings. This happens even with the most nearly perfect lens; it is a result of the wave nature of light itself. Thus, if you try to look at a *binary* (double) star, which consists of two separate stars close together, a small telescope may not separate them, even if you use a very high magnification. This is because the image disk of each star would spread over the other. If you used an eyepiece that magnified more, the disk would look larger, but you still wouldn't separate the two images.

The larger the diameter of the front telescope lens (the *objective*), the smaller is the disk. Then the images of each star may be separate, and a high-power eyepiece would show them clearly. The same thing applies in looking at planets and the Moon. With a large telescope you can see details much finer than those visible with a smaller instrument.

CELESTIAL CAMERAS

Actually, in a modern observatory, astronomers spend relatively little time looking through telescopes except to keep one accurately aimed during a long photographic exposure. The telescope may feed light into a spectroscope, or it may be used as a camera. The objective lens then forms an image on a photographic film or plate. One advantage is permanence. The plate, after it is developed, may be preserved and studied for years.

But, in addition, astronomers photograph objects too faint to be seen through any telescope. If you look at a faint nebula, it doesn't help to watch a long time. Continued observation doesn't increase the ability of the eye to see faint objects, as it does for the photographic plate. Even with an ordinary camera, when you take a time exposure of an interior, the less light there is, the longer you have to expose. With a certain light value, you may expose for a second; at a tenth of that amount of light, the exposure must be ten seconds. And if it's only a hundredth as bright, you'll have to expose for a hundred seconds. The long exposure gives the light time to soak into the film, and this makes up for low intensity. Astronomical exposures of faint objects may run to many hours, or may be spread over several nights.

While lenses have been mentioned as forming the telescope image, the largest instruments use mirrors rather than lenses to do this. Lens telescopes are called refractors; the glass bends or *refracts* the light rays so that they form the image. The biggest telescopes, however, are reflectors; a concave mirror, formed to a very accurate shape, reflects the parallel bundle of light rays from a distant star and thus focuses them. Usually the mirror is made of glass, which is merely a support for the reflecting metal surface, formerly silver, now usually aluminum. The light never passes through the glass, as it does in common household mirrors, which have the silver on the back; see Fig. 8.

The largest refractor is the telescope at the Yerkes Observatory of the University of Chicago, located at Williams Bay, Wisconsin. The lens, 40 inches in diameter, consists of two pieces of glass, each supported only around the edge. Though glass is considered quite rigid, it is not entirely so, and with larger lenses there would probably be some bending as the telescope was raised to study an object high in the sky. The accurate figure of the lens would thus be affected.

But the mirror of a reflecting telescope can be supported over the entire back. The largest telescope yet made—the Hale Telescope located on Mount Palomar in California and owned by the California Institute of Technology—has a mirror 200 inches, or nearly 17 feet, in diameter.

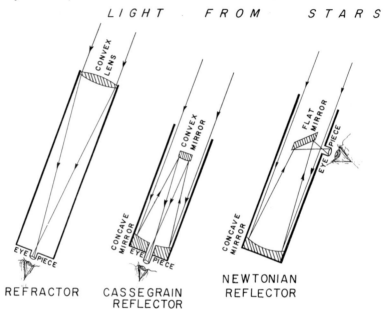

LIGHT   FROM   STARS

REFRACTOR   CASSEGRAIN   NEWTONIAN
                   REFLECTOR   REFLECTOR

Fig. 8. Three types of telescope. In the refractor, a lens forms the image, which is viewed through an eyepiece. A concave mirror is used in a reflector to bring the light rays to a focus. The Cassegrain type has also a convex mirror, which reflects the light rays, through a hole in the main mirror, to the eyepiece. The Newtonian type has a flat mirror, at a 45-degree angle, to reflect the rays to the eyepiece on the side of the tube.

Even though it is used as a camera, an observer has to remain at the telescope during an exposure, in order to keep the telescope accurately pointed. With the Hale telescope, he rides in a small cylindrical cabin right at the top of the instrument, for the diameter of the cabin cuts out only a small portion of the light beam that is on way to the mirror. With smaller reflecting telescopes, this cannot be done. One method, that of Newton, who invented the reflecting telescope in 1672, uses a small flat mirror, set at a 45-degree angle, to reflect the image off to the side. In other systems the second mirror is convex and placed at the top of the instrument, so as to reflect the light back through a hole in the center of the main mirror.

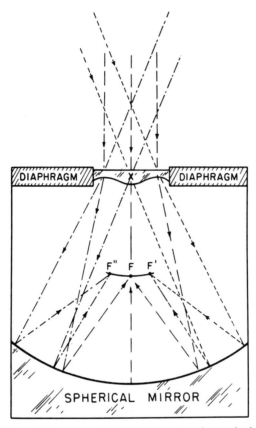

Fig. 9. The Schmidt camera. It has a correcting lens which bends the light rays before they hit the main spherical mirror. They are then reflected to the focal surface, F″FF′, where the photographic film, curved to fit, is placed. (By permission from *Elementary Astronomy,* by Otto Struve, Beverly Lynds, and Helen Pillan. Copyright, 1959, Oxford Univ. Press, Fair Lawn, N.J.)

Another important type of astronomical camera is the Schmidt telescope, named after its inventor, Bernhard Schmidt of the Hamburg Observatory in Germany. It is a reflector, with a concave mirror to focus the light rays, but the mirror surface forms part of a sphere. In other reflecting telescopes the surface of the mirror is a paraboloid, which focuses light rays at the same distance no matter whether they fall at the edge or the center of the mirror.

A spherical mirror does not do this. The parallel rays that come from a distant star and that strike the edge would be focused at a shorter distance than those rays reflected from the center. This would prevent use of the spherical mirror alone in a telescope. Schmidt added a correcting plate of glass in front of the mirror. This alters the path of the light rays before they are reflected, so that they are focused at the same distance, as shown in Fig. 9. The photographic film, which is curved to the proper shape, is placed between the correcting plate and the mirror.

A Schmidt camera can photograph clearly and rapidly a large area of the sky. Such instruments have been installed in many observatories. The largest is the one at Mount Palomar (shown in Plate 2a). A photograph taken with it, as part of the National Geographic Society—Palomar Observatory Sky Survey photographic atlas of the northern heavens, is shown in Plate 13a.

ASTRONOMICAL TELEVISION

While photography is now the main method used for astronomical observations, electronic techniques, closely related to those of television, show promise of even greater sensitivity. Faint sounds are picked up with a microphone, then amplified to enormous volume through a loud-speaker. Somewhat analogous in operation to the loud-speaker, is the image converter, which has been used to amplify faint X-ray shadows. Experiments have been made with converters at several observatories; perhaps these methods will allow astronomers to record telescopic images too faint to be photographed.

Such amplified images may be photographed, for a permanent record, or may be sent by television to other locations, so that various groups of scientists could watch simultaneously. This might be a great convenience, because many observatories are located far from cities, often on mountain tops, or on high plateaus.

There are two reasons for this. Near a city, the atmosphere is usually thick with dust and smoke, which considerably reduces the transparency; thus, the stars look considerably fainter than they do from a more remote site. Moreover, there is the glare of city lights, which reduces still further the visibility of fainter objects.

In 1957, to get even higher than available mountain tops, the U. S. Office of Naval Research sponsored a series of experiments

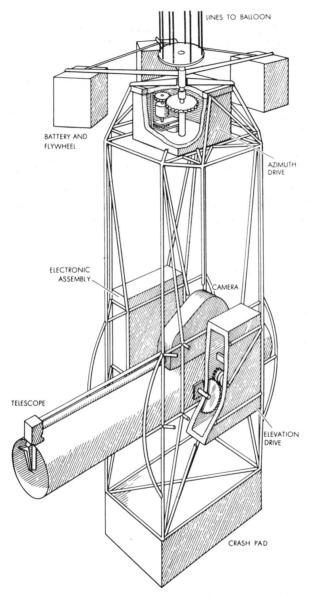

LINES TO BALLOON

BATTERY AND
FLYWHEEL

AZIMUTH
DRIVE

ELECTRONIC
ASSEMBLY

CAMERA

TELESCOPE

ELEVATION
DRIVE

CRASH PAD

Fig. 10. Simplified diagram of a balloon telescope. Used to photograph
the Sun from an altitude of 40 miles, it is shown in the operating position. As it
is carried aloft, the telescope is stowed within the mounting. (By permission from
Scientific American. Copyright, 1960, Scientific American, Inc.)

in taking celestial photographs with a 12-inch telescope carried aloft by a balloon; see Fig. 10. Martin Schwarzschild of Princeton University directed this project. The balloons were unmanned, but the instruments, with their films, were recovered after they came down. Photographs of the Sun's surface of far greater clarity and detail than any ever taken from much larger instruments on the ground were the result of this project, called Stratoscope I.

Late in 1958 the National Science Foundation announced plans for Stratoscope II. A 36-inch telescope was to be equipped with television links to the ground station, so that it could be pointed at celestial objects by remote control. The astronomers in charge will use the 12-inch Stratoscope I telescope for solar observation, while the larger one will take high-resolution photographs of other objects, such as the planets, nebulae, and galaxies. At altitudes of as much as 15 miles, such air-borne observations would be far above atmospheric disturbances. Truly remarkable results may be expected as this program gets under way during the 1960's.

And, looking still further into the future, astronomers are talking about telescopes on manned satellites, at altitudes of hundreds of miles, or even on the airless surface of the Moon. When these developments are accomplished, astronomy will make advances even more spectacular than those which occurred as the telescope replaced the earlier naked-eye observations.

3

Radio Astronomy

Even though the electromagnetic spectrum had been extended downward to the gamma rays and upward to radio waves of thousands of feet or more in length, man's studies of the universe were dependent on waves of visible light—and those a little shorter or longer—until 1931. Then a new window was opened slightly.

But long before this, it had been suspected that radiations other than visible light, infrared, or ultraviolet might be coming from the Sun. During the decade of the 1890's, when Marconi and others were performing early experiments with radio, it was realized that radio waves differed from light only in that they were much longer. An English physicist, Sir Oliver Lodge, at that time a professor at University College in Liverpool, tried to pick up radio waves from the Sun. The experiment did not succeed, but he apparently felt that in some isolated country location, far from the sources of interference present near a large city, and with highly sensitive equipment, radiation could be detected.

In 1927, trans-Atlantic radio telephony was introduced as a regular service and was followed shortly by communication to ships at sea. As receivers were made increasingly sensitive, static interfered more and more with these circuits. The Bell Telephone Laboratories began an intensive study of static to learn about its causes and characteristics.

On what had been a potato farm at Holmdel, New Jersey, they set up an experimental station, equipped with a special antenna a hundred feet long that could be slowly rotated, like a merry-go-round. Responsible for its construction and operation was a young radio engineer named Karl Jansky.

In 1931 the operation of this station began. As the antenna swept around and around, once in 20 minutes, he picked up plenty of static. Sometimes it came in loud crashes, from nearby thunderstorms. More faint was that from distant storms, a hundred miles or more away. Also there was a weak and steady hiss that could barely be detected above noises that are heard from any electronic circuit when highly amplified. But the hiss, on a wave length of 15 meters, was not heard all the time. Sometimes it disappeared completely.

Jansky soon eliminated the possibility that this noise resulted from power lines or radio transmitters, or from thunderstorms. From the position of the antenna, he could tell the direction of the source, and it seemed to follow the Sun: east in the morning, south at noon, west in the evening, and disappearing entirely at night. A month later, however, the noise was two hours ahead of the Sun, so evidently that body was not the source. Six months later the noise was coming from a point in the sky directly opposite the Sun, and a year later it was with the Sun once more.

BROADCASTS FROM THE STARS

The significance of this became apparent to Jansky as he began to study astronomy. The Earth makes one revolution around the Sun each year. In June we are in such a direction from the Sun that the stars behind it, invisible because of the glare, are those of the constellation of Gemini, the twins. Six months later, in December, we have moved to the opposite direction, and the stars of Gemini are visible in the south at midnight. The Sun's background stars are those of Sagittarius, the archer, which is visible, in the south, at midnight in June. Thus, the source of Jansky's hiss did not keep step with the Sun, but it did come from the same part of the starry sky. Actually, it was coming from Sagittarius.

This constellation is important because it is the brightest part of the Milky Way. To anticipate matters to be discussed in more detail in a later chapter, this is the direction of the center of our Galaxy, the grindstone-shaped system of something like a hundred thousand million stars, of which our Sun is a very minor member, located about halfway from the center to the edge. So the radio waves that Jansky detected were coming from the heart of the Galaxy.

The Milky Way actually consists of a swarm of stars so numerous and so distant that their light seems to merge into the familiar luminous pathway through the sky. Therefore, it seemed as if the Sun, nearest star of all, should be a prominent source. Jansky did make a special effort to pick up its radiation, but couldn't find it. Although he published papers promptly about these studies, radio waves from space were quite far removed from the interests of the Bell Telephone Laboratories. His last paper on the subject was presented at a meeting of the Institute of Radio Engineers in 1937. He continued his work on static and other sources of radio "noise" until his death, in 1949, at the early age of forty-four.

At this time, as indeed for a number of years to come, celestial radio was an orphan which no one wanted. Few astronomers had heard about it, and even they could not appreciate what it would mean to their science. And to the radio engineers generally it was interesting, but of little importance. Not, however, to Grote Reber one of the two founders of radio astronomy.

He was a radio engineer working for a radio firm in Chicago; he lived in Wheaton, Illinois. While in his teens he had been an enthusiastic, amateur radio operator, conversing regularly with other "hams" in distant parts of the Earth. But they were only a few thousand miles away, and he wanted to get still greater distances. To accomplish this, he thought of picking up radio waves reflected from the Moon, 240,000 miles away, and even made some efforts to do it—which were unsuccessful.

Then he read Jansky's early papers and decided to follow radio astronomy as a hobby. In the summer of 1937 he built, at his home in Wheaton, a radio reflector made of sheet iron supported on a wooden framework and shaped like an upside-down umbrella 31 feet, 5 inches in diameter. This picked up the radio waves and focused them on the actual antenna, like a searchlight in reverse. In other words it was a reflecting telescope for radio waves; by pointing it toward different parts of the sky, he could pick up radiations, if any, from these directions.

Actually, his telescope could only be moved along the meridian —northward or southward. But the Earth itself turns each day, so the telescope would sweep across the sky from west to east. In this way any part of the sky visible from Wheaton could be reached. This type of mounting, by the way, is similar to that of a form of telescope known as the meridian circle, used to determine time by accurately checking the moment at which a particular star crosses the meridian.

The radio waves that were picked up by this 31-foot dish were carried by wires to the actual receiver, with its detector and other tubes, in the cellar of his house. Through a pair of headphones any received signal could be heard, while its intensity would be indicated on a meter.

To avoid, as far as possible, the interference from passing automobiles and other earthly sources, Reber did most of his observing between midnight and six A.M. Then he had to drive 30 miles to his regular job in Chicago. In the evening he would return, get his supper, sleep until midnight, and then start observing.

In the spring and summer of 1938 he made his first tests, attempting to pick up waves 9 cm. (about 3½ inches) in length. No results! He improved his equipment and tried for 33-cm. (13-inch) waves, but still none were detected.

More alterations—and a change in wave length to 1.85 meters (about 6 feet). Then, early in 1939, came his first success. As certain parts of the Milky Way moved across the field of the telescope there was a steady hissing in the receivers—and a movement of the needle on the dials of his meters.

This brought a much-needed confirmation of Jansky's earlier work. Unlike that pioneer, Reber was doing it as a hobby, not as a job, and could keep at it without any boss telling him to do something else! As his results improved, he made two surveys of the radiation from various directions along the Milky Way and found some "hot spots," regions from which radiation was particularly strong. One was in Sagittarius, where Jansky had found it. Others were in Cygnus, the swan; Canis Major, the big dog; Cassiopeia, the seated lady; Aquila, the eagle; etc.

Since the Milky Way consists of stars, it would seem that stars might be the source of the radio waves from space. If so, then a much closer bright star should be another copious source. But when he "looked" at some of the brightest stars in the sky, no waves could be detected at all. Nor could he get any from the Sun, nearest star of all. And while some of the radio "hot spots" were parts of the Milky Way, rich in stars, others were in dark areas with very few stars visible, even through good-sized telescopes.

In 1940, Reber reported his results in two papers: one for the radio fraternity, in the *Proceedings of the Institute of Radio Engi-*

neers; the other for the astronomers, in the *Astrophysical Journal.* But still neither group showed any very great interest.

RADAR PAVED THE WAY

The exigencies of warfare, however, soon brought a change. Radar was developed in the early days of World War II. This is a radio device which sends out brief pulses of radio waves in a narrow beam and focused, like the light beam of a searchlight, by a parabolic dish similar to that which Reber used to pick up signals. The radio pulse goes out at a speed of 186,000 miles per second, hits a distant ship or airplane, is reflected, and comes back to its source. Now the transmitting antenna becomes a receiver. The dish collects the waves of the echo, they are detected, and ingenious electronic devices tell to a millionth of a second how long the total journey took. Knowing the speed of the waves, the distance of the ship or plane can be determined; the direction is given by noting how the dish is aimed.

Even though the outgoing waves are in a beam, they weaken considerably with distance. The returning echo, faint at best, goes out in all directions, and there is still more weakening of the signal. To pick up these waves, it was necessary to develop radio receivers far more sensitive than any that Jansky or Reber had available.

Radar is credited with having saved England in the early days of World War II. With its aid, flights of German bombers were detected soon after they left their fields on the continent, and the limited forces of the R.A.F. were dispatched to meet them. Without such aid, the British would have had to cover so large an area continually that the defense would have been spread too thin to have been effective.

As the Nazis launched their V–1 "buzz bombs" against London in 1944, radar was again of service. Coupled to an "electronic brain," developed in the United States by the same Bell Telephone Laboratories for whom Jansky had worked, radar automatically aimed the antiaircraft guns which brought down 90 per cent of the bombs before they could do any damage.

But then came the V–2 rockets, many times faster and harder to locate. It was necessary to detect them almost immediately after they were launched and this required still more improvement in the defending radar equipment. Intelligence reports brought warning that the V–2 was being prepared; to meet them the Royal Anti-Aircraft Command began at once to develop the radar that would have to be used. A young scientist named Stanley Hey was placed in charge and in 2 months he did produce a device that could pick up the V–2 rockets.

Much of the time this worked beautifully but, on some occasions, there was interference which drowned out the echoes from the rockets. The delicate equipment was picking up the radio waves from the depths of the Milky Way, which were stronger than the radar echoes.

This was not Hey's first experience with something of this sort. Earlier in the war—in 1942—radar working on a wave length of 4 to 6 meters (about 16 feet) was employed to detect enemy aircraft and furnish data for aiming antiaircraft batteries. But in February these radar sets were often inoperative on account of some kind of interference. The Germans had developed some new form of jamming as a countermeasure, the British first supposed. Hey, then a member of the Army Operational Research Group, was assigned the task of correlating the reports and determining the exact trouble. The radar sets had been pointing toward the Sun when the troublesome interference was observed, and that body, indeed, was the source of the interference!

It appeared, then, that the Sun actually was broadcasting radio waves, but why had they not been noticed before? Principally because the Sun's activity, as we shall see in a later chapter, is not constant, but varies over a cycle of about 11 years. During the thirties, when Reber had sought for solar waves, the Sun had been quiescent, and even if his equipment had been many times more sensitive he could not have detected them. Most of the interference in February, 1944, proved to be associated with one large sunspot.

Hey wrote a report on his conclusions, as he did later in connection with his 1944 work on the V–2; but both were top secret, and it was not until 1946 that a limited account was made public.

In 1942, at the Bell Telephone Laboratories, George C. Southworth was seeking some sort of solar radiation on wave lengths between 1 and 10 cm. (about an inch or two), and he showed that it was coming in steadily. This was quite different from the meter radiation which Hey found the same year as that radiation varies with the activity of the Sun. The centimeter radiation is the "blackbody" radiation emitted by any hot object. It might be considered

as very long infrared radiation. Such rays are emitted by all hot
bodies, whether they give off visible rays or not.

SIGNALS FROM THE PLANETS

Not only the Sun, but the Moon and some of the planets are
also sources of radio waves. For the Moon, Mars, and Venus, black-
body radiation is again responsible; the emission is what would
come from any object at the same temperature. Even though the
Moon is about 240,000 miles distant, radio pulses sent out from the
Earth have often been detected as they echoed back. Similar echoes
have been obtained from Venus.

Venus is nearer the Sun than the Earth is and therefore is
hotter; Mars is farther out, but still near enough to the solar
system's central fire to keep at a not too unreasonable temperature.
Jupiter, on the other hand, is much farther out and far colder; so
the black-body radiation from it would be quite feeble. But in
1955, at the Department of Terrestrial Magnetism of the Carnegie
Institution of Washington, two scientists, Bernard Burke and Ken-
neth Franklin, picked up signals which they thought at first
originated nearby, perhaps on tractors on nearby farms. Several
years earlier an Australian worker had found similar signals, which
he could not explain. But Burke and Franklin soon found that
the signals came from Jupiter, despite its coldness.

It was not, however, black-body radiation. Instead of coming
as a steady hiss, as it does from the Moon, it is variable, like the
sudden bursts of static you can hear on your home radio from a
nearby thunderstorm. Perhaps the bursts are caused by some sort
of lightning in the clouds above Jupiter, whose atmosphere is
mainly ammonia and methane. If so, it must be far more powerful
than any lightning we know on Earth. This radiation occurs most
prominently on wave lengths of about 15 meters or 50 feet. The
Jupiter bursts last as long as a second.

J. D. Kraus, at the Ohio State University in Columbus, confirmed the findings of Burke and Franklin of emissions from
Jupiter and made an important new contribution when he found
similar waves coming from Venus. These irregular bursts were in
addition to the steady black-body transmission. So perhaps the
clouds above Venus which continually hide its surface from our
view may also have violent thunderstorms. The Venus signals are

only about a three-hundredth as strong as those from Jupiter and of shorter duration, lasting but a small fraction of a second. Thus, they are more like terrestrial lightning strokes.

The physicist speaking of sound uses the term *noise* to indicate a mixture of waves of various and unrelated frequencies, as opposed to a musical note, which consists of vibrations at a particular frequency or group of related frequencies. From acoustics, the radio engineer has borrowed the name. He often uses it to designate a random mixture of radio frequencies, which is very different from the transmission from a broadcasting station or other transmitter, where great pains are taken, as required by government regulations, to maintain transmission on a particular frequency. Static, of course, is a form of radio noise, and so is the mixture of waves received from the Milky Way, the Sun, the Moon, Jupiter, etc.

In the previous chapter we found how atomic changes, particularly the return of an electron from an abnormal position to its usual place, would cause radiation of light on a particular wave length, thus producing the lines of spectrum. Such lines appear not only in the visible part of the spectrum, from violet to red, but they also appear in the ultraviolet and the infrared part. Thus, it seemed reasonable to suppose that there might be similar lines in the radio spectrum being observed from the sky. These would be radio "notes" instead of noise.

Space between the stars is not actually a void, although it is much emptier of matter than the best vacuum we can produce in earthly laboratories. The stuff between the stars is mainly hydrogen; and even though it is spread thinly, perhaps 40 or 50 atoms in a cubic inch, there is so much space that the total amount of hydrogen is very large. But, at the low temperature of interstellar space, there occur none of the atomic shifts that produce visible light.

FLIPPING HYDROGEN ATOMS

In 1945 Hendrik C. van de Hulst, a young Dutch astronomer at the University of Leiden, suggested, however, that there might be a change in the hydrogen atoms out in space that would cause them to emit radiation. The proton that forms the hydrogen nucleus and the electron that revolves around it not only carry electrical charges but each is in rotation. A rotating charge produces a magnetic field. The electron in its ground state, when it has the lowest energy, is about two billionths of an inch away from the nucleus. However, this distance differs slightly, depending on whether the electron and proton are rotating in the same or in the opposite sense.

If the two particles are spinning in the same direction, there is a reaction between their magnetic fields which push them farther apart. Then, if the electron should suddenly flip over so that it turned in the same direction as the proton, it would move in a little. And, as we have seen, a shift in the position of an electron toward the nucleus means release of energy in the form of radiation. Such radiation would have a wave length of 21 cm. (about 8¼ inches). Later, the atom might absorb energy from a collision with another atom. Then the electron flips back again to its higher energy state, and it would then be ready to rotate the other way once more.

For individual atoms, such a flip-over is very rare. Van de Hulst estimated that, on the average, the lifetime of the atom in the higher energy state would be about 11 million years; i.e., it would take that long for the transition from the state of parallel directions to that of opposite directions. But, even though there are so few atoms to each cubic inch of space, there is so much space that there are lots of atoms, and shifts would be occurring all the time. The result: such 21-cm. radiation should be coming in toward the Earth continually, and proper equipment should be able to detect it.

Six years passed before the discovery was made. Two Harvard physicists, Edward Purcell and Harold Ewen, identified the 21-cm. hydrogen radiation on March 25, 1951, and reported it shortly afterward at a meeting of the American Physical Society.

Van de Hulst happened to be visiting Harvard at the time, and he immediately notified his colleagues back in Holland by trans-Atlantic telephone. At Kootwijk, near Leiden, the Dutch were constructing a new radio telescope especially designed to pick up hydrogen waves. By May it was completed, and they confirmed the findings of the Harvard group. Then W. N. Christman and J. V. Hindman, who were in Australia where important work in radio astronomy was already going on, hurried to construct a 21-cm. radio telescope. Within a few months they, too, had tuned in on the broadcasts of interstellar hydrogen atoms.

While some astronomers, prior to 1951, had realized that radio astronomy might supplement their observations with optical telescopes, few had shown any great enthusiasm for this new tool. This is hardly surprising since the electronic techniques that it required were so different from any they had used before. But a few months after his paper to the American Physical Society, Ewen presented an account of his findings at a meeting of the American Astronomical Society. Many astronomers then began to understand some of the things that radio could do for them. In December, the Astronomical Society met again, and at that time Jan H. Oort, director of the Leiden Observatory and a distinguished astronomer who had been closely associated with van de Hulst in his work, attended and explained the significance of radio observations as a branch of astronomy. Since then, astronomers have adopted it with enthusiasm.

Hydrogen radiation, due to the flipping-over of the electron, has been produced and measured in the laboratory; work at Columbia University placed its wave length at 21.1049 cm. However, when Ewen and Purcell first detected it in March, 1951, they found it to be slightly shorter than that. The cloud of hydrogen which they had observed was in the direction of Ophiuchus and happened to be moving toward the Earth; the resultant Doppler shift, therefore, squeezed the waves together so that they were shorter than normal when they arrived.

Since the pioneer observations, many radio observatories in all parts of the world have tuned in on hydrogen broadcasts. Sometimes the waves are short, due to an approach of the clouds, and at others they are long, because the masses of hydrogen are receding from us. The Dutch astronomers have detected as many as three or even more wave lengths at the same time and from the same direction. This means that the astronomers were looking toward, and through, several hydrogen clouds, each cloud moving at a different speed toward or away from the Earth. By analyzing such observations, astronomers have learned a great deal about the structure of the Galaxy. But for these details we must wait until a later chapter.

RADIO OBSERVATORIES

Radio telescopes are of many kinds. The kind Reber used is basically the same as the reflecting telescope at Mount Palomar, in which a concave mirror, coated with aluminum, picks up the light rays from the distant stars and brings them to a focus.

The big dish of this type of radio telescope picks up the faint radio waves from space and focuses them on an antenna, such as a dipole. This is simply two rods in line, separated by a small space in the middle; their combined over-all length is equal to half of the length of the waves to be detected. A pair of wires, one connected to the inner end of each rod, carries the energy, feeble though it is, to the detectors, amplifiers, and other electronic devices which translate the waves into a wavy line, made by a pen on a moving strip of paper, or whatever other type of record may be desired.

Instead of a dipole, a precisely formed tube, or *wave guide*, may be placed with its open end at the focus of the dish. Somewhat as sound waves travel through a speaking tube, so the short radio waves pass through the guide to the detecting equipment. Both the length of the dipole and the size of the wave guide are determined by the wave length to be picked up. Thus, the same dish can be used for waves of many different lengths by changing the antenna at the focus.

The larger the dish, the more the energy collected. Just as the 200-inch mirror at Mount Palomar can detect objects considerably fainter than the 100-inch telescope can, and that telescope can observe fainter objects than a 60-inch telescope can; so the bigger the parabolic dish on a radio telescope, the weaker the radio sources the telescope can observe. The largest radio telescope yet built, at Jodrell Bank near Manchester, England, is one with a bowl 250 feet in diameter.

But there is another great advantage to the big dish, aside from its increased capacity to detect minute amounts of energy. Just as with an optical telescope, it is desirable to detect, as separate, two objects that are in nearly the same direction. This is determined by the resolving power; the greater the power, the nearer to each other the separate sources can be and still be identified. For the optical telescope, this may involve seeing as separate the two parts of a close double star, or observing fine details on the Moon. In radio astronomy, similarly, close radio sources may have to be separated.

The resolving power of a telescope, either optical or radio, depends on its diameter in terms of the wave length of radiation used in the observation. With visible light waves about 1/50,000 inch long, a modest 10-inch telescope, for light, would measure 500,000 wave lengths in diameter. With it, fairly close double stars may be observed. But to obtain similar resolution with the 40-foot waves on which radiation has been observed from Jupiter, the telescope would have to be 500,000 times 40 feet in diameter; i.e., 20 million feet or nearly 3,800 miles, which would be somewhat impracticable! Even to get comparable resolution on the shorter 21-cm. (about 8.26 inches) radiation of hydrogen, a 780-mile telescope would be needed.

BIG EFFECTS FROM LITTLE INSTRUMENTS

While it does seem impossible to build radio telescopes with the reflecting dish big enough to give fine resolution, there are some other dodges that may be used to improve it. One makes use of the phenomenon of *interference,* mentioned before in connection with light waves. If light comes from each of two pinholes, perhaps an inch apart, and shines on a white surface an inch or so away, the illumination of the surface is not continuous but is a series of light and dark bands. For a point exactly in the middle and precisely the same distance from each pinhole, the two sets of light waves reach the surface together, in step. But, a little way to either side, one of the pinholes is a little nearer. At a particular point, one pinhole may be exactly half a wave length of light closer, or farther, than the other. This means that the crest of one wave will come at the trough of the other, they will counteract each other, and there will be darkness. Go a little farther and the difference in distance becomes a whole wave length. Then the waves are in step again, and they reinforce each other. After that, a place comes where there is interference and darkness again, and then another point of reinforcement. Thus come the series of bright and dark bands.

The same thing occurs with radio waves, on a larger scale. Take two dipole antennas fed by the same transmitter and separated a little. The area in which the waves are "shining" is not illuminated with visible light but with radio energy. Now, if you move a receiver across these beams, you will find places where the waves from each transmitting antenna are in step and the signal is extra strong. These correspond, as with light interference, to places where the difference in distance from the two antennas is a whole number of wave lengths, so that the waves arrive in step. In between are "dark" areas where there is no signal. There is an extra half wavelength difference in the paths; therefore, the two sets interfere.

Now put a receiver where the transmitter was and connect it to the pair of antennas. Move a transmitter along the line that the receiver was moved before. When transmission comes from places where there were "bright" bands, the signal comes in strongly; from the locations in between, there is no signal. This is the principle of the radio interferometer. Each *lobe* of such a pair, each direction from which a strong signal comes, is much more sharply defined than any directional effect that could be obtained with a single antenna.

One of the pioneer interferometers of this sort stands in Australia on a 250-foot cliff overlooking the sea. It was a radar station during the war, and it has only one antenna, which happens to be a dish. Since a water surface makes a good reflector for radio waves, however, the dish picks up two signals—one from the source directly, the other from its reflection in the sea—and thus the interferometer effect is obtained.

Not one, but a number of antennas may be used to get still finer resolution. Another interesting arrangement in Australia is located on a hill near Sydney. On each of two adjacent sides of a city reservoir, there is a row 712 feet long—more than a city block—of thirty-two antennas, each with a dish 6½ feet in diameter. One row is north and south, the other east and west.

From the east-west array, strong signals are picked up from north-south strips across the sky. Each strip is 3 minutes of arc, about a tenth of the Sun's diameter, in width. The strips are about 1.7 degrees apart, which is more than three times the diameter of the Sun; therefore, the Sun can only be on one strip at a time. Thus, as the rotation of the Earth carries the Sun across the sky from east to west, radio waves coming from a narrow region on the Sun's surface may be identified. For the north-south antenna array, there are similar east-west strips to which the device is sensitive. In this way, a small region on the Sun, where the two strips cross, and perhaps a single spot can be isolated.

Considerably larger, but embodying similar principles, is the Mills Cross (named after Bernard Mills, who devised it) located on farm land near Sydney. There are 500 dipole antennas along an east-west line more than a third of a mile in length. Intersecting the center of this line is another, running north and south, so that the lines form a huge cross. The two groups are connected to the receiver in such a way that only signals coming through both sets are used, and the effective area of the sky from which it picks up a signal is a square only 50 minutes on a side, less than twice the diameter of the full Moon. The Mills Cross works with waves about 11 feet in length.

With the lines of antennas each more than a third of a mile long, the whole thing is fixed on the ground and cannot be moved to point to different parts of the sky. However, by adjusting the individual antennas in the north-south arm of the cross, the beam may be shifted about 45 degrees to the north or south of the zenith. Those of the east-west arm are fixed, but this beam sweeps across the sky as the Earth itself turns. Thus a considerable area of the sky is covered. Since he made this first installation in Australia, Mills has aided the Carnegie Institution to build a similar cross, even larger, near Washington.

Comparing the radio telescope with its optical counterpart, we see an essential difference. Ordinarily, photographs (made with light) combine a wide range of wave lengths of colors, perhaps even extending outside the visible spectrum into the infrared or the ultraviolet. With narrow-pass filters, it is possible to isolate particular colors. Also the spectroscope can be used to sort them out.

The radio receiver is tuned to a particular wave length, so it automatically acts as the narrow-pass filter does to light. Sometimes the radio astronomer wants to narrow it down even more. The 21-cm. hydrogen radiation normally is exactly this wave length, with a frequency of 1,420 megacycles. This occurs when the flipping hydrogen atoms that generate the radiation are moving neither toward nor away from the earth. If they are moving, the wave length becomes shorter or longer, on account of the Doppler effect, and it is important to measure the exact shift to determine the speed of the movement.

THE RADIO SPECTROMETER

This is done with a radio spectrometer, which the electronic experts have developed for astronomical use. The wave length to which it is sensitive may be shifted back and forth, from a little above to a little below that of the normal hydrogen waves. The displacement of the waves may be measured, and from this one can determine the relative speed of the atoms from which they come. Such data have led to important conclusions about the shape of our Milky Way system—the Galaxy which will be described in a later chapter.

With so many different radio telescopes tuned to a wide variety of wave lengths, there are plenty of data from which we can determine the relative strength at different frequencies. This does not seem to change very much except for the bursts of radio emissions that sometimes pour out of the Sun, where the changes are large and rapid.

Two other Australian radio astronomers, J. P. Wild and L. L. McCready, have devised a receiver which will sweep across the wave lengths from about 4 feet to 25 feet, in a fraction of a second. Actually, their device uses three separate aerials, each with its own receiver, since one receiver could not cover the desired range. The results obtained with this equipment are called dynamic spectra.

Though there are methods by which installations that are relatively modest can do valuable work in radio astronomy, the big reflectors have many advantages. One of these is the 250-foot dish at Jodrell Bank, near Manchester, in England, which is shown in Plate 2b. One of 210 feet is under construction in Australia. These are "steerable"; i.e., they may be pointed toward any part of the sky and accurately aimed at the region to be studied.

In the United States the principal center of radio astronomy is the National Radio Astronomy Observatory, established at Green Bank, West Virginia, with U.S. government funds supplied by the National Science Foundation. This location was selected, after an investigation of many sites, because of its accessibility and its relative freedom from radio static, which would interfere seriously with the researches.

Reber's historic 30-foot telescope has been re-erected at Green Bank and is still doing useful work. Still larger is a radio telescope, 85 feet in diameter, similar to several at other observatories. Another of 140 feet is being built.

The original plans called for a fully steerable telescope, 600 feet in diameter, and another of 300 feet. However, these were abandoned when U.S. Navy officials decided to build a 600-foot steerable instrument. Recognizing the advantages of West Virginia, they selected Sugar Grove, about 30 miles east of Green Bank,

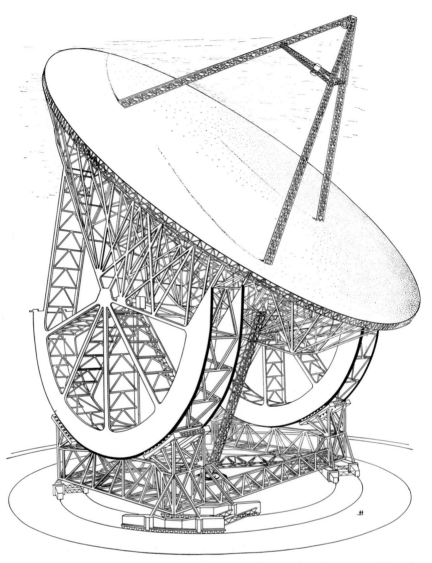

Fig. 11. Drawing of the 600-foot radio telescope to be erected by the U.S. Navy at Sugar Grove, West Virginia. It will stand 665 feet high and will incorporate 20,000 tons of steel and 600 tons of aluminum. The scale is suggested by the tiny human figures at lower right. (By permission from *Scientific American*. Copyright, 1960, Scientific American, Inc.)

as the location. This huge telescope, with a height of 665 feet, about that of a 65-story building, will appear as shown in Fig. 11. Half of its time will be devoted to classified Navy projects, concerned with the physics of the upper atmosphere, communication, and navigation. But the rest of the time it will be available to astronomers, and there should be close cooperation between Sugar Grove and Green Bank.

With 21-cm. hydrogen radiation, the 600-foot telescope will be able to concentrate on a region about a sixth the apparent diameter of the full Moon. It will serve not only as a receiver, but as a transmitter as well, sending out signals and picking up their echoes from the Moon, Venus, Mars, and perhaps even Jupiter. Timing these echoes will fix distances in the solar system with great precision and will provide data useful in space navigation.

PROJECT OZMA

Nature, which has been published every week in London for nearly a century, is perhaps the most generally respected of all scientific journals. In September, 1959, some readers were surprised to find in its dignified pages an article that, a few years earlier, could hardly have appeared in any but a science fiction magazine. This was "Searching for Interstellar Communications," by two Cornell University physicists, Giuseppe Cocconi and Philip Morrison.

As we shall learn in a later chapter, the process of formation of planets around a star no longer seems as rare as it once did. So, they argue, there seems to be no good reason why other stars that are similar to the Sun should not also have planetary systems. Moreover, there are two planets in the Solar System (Earth and, "very probably, Mars") which have life on them, so it seems likely that life would have started elsewhere.

On some of these other life-bearing planets, of course, it may not have developed very far, but on others it may well have developed into a society far more advanced, scientifically and intellectually, than ours.

"To the beings of such a society," write Cocconi and Morrison, "our Sun must appear as a likely site for the evolution of a new society. It is highly probable that for a long time they will have been expecting the development of science near the Sun. We shall assume that long ago they established a channel of communication that would one day become known to us, and that they look forward patiently to the answering signals from the Sun which would make known to them that a new society had entered the community of intelligence."

Because of such considerations, Project Ozma has been set up at the Green Bank Observatory. It is named after the queen of the imaginary land of Oz. Using the 85-foot telescope, and the 140-foot telescope as that comes into use, the radio astronomers listen carefully for possible signals from the direction of stars that resemble the Sun.

As for the nature of these signals, it seems that radio waves might well be used, since electromagnetic radiation is so widely spread through the universe. Frequencies above 10,000 megacycles are stopped by our atmosphere, while those below 1,000 mc. might be drowned out by the radio "noise" from the Galaxy. Thus a frequency between these limits seems most probable, assuming that the intelligent beings on the distant planets would realize this. But it would be a difficult task to search this whole range. Is there any particular frequency that might very well be used?

"Yes," answer Cocconi and Morrison. The 1,420-mc. radiation of interstellar hydrogen comes in the right part of the spectrum and would be a reasonable selection. Artificial transmission on this frequency could be easily coded, so that it could be identified and not confused with the natural radiation from space. It might, for example, consist of a succession of prime numbers (1, 3, 5, 7, etc.) or a series of simple arithmetical sums, which would indicate some intelligence behind it.

Even the nearest stars are many trillions of miles distant; but our present radio telescopes are sufficiently sensitive, so that they could pick up messages from planets at a distance of not more than 10 or so light-years and which were sent by transmitters only a little more powerful than those we already have.

Not more than 15 light-years away there are seven stars that resemble the Sun, and which might have planetary systems. Some of these are too far south in the sky to be reached from Green Bank and others are in the same direction as the Milky Way. Their signals might be hard to disentangle from the background of natural radiation. Tau Ceti (in the constellation of Cetus, the whale) and epsilon Eridani (a star in Eridanus, the river) seem most suitable and are being examined first. Within 50 light-years there are about a hundred stars of solar type; later, perhaps, the investigation will be extended to some of these.

And what if some signal is received? Then, of course, we shall have to answer, beaming a signal carrying some kind of coded intelligence to the right part of the sky. For a star at 10 light-years, it would take 10 years for their signal to reach us, and 10 more for our reply to get back, so this is a long-term program. Communication, if it is ever achieved, will be slow at best.

Cocconi and Morrison admit that their speculations might seem to belong to the domain of science fiction, but they submit that "the presence of such interstellar signals is entirely consistent with all that we now know, and that if signals are present the means of detecting them is now at hand."

They concluded their paper with these challenging words: "Few will deny the profound importance, practical and philosophical, which the detection of interstellar communications would have. We therefore feel that a discriminating search for signals deserves a considerable effort. The chance of success is difficult to estimate; but if we never search, the chance of success is zero."

Even if Project Ozma is not successful, radio astronomy has opened up a period in celestial science comparable with that of the seventeenth century, when the telescope was first being applied to the heavens. That instrument yielded knowledge which previously had seemed completely out of our reach.

Then it seemed that, from the distance of the Earth, we could never find what the stars are made of. But the spectroscope made that possible, and gave other important data as well.

Radio astronomy will mean just as great a revolution in astronomical research. Of course, the radio telescope will not replace its optical counterpart; in spite of the importance of spectroscopy, direct observations or photographs through telescopes of all sizes are still made. Radio studies will take their own place as an important new tool in telling man about the nature of his universe.

4

Atomic Energy in the Stars

The sciences of physics and astronomy probably come closest in the study of the interior of the stars. Thus has arisen the combination science of astrophysics. The light that reaches us from the stars is picked up by telescopes, recorded on photographic emulsions, and analyzed by spectroscopes; then it tells us what is happening in the stellar atmospheres. Only indirectly can we infer what is happening in the interior thousands, sometimes millions, of miles below the surfaces of the star.

Fortunately, the physicist can give very effective help. He is now just beginning to reproduce conditions that occur inside the stars. Despite this, a knowledge of what happens in laboratory experiments, extended by theoretical considerations, permits the astrophysicist to surmise, with some assurance that he is approaching the truth, how atoms and parts of atoms behave under the extreme conditions of temperature and pressure that exist in a stellar interior.

He makes the fundamental assumption that basic laws of physics apply in the distant reaches of the universe, just as they do on Earth. This assumption, of course, is the foundation of all science. If its laws and principles were capricious, science would hardly be possible.

Early man, like his descendants in relatively recent times, knew only fire as the source of heat or light. When he found both light and heat coming from the Sun, he assumed that combustion was its source, that the Sun was a vast conflagration. It differed only in size, he thought, from the fires he kindled on the floor of his cave and, later, in fireplaces and stoves.

As geologists began to delve into the past history of the Earth, they soon realized that our planet had existed in a state very much as it is now for thousands—even millions—of years, and that the Earth must have received heat from the Sun at a similar rate over all this period. Huge though the Sun is, its fires could not possibly have burned so long—unless they were continually stoked with new fuel.

COULD THE FUEL BE METEORS?

With the realization, in the early part of the nineteenth century, that the Earth was being constantly bombarded from space with material that appeared in the sky as meteors and occasionally as a meteorite landing on the ground, it seemed that this material might supply the Sun with fuel. But this theory was inadequate. As a great American astronomer of the past century, Simon Newcomb, expressed it in his book, *Popular Astronomy,* published in 1878, "in order to keep up this solar heat, a mass of matter equal to our planet would have to fall into the sun every century."

But, he continued: "This quantity of meteoric matter is so far beyond all reasonable possibility that it requires little consideration to show that the supply of solar heat cannot thus be accounted for. Only a minute fraction of all meteoroids or other bodies circulating through space or revolving around the Sun could strike that luminary. In order to strike the Sun they would have to drop directly into it from space, or be thrown into it.... If meteors were as thick as this, the Earth would be so pelted with them that its whole surface would be made hot by the force of the impact, and all life would be completely destroyed. While, then, the Sun may, at some past time, have received a large supply of heat in this way, it is impossible that the supply could always be kept up."

Then came a suggestion by the German physicist, Herman von Helmholtz. When you take a weight from the ground and raise it, say, a hundred feet, you expend energy. The weight now has additional energy—potential energy—by virtue of its elevated position. As it falls, it gives up this energy in the form of heat. Thus, the temperature at the bottom of a waterfall is slightly higher than at the top. In falling, the potential energy of the water at the upper level has been converted to heat energy.

Helmholtz proposed that the outer layers of the Sun were slowly falling to the center; i.e., it was slowly but continuously shrinking.

Such a contraction, reducing the solar diameter by about 200 feet per year or about 4 miles in a century, would be enough to maintain the output of the solar powerhouse, according to Kelvin, an English physicist. With the Sun's diameter of about 866,000 miles, this would be far too small to detect, except over many thousands of years.

On this basis, the past history of the Sun was pushed back about 18 million years. While this was a lot better than the few thousand years that burning provided, it still did not give all the time demanded by geologists; but no other explanation seemed satisfactory.

However, after Madame Curie and her husband discovered radium, scientists realized that there were other possible sources of energy. In his *Manual of Astronomy*, published in 1902, Charles A. Young, of Princeton University, wrote:

"If we could assume that the amount of heat yearly radiated by the solar surface had remained constantly the same throughout all those ages, and, moreover, that all the radiated heat comes only from the slow contraction of the solar mass, apart from any considerable original capital in the form of a high initial temperature and without any reinforcement of energy from outside sources,— *IF we could assume these premises* [italics his], it is easy to show that the Sun's past history must cover about fifteen or twenty million years. But such assumptions are at least doubtful; radium and its congeners may have played an important part, and the Sun's age may be many times greater than the limit we have named."

Even though Young, and others, raised such questions and suggested that the answer might lie deep within the atom, they could find no actual mechanism—no process allied to that by which radium continually yields energy and which could stoke the furnaces of the Sun and other stars. As late as 1920, teachers of astronomy were still telling their students that contraction was the process.

By 1930, however, a change in our thinking had begun. Einstein's theory of relativity had been verified, and part of the theory was that mass and energy are basically the same. Matter, in theory at least, could be converted into energy. Cockroft and Walton, at the Cavendish Laboratory of Cambridge University, were soon to show (in 1932) that lithium could be transmuted into helium. There was a slight loss of mass, which reappeared as energy, exactly in accord with the Einstein formula: $E = mc^2$.

About 1925 Arthur Eddington, astronomer at Cambridge University, proposed that conversion of some of the solar mass into energy kept the Sun fueled. One school of thought proposed that it was a complete conversion process; but this suffered from an objection opposite to that which had doomed the contraction theory, because it gave too much time. This explanation allowed the Sun an age as great as a trillion years, and astronomers didn't know what to do with it.

The other suggestion was that only a part of each atomic nucleus would be converted. Helium was known to exist in the Sun; indeed, it had been discovered there before it was found on Earth. Considering hydrogen as the building block of heavier elements, it takes four hydrogen nuclei to build one nucleus of helium. With the mass of each hydrogen nucleus as 1, the mass of helium should be 4. But it isn't; it is only 3.97. If the missing 0.03 units of mass from each quartet of hydrogen atoms assembled to form one of helium were converted to energy, it seemed about right.

THE CARBON CYCLE

Still there was the puzzle: "How does it work?" One answer came in 1936 when, independently, Hans A. Bethe, of Cornell University, and Carl Friedrich von Weizsäcker, in Germany, proposed the famous "carbon cycle." The fuel is hydrogen; carbon (the ordinary kind) acts as a catalyst. That is, without suffering any permanent change itself, the carbon makes possible profound changes in other elements. A catalyst has been termed a *chemical parson,* for a clergyman can produce a great change in the lives of two persons whom he marries; yet, he does not change himself!

The carbon cycle starts with ordinary carbon of 12 units mass; see Fig. 12. Along comes a proton, with which it collides. They stick together. The nucleus is now one of nitrogen, not ordinary nitrogen (which weighs 14 mass units) but a light isotope: nitrogen 13. A little mass is lost, which comes off as energy in the form of a gamma ray. On the average, it takes 2,500,000 years for a carbon nucleus and a proton to get together in this way; but there are lots of carbon atoms, and protons too, in the Sun.

Nitrogen 13, however, is unstable. In less than 10 minutes it gives off a positive electron (ordinary electrons, it will be recalled, are negatively charged). Since the number of positive charges determines what an element is, and one of these charges has been lost, we no longer have nitrogen. It has reverted to carbon, not the ordinary isotope but a heavier one: carbon 13.

Then another proton comes along (in 500,000 years, on the average) and hits the carbon 13 nucleus. Once again it changes to nitrogen; this time the ordinary variety, nitrogen 14. Again some mass is lost; another gamma ray carries off the energy.

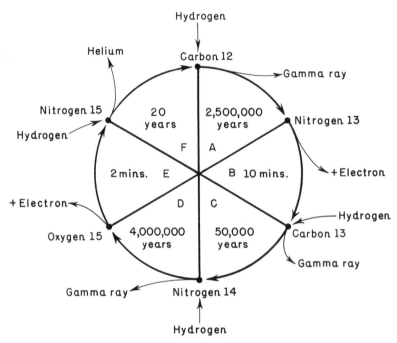

Fig. 12. The carbon cycle. The source of energy in stars hotter than the Sun. Carbon is changed to nitrogen and then back to carbon, leaving helium as the ash. (By permission from *Electrons in Action,* by James Stokley. Copyright, 1946, McGraw-Hill Book Co., Inc., New York.)

Some 4 million years later, our nitrogen 14 nucleus is hit by still another proton. It changes to a light form of oxygen with 15 mass units instead of 16, the more usual value. A third gamma ray carries off more energy.

Oxygen 15 (like nitrogen 13) is unstable; in just over 2 minutes it gives off a positive electron, thereby changing to a heavy isotope of nitrogen, N 15.

Now comes the final step in the process, in some 20 years. A fourth proton hits the nitrogen 15 nucleus. There is a momentary combination which immediately splits apart, leaving a nucleus of ordinary helium, and also one of ordinary carbon (which is just what we started with some 6.5 million years ago!). Four protons—hydrogen nuclei—have been used up; they were the fuel. One helium nucleus remains as "ash" from this solar "fire." And the carbon 12 nucleus, magically restored to its original form, is ready to meet another proton and to begin the process all over again!

The carbon cycle seemed to meet the astronomer's demands precisely and was generally accepted. The author of one leading textbook, published in 1947, stated categorically that, at least as it concerned a star of the size and mass of the Sun, "the sole source of energy production is the carbon cycle."

While physicists realized, during the decade of the thirties, that some such nuclear process seemed to explain the source of solar and stellar energy, it still seemed that a long time would pass before any comparable process could be applied on Earth. Perhaps, indeed, such human application of these celestial processes could never be made. But, even then, preliminary work was going on, destined before the decade ended to lead to a series of discoveries that were to cause a world revolution.

NEUTRONS AS BULLETS

About 1934, the Italian physicist Enrico Fermi (later to emigrate to the United States) showed that neutrons were effective bullets for atom-smashing experiments. These particles, it will be recalled, are one of the two kinds of bricks out of which atomic nuclei are built; protons are the other. He found neutrons could be used to initiate changes in much heavier atoms than those which had been altered in past nuclear experiments.

Most changes of elements that had been observed were changes to those elements slightly lighter (or, in some cases, slightly heavier) than the original. When Fermi fired neutrons at uranium, then the heaviest element known, he obtained something which was apparently not lighter. Thus, he concluded that he had produced a new kind of atom, heavier than uranium. Later such trans-Uranium elements were made (ten are now known) but this did not seem to be the explanation of Fermi's results. A German woman scientist, Ida Noddack, suggested that the neutrons had split the uranium nuclei into two roughly equal parts; but that seemed so radical a proposal that no one accepted it at that time.

In 1938, however, another German, Otto Hahn, found that, when uranium was bombarded with neutrons, a considerably lighter element appeared. This was finally identified, in France, as barium, number 56 in the list of atoms, far below uranium, whose atomic number is 92.

Then, in January, 1939, another German woman scientist, Lise Meitner, who had moved to Denmark because of the Nazi persecution of her race, and her nephew, O. R. Frisch, revived Noddack's proposal. They suggested that Hahn's curious results could be explained by what they termed *fission*, borrowing a word from biology. Perhaps the uranium nucleus had split into two, one nucleus of barium (56), the other of krypton (36). The atomic numbers of these two elements total 92, so none of the protons from the original uranium nucleus had been lost.

This was the discovery of nuclear fission; it was to lead to the atomic bomb as well as to atomic power plants and all the other applications of atomic energy. In December, 1942, Fermi, by that time at the University of Chicago, operated the first nuclear reactor. By means of a chain reaction utilizing the fission process in uranium, a controlled release of atomic energy was accomplished for the first time. The atomic age had begun!

Fission—the splitting of very heavy atomic nuclei—is one of two ways whereby nuclear energy may be released. The other is fusion; it occurs in the Sun and other stars. Very light nuclei, usually hydrogen, fuse together to form a heavier nucleus, such as helium. In other words, starting from either the upper or lower ends of the list of atoms, ranked by increasing mass, and going toward the middle, energy is released.

On the other hand, starting with number 65 (terbium), a change to either lighter or heavier elements will require energy to be absorbed. You may think of hydrogen at the top of one hill, uranium on another, with terbium at the bottom of the valley between. A road connects them, and the other elements along the way. You can coast down from either height toward the bottom; energy is released. But it takes energy to get from the bottom to either hilltop.

Even in 1936, when the carbon cycle was originally proposed, physicists realized that four protons could combine to form helium in a more direct manner, without the intervention of carbon and nitrogen. First two protons would combine. When this happens, a positively charged electron emerges from the combination, carrying away one of the positive charges. Thus only the mass of a proton, without charge, is left. In other words, one of the protons changes to a neutron. With one proton, a neutron forms hydrogen, not the ordinary kind, but heavy hydrogen, also called *deuterium*. The nucleus of this atom is called a *deuteron*. Now comes along another proton, which combines with the deuteron. Since

PROTON-PROTON REACTION

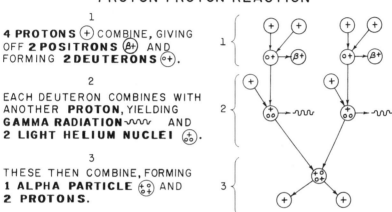

1
4 PROTONS (+) COMBINE, GIVING OFF **2 POSITRONS** (β+) AND FORMING **2 DEUTERONS** (∘+).

2
EACH DEUTERON COMBINES WITH ANOTHER **PROTON,** YIELDING **GAMMA RADIATION** ∿∿∿ AND **2 LIGHT HELIUM NUCLEI** (⁺∘∘).

3
THESE THEN COMBINE, FORMING **1 ALPHA PARTICLE** (⁺∘∘⁺) AND **2 PROTONS.**

Fig. 13. The proton-proton reaction. The source of energy in stars like the Sun.

the resulting nucleus has two protons, it is no longer hydrogen, but helium. Its total mass is only 3, not 4 like normal helium. That is, it is a light isotope of helium.

This helium-3 nucleus must now be converted into helium 4, the normal kind, in various possible ways. The most likely manner, as far as stellar reactions are concerned, is for two helium-3 nuclei to combine. Two protons are ejected from the combination, leaving a nucleus with two protons and two neutrons—in other words, helium 4; see Fig. 13.

TEMPERATURE DETERMINES THE PROCESS

It seems to be a matter of temperature that determines whether the carbon cycle or the proton chain operates in a particular star. At about 10 million degrees on the Centigrade scale (about 18 million degrees Fahrenheit), the proton chain would occur, virtually to the exclusion of the carbon cycle. At 30 million degrees centigrade, however, the carbon cycle would occur exclusively. Somewhere in between there would be a temperature at which both would occur equally. The Sun's internal temperature is 15 million or so degrees centigrade. Is this above or below the change-over point?

Earlier work indicated that in the Sun the carbon reaction would predominate but, with further studies, estimates of the temperature at which the two methods would be equally likely climbed higher and higher. "It now appears," says Lawrence H. Aller of the University of Michigan, "that the Sun derives its enery almost entirely from the proton-proton reaction. This reaction fails to provide sufficient energy only in the hotter... stars where it appears that the carbon (or carbon-nitrogen) cycle may be the principal source of energy." *

In very hot stars, the carbon cycle provides energy; in stars similar to the Sun, the proton chain predominates. And perhaps, in considerably cooler stars, the old Helmholtz contraction process may operate. This might occur after the star's supply of hydrogen has been completely converted to helium and no fuel is left to supply either the carbon or proton process.

As the star contracts, it will get hotter and hotter inside. At a hundred million degrees or so, another nuclear process may begin to supply energy, this time with the helium that had been formed previously as fuel. Contraction increases the density to perhaps 20,000 times that of ordinary water. Under these conditions, it seems, three helium nuclei may combine to form one of carbon 12. Since this conversion is still toward elements of middle weight, again energy would be yielded.

THERMONUCLEAR REACTIONS

These are examples of *thermonuclear* reactions where high temperatures make possible effects that could not occur in cooler bodies because of the mutual repulsion of particles with similar electrical charges. Two protons, for example, each with its positive charge, repel each other, and they cannot come together in order to unite and carry on the proton chain. But when hot enough, they have the extra energy needed to overcome repulsion, and then union can take place. Because this requires temperatures of the order of 10 or

---

* L. H. Aller, *Astrophysics: Nuclear Transformations, Stellar Interiors, and Nebulae.* Copyright, 1953, The Ronald Press Co., New York.

20 million degrees, it seemed as if such processes were forever beyond hope of duplication on Earth.

However, when an atomic bomb is exploded, such high temperatures are produced momentarily, which can be utilized in a hydrogen bomb. A fission bomb, using uranium, serves as a trigger that provides the high temperatures needed. The hydrogen nuclei then unite in a process closely similar to that which occurs in the Sun and other stars.

Soon after the atomic bomb was developed, the fission process was applied to make nuclear reactors—atomic furnaces—in which atomic energy could be converted into useful power. Today, atomic power plants are generating electricity in land-based plants and are driving submarines and other ships. Small wonder, then, that the atomic scientists and engineers looked wonderingly at the hydrogen process, to consider whether that too could be applied constructively and not just destructively in a bomb.

The solar process, involving a union of protons, takes millions of years to complete; therefore, it would hardly be suitable. But there are similar processes, using the heavier isotopes of hydrogen, which seem more promising. One involves deuterons, nuclei of heavy hydrogen, which occur in nature.

There is a process, the *D-D reaction,* involving the union of two deuterons, which consist of a proton and a neutron each. Three of the four particles from the two nuclei combine; the fourth is ejected. Thus, there are two possibilities. In one case, the result is a nucleus with two protons and one neutron, helium 3. The other result has two neutrons and one proton, tritium, or extra heavy hydrogen. Either process, however, gives off energy; thus the reaction may be a practicable method of obtaining thermonuclear power.

One trouble is that this reaction requires a temperature of something like 100 million degrees. However, there is another, which will work at around 30 million degrees, called the *D-T reaction* since it involves deuterium and tritium. The deuteron, you will recall, has a proton and a neutron; the *triton* (the tritium nucleus) has a proton and two neutrons. When a deuteron and triton unite, they form a helium nucleus with two protons and two neutrons. The third and extra neutron is ejected. This reaction gives off even more energy than the D-D reaction, and is probably the one used in the H-bomb.

Tritium does not occur in nature; it must be made, in a nuclear reactor, by bombarding lithium with neutrons. Moreover, it cannot be stored very long because of its radioactivity. If you have a pound of tritium now, you will have only half a pound 12 years from now. The other half pound will have changed to helium 3. With deuterium, however, ample quantities are available in nature; since, even with the natural proportion of one part to 6,000 of ordinary hydrogen, there are some 200 trillion tons of it in the oceans of the world. It is not difficult to extract, and it has been estimated that the amount in the oceans of the world would be able to supply power, at the rate energy is now being used on Earth, for some 20 billion years! No wonder the United States, Britain, the U.S.S.R., and other nations are devoting major efforts to harness this process.

The difficulty of applying it, however, involves more than selecting a suitable fuel and heating it to a hundred million degrees. Even after this temperature is attained, some way must be found of containing the reaction. The Sun—nearly a million miles in diameter—is so enormous and so massive that the force of gravitation holds the hot mixture at the center. The process takes place extremely slowly, but there is so much material that the steady output of energy is enormous.

On Earth another method is required, but no usual construction material will remain solid at temperatures as low as 10,000 degrees, to say nothing of 100 million. Therefore, some other means of confinement must be found.

At the temperatures needed, the atoms of deuterium and tritium are completely ionized; i.e., there are no electrons moving around the nuclei. As a result, the nuclei are electrically charged. Unlike ordinary unionized and uncharged atoms, magnetic forces will act on them, and this has led to the concept of containing the plasma, as such a mixture of atomic nuclei is called, in a magnetic "bottle." That is, properly designed magnetic fields may be able to hold the plasma at the center of a solid container, away from the walls.

Although many scientists working in the field are optimistic that these problems can be solved, the answers have not yet been found. It seems that a practicable thermonuclear power plant is still far in the future. We will have to continue to depend largely on the one we already have and have been using for past ages and ages: the Sun, which continues to shower its radiation upon us.

5

The Sun

When early men worshiped the Sun, as they often did, they must have had some appreciation of the importance of that body to the inhabitants of Earth—an importance fully substantiated by modern science. No life could exist on this planet without the beneficent radiation of light and heat from the Sun; indeed, it has been the source of all the energy used on Earth during past ages. Now, with atomic power a reality and thermonuclear power in prospect, we may become partially independent of the Sun as the Earth's powerhouse; but there seems no doubt that it will continue to be a major source of our energy.

The heating effect of the Sun evaporates water from lakes, rivers, and oceans; the vapor ascends into the sky. In doing so, it acquires energy from the Sun; and when the vapor condenses and falls to Earth as rain, some of this store of energy is released. More is released as the water flows from high lands to low and on the way, perhaps, turns the turbines of hydroelectric plants. Thus, all water power originates in the Sun.

Suppose we burn wood, once part of a living tree. As the tree grew, solar rays, by that marvellous process known as *photosynthesis*, built up cellulose—a compound of carbon, hydrogen, and oxygen of which wood mainly consists. Again solar energy is stored; to be released when, in the process of burning, the cellulose is broken down into carbon dioxide and water. And when we burn coal, we are burning vegetation that lived millions of years ago and acquired solar energy in the same way. Similarly, oil and natural gas resulted from the fossil decay of other organisms which, while living in past ages, likewise took up energy from the Sun. Power from the wind depends on the Sun; the movement of air masses across the surface of the Earth is basically dependent upon the heating of certain areas where the air rises, so that more air has to flow in to take its place.

As thermonuclear processes take place in the heart of the Sun, converting hydrogen into helium, and as the resultant energy finally reaches the solar surface, there is a tremendous outpouring of radiated energy. In terms of the unit familiar to us in rating electric equipment, the whole Sun is continually putting out 5.1×10^{23} kilowatts. But space is so nearly empty that most of this travels on and on. Only about one part in two billion is intercepted by the Earth, but this is still an enormous quantity.

ONE HORSEPOWER PER SQUARE YARD

Roughly, the energy received by a square yard of Earth's surface, in the United States, would yield about one horsepower if it could be fully utilized. The energy falling on an area of 10×20 miles would, theoretically, be enough to supply the needs of the world at the present rate of consumption. Why, then, is it not used?

Actually, of course, no process of energy production is completely efficient, so not more than a very small proportion of that falling on an area could be converted into useful electrical current. Moreover, the best place for a solar energy plant would be a desert region, with very little cloudiness. But such areas are generally far from the places where power is needed. This would entail additional losses in transmitting the electrical power over considerable distances. However, much study is being given to solar energy; it may well prove as important in the future as energy from nuclear sources.

For a number of years a house near Boston has been heated by solar rays which shine on a glass-covered blackened chamber on the south side. As in a greenhouse, the air becomes heated. It is pumped through ducts to the basement, where it gives up its heat to cans of magnesium sulfate (Glauber's salts), causing the solid chemical to change to a liquid form. In this way the heat energy is stored. As the solution solidifies, heat is given off, to warm the air carried through the house. Thus, even through long winter nights, or after several cloudy days, there is still enough heat stored to keep the house warm.

Use of an ordinary magnifying glass as a "burning glass," to focus the Sun's rays on a piece of paper and to ignite it, is a familiar experiment which everyone has performed. Many years ago the California Institute of Technology erected, on top of their Astrophysical Laboratory in Pasadena, a solar furnace embodying exactly similar principles. An array of lenses and mirrors, mounted like an equatorial telescope so that it would follow the Sun, formed an intensely hot spot the size of one's little fingernail. Here a temperature of many thousands of degrees was reached—enough to melt and even boil a brick in a few seconds.

Some of the most extensive work of this sort has been carried on at the Solar Energy Laboratory on Mont Louis, in the French Pyrenees. A parabolic reflector about 35 feet in diameter is used to focus the Sun's rays and to form an image about 5 inches in diameter, with a temperature of some 5,500 degrees Fahrenheit. Since it would be very difficult to make a solid mirror so large, more than twice the size of the Hale telescope mirror on Mount Palomar, the reflector is actually constructed of 3,500 smaller glass mirrors. Each is held in a frame which is bent slightly so that it forms a concave mirror shape and is capable of bringing the Sun's rays to an approximate focus. The bending of each element is controlled so that each comes close to what it would be if it were part of one big mirror. Optically, of course, the image is poor, but the reflector doesn't need to be as accurate as a telescope. All that it does is to act as a funnel to concentrate a lot of solar energy into a small region.

The mirror is too big to be easily moved around to follow the Sun, so it is fixed in a vertical position. Sunlight is fed into it from a flat mirror, about 38 feet square, likewise made up of smaller sections—540 of them. These are not bent but are as flat as they can be made. The whole assembly is mounted so that it can move to follow the Sun. Thus, a steady beam of sunlight shines for hours on the concave mirror, and the rays are focused on the equipment used in the experiments. According to the head of this laboratory, F. Trombe, the reflector collects sufficient energy for a power yield of about 75 kw. Also, he has said, such equipment seems capable of commercial use in a number of processes requiring high temperatures, particularly refining various metals.

The same idea has been applied on a miniature scale for more familiar uses, namely, cooking. In Russia, for example, a "solar kitchen" has been developed for a family of 3 or 4 persons. This uses a mirror, a little less than 4 feet in diameter, made of polished aluminum. The mirror can be quite inaccurate in its shape, since it is not intended to give a perfect image. It is mounted so that it can be moved by hand, focusing the solar rays on a cooking pot. On a sunny day this can do the work of a 600-watt electric stove. Such solar stoves may find wide use in India and other tropical countries where fuel for cooking is scarce and expensive.

In the United States, as well as elsewhere, promising experiments have been made in the distillation of sea water by solar heating, using relatively simple devices. People in many parts of the world are increasingly plagued by the ancient mariner's plaint: "Water, water, everywhere, nor any drop to drink," as their supplies of fresh water diminish, while they see plenty of ocean water nearby. Perhaps solar energy will solve this problem.

THE SUN AS A STAR

But the Sun, entirely aside from its importance as the source of terrestrial energy, has great scientific significance because it is the nearest star—the only one, in fact, that we can observe in detail. The next nearest, in the constellation of the Centaur, a group not visible from northern countries, is some 2.7×10^5 times as far. Not even the largest of telescopes will show it as more than a single point of light. Yet the Sun appears about the size of a penny (which is $\frac{3}{4}$ inch in diameter) held 80 inches away. This is an angular diameter of about half a degree, which is the angle between two lines from points diametrically opposite on the solar edge and meeting at the Earth.

Curiously enough, it is not necessary to observe the Sun to find its distance. Many years ago the German astronomer, Johann Kepler, discovered the laws that control the movements and distances of the planets as they revolve around the Sun. One states that if you divide the square of the period of a planet (i.e., the time it takes to make one revolution around the Sun) by the cube of its mean distance from the Sun, you get a constant. The period is easy to find, for that can be measured by watching the movement of the planet in the sky. Then, if you know the constant, you can work the formula in reverse and calculate the distance. But even if the constant is unknown, you can assume some arbitrary value and find the relative distances from the Sun of all the planets. That is, by Kepler's law, you can draw an accurate map of the solar system; all that is lacking is the scale of miles. Then, if you are able in some way to find the distance of any one planet from the Sun, you have the scale; and, from the map, any other distances may be determined.

In addition to the major planets, there are thousands of asteroids (which are tiny planets), some only a few miles in diameter. One of these, called Eros, came within 16 million miles of Earth in 1931. At this short range, its distance could be measured accurately by observations made from observatories in widely scattered parts of the Earth. Being so near us, its position against the background of distant stars was altered greatly as it was observed, for example, from Cape Town and from a place in the United States. Thus the scale for our map was established, and the Sun's distance was found to be 93,005,000 miles.

SUN NEAREST IN WINTER

However, it should be noted, this is the *mean* distance, for the Earth moves around the Sun in an ellipse. We are closest in January; then we are about 3 million miles nearer than we are in July, and this alteration of distance causes a variation of about 7 per cent in the amount of light and heat reaching the Earth.

There is another, entirely different way to find the Sun's distance; this method is not as precise but gives a good confirmation. This method uses the Doppler shift of lines in the spectrum of the stars and depends on whether the stars' distance is lengthening or shortening. This is shown in Fig. 14, where A, B, and C represent three different positions of the Earth in its annual revolution around the Sun, while D is the direction of the distant stars, which we will assume to be stationary. At A the Earth is approaching the stars with the full speed of Earth's motion around the Sun; at B it is not changing its distance; and at C it is receding with full speed. Thus at A the lines in the spectrum of the stars will be shifted toward the blue end; at B they will be in their normal positions; and at C they will be shifted toward the red.

From these shifts the actual velocity may be found; and, since the star is assumed to be at rest, it means that the Earth was approaching the star with a speed of 18.5 miles per second at A and is receding from it with the same velocity at C. This, then, is the orbital speed of the Earth. Multiplying this by the number of seconds in a year (31,558,464), we get the circumference of the Earth's orbit—about 585 million miles. Dividing this by 3.1416 gives the mean diameter of the Earth's orbit (186 million miles), and half this is the radius—the mean distance of the Earth from the Sun, or 93 million miles.

Of course, the stars are not stationary, as we have assumed, but are themselves moving; some toward us and some away from us.

Fig. 14. Determining the distance of the Earth from the Sun. By means of the Doppler effect, we can measure the average speed at which the Earth approaches, or recedes from, distant stars. This is the speed of the Earth's annual movement around the Sun. Knowing the time it takes us to go around the Sun, we can calculate the circumference of the Earth's orbit, its diameter, and hence the distance of the Earth from the Sun. (By permission from *Our Sun*, by Donald H. Menzel. Copyright, 1949, Harvard Univ. Press, Cambridge, Mass.)

But if such measurements are made of a great number of stars, their individual motions will be eliminated.

How big is the Sun? A penny (as we have seen) will just cover the Sun when held at a distance of about 80 inches. This is about 107 times the penny's diameter (¾ inch). If you divide the Sun's distance by 107, you get its diameter, which has been accurately determined as 865,370 miles.

How much does the Sun weigh? Actually, we should ask: What is the mass of the Sun? Weight is a measure of the attraction of the Earth on a body near its surface and depends on the body's mass, which is the amount of matter it contains. Practically, here on Earth, mass and weight may be considered the same thing, but weight has no meaning for a body out in space.

To get the Sun's mass, it is necessary to know that of the Earth itself, which is 6.59 × 10²¹ tons. At the surface of the Earth a body that is allowed to fall has dropped 16.1 feet after one second. From zero speed at the start of its fall, it has increased to a velocity of 32.2 feet per second. Its speed continues to increase, and every second of its free fall it accelerates by this same amount. Thus we say that the acceleration of gravity is 32.2 feet per second per second.

The Earth itself is falling toward the Sun, even though we are not likely to reach it in the foreseeable future. If it were not for the Sun's gravitational pull on the Earth, we would fly off into space in a straight line. The falling, then, pulls us out of this straight line, so that we move in approximately a circle (actually an ellipse) about the Sun. Every second the Earth deviates about ⅛ inch from the straight line; therefore, the acceleration of the Sun's gravity, at this distance, is ⅛ inch per second per second.

The acceleration of gravity for two different bodies is proportional to their masses provided they are the same distance from the gravitational center. The pull of gravity weakens with the square of the distance; i.e., if an object is twice as far, the pull is not ½ but ¼, since 4 is the square of 2. This means that the acceleration of gravity is inversely proportional to the square of the distance. Thus, allowing for the fact that the distance of the Earth from the Sun is so much greater than that of an object on the Earth's surface from its center, you can calculate that the Sun is 333,434 times the mass of the Earth. This is nearly 2.2 × 10²⁷ tons. Now, knowing the Sun's mass and volume (which is easily calculated from the diameter), we find that its average density is about 1.4 times that of water. At the center, the density is many times greater than this; it is much less at the surface.

SPOTS ON THE SUN

Generally, the Sun is so brilliant that to look at it directly would injure the eyes. Some sort of protection is needed: the traditional smoked glass, a pack of several very dense photographic negatives, or a very dark glass like that used by arc welders to watch their work. But sometimes, when the air is very hazy, especially when the Sun is just rising or setting and its light must pass through considerable thicknesses of atmosphere, you can look at the Sun directly. Usually it presents an unblemished surface, but dark spots may appear on it. These were noticed by the Chinese as early as 28 B.C.

People in Europe saw them later and supposed that they were due to some planet or other body passing in front of the Sun. In those days it was believed that the Sun, as a celestial body, must

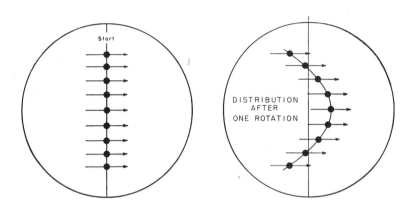

Fig. 15. Schematic demonstration of solar rotation. The Sun's surface rotates at different speeds, depending on the latitude. If a row of spots were lined up from north to south (left), after one rotation those at the equator would be farthest ahead and those toward the poles would lag farthest behind. Equatorial spots complete their circuit in 25⅓ days; those at latitude 40° take 27½ days. (By permission from *Our Sun*, by Donald H. Menzel. Copyright, 1949, Harvard Univ. Press, Cambridge, Mass.)

be perfect, and thus it could never be marred by any spots! But in 1611, Galileo, the first astronomer to use a telescope to good advantage, observed the spots and recognized that they were on the surface of the Sun itself, from the way they changed in detail. Moreover, from their progression across the Sun's face, he concluded correctly that the Sun was rotating.

The period of solar rotation is 25.14 days, i.e., about 25 days, 3 hours, 22 minutes. This, it should be emphasized, is the mean, an average. Actually, the Sun does not turn like a solid sphere, such as the Earth. The solar equator rotates most rapidly; a spot there would travel around in 25.33 days; one at 40 degrees north or south of its equator, the highest latitude in which these spots normally occur, requires 27.5 days for one revolution; see Fig. 15.

At 75 degrees latitude, the period is more than 33 days, as determined by spectroscopic observations.

Sometimes many spots are visible; at other times weeks may
pass without one. In 1843 a druggist and amateur astronomer of
Dessau, Germany, Heinrich Schwabe, realized, after some 20 years
of observing sunspots, that they came in a definite cycle. Every
11 years, roughly, spots are at minimum; in between, they rise to
a maximum. However, the length of the period varies considerably; the mean is 11.1 years, but there have been periods as short
as 7.5 years, or as long as 16 years. And during the past half century the periods have tended to be shorter than previously, with a
mean close to 10.2 years.

By terrestrial standards, sunspots are enormous. Even a small
one is large enough to engulf the entire Earth. One of the greatest
ever recorded, seen in April, 1947, covered an area on the solar surface of more than 5 billion square miles. Its diameter, at the time
of full development, was about 40,000 miles.

A typical spot consists of a dark inner portion called the *umbra;*
around this is the *penumbra,* lighter but still much darker than the
surrounding solar surface. Bridges of lighter material from the
penumbra may cross the umbra, making it look as if it were in
several parts.

Usually sunspots appear in groups with a number of spots of
somewhat comparable size. Or, as in the case of the April, 1947,
monster, one huge spot may dominate the entire group. This group,
like the spot, was the largest ever recorded. It covered a total area
of more than 7 billion square miles.

SPOTS ACTUALLY BRIGHT

A spot appears dark only by contrast with the surrounding
solar surface; actually it is very bright—more brilliant, in fact, than
an electric arc. The spot is really a storm area in the Sun's atmosphere—an area where the pressure is lower, and the gases rise and
expand. In their expansion they are reduced in temperature from
about 10,000 degrees Fahrenheit (that of the Sun's surface normally) to about 7,500 degrees Fahrenheit. The spot gives out
about 10 per cent as much energy as a similar unspotted area. If
at the time that a single large spot group was visible all the rest of
the Sun's surface was covered, the Earth would still receive illumi-

nation equivalent to that from a hundred full Moons! If you looked at it directly, your eyes would be dazzled by its brilliance.

Although there is a record of one spot, in 1840-1841, which survived for 18 months, they are generally very transitory. Small ones last only a day or two. Big ones may survive for weeks, long enough to be carried behind the Sun by its rotation, and brought into view a second time. The huge group of 1947 was first detected early in February. Then it passed out of sight; and, when visible again, in the beginning of March, it had an area of 5,400 million square miles. It came into view again and, in April, its maximum area was more than 7,000 million square miles.

Large spots may be seen with small and imperfect telescopes as well as with the naked eye; larger and better instruments reveal details which attest to the turbulence of the solar atmosphere in unspotted regions. This surface is not uniform, but shows a granular appearance. This is sometimes called the *rice grain* structure because it looks like rice grains floating in a bowl of soup—or, at least, the way that rice grains would look if they did float, rather than sink to the bottom of the dish! These grains show up best near the center of the disk. One such grain may be as much as several hundred miles across, a brilliant patch contrasting markedly with the darker surroundings. Their lives are counted in minutes, as they are hurled around in the solar atmosphere by winds as high as 90 miles per second.

Sometimes these granulations separate, and a dark area known as a pore, perhaps a few hundred miles in diameter, may be formed. Then several pores may join to form a spot. There is a tendency, at the beginning, for pores to cluster around two centers of activity, called the *leading* and *following* spots. That is because the Sun rotates from east to west, and the spot that is toward the west "leads" the procession. However, the following spot, during the first several days, may seem to lag behind, for the two draw apart in longitude as they grow in area. In about 10 days, in a typical case, the spots reach maximum size; they are now about 10 to 15 degrees of longitude (perhaps 100,000 miles) apart and no longer continue to separate. Usually the leading spot lasts about four times as long as the follower, which generally has a more irregular shape, and quickly vanishes after it has attained its largest growth.

Before a spot becomes visible, there is some disturbance below the visible surface. Patches of bright material called *faculae,* "little torches," may appear long before a spot breaks into view. They may form a vast veined network around the spots and may remain visible long after the spot has vanished.

According to one solar authority, Donald H. Menzel, faculae form a sort of solar "mountain," not permanent mountains like those on Earth, of course, but regions where the bright solar surface —the *photosphere*—rises from 5 to 100 miles above the "plain." He has suggested that they are volcanic mountains, for from them rise geyser-like eruptions, flares, and jets of luminous gases to heights of 25,000 to 50,000 miles or even higher. These are the *prominences* which will be described a little later.

So far we have not mentioned the largest part of the Sun—a part that relatively few people have ever seen. This is the *corona*, a pearly halo, continually changing, that extends out from the Sun to a distance of 10 million miles or more. It is about half as bright as the full Moon; about a millionth of the brightness of the Sun itself. If you were observing from the Moon (which has no atmosphere) or from an artificial satellite above our atmosphere, all you would need to do to see it would be to hold a finger in front of the Sun's disk. With the glare eliminated, the corona would be easily visible.

We observe the Sun from the bottom of an ocean of air, which is brightly illuminated in the general direction of the Sun, and this ordinarily hides the faint corona. Something outside the atmosphere has to come in front of the Sun to make the corona visible.

ECLIPSES OF THE SUN

Fortunately, there is something that can hide the Sun. It is the Moon. Every time the Moon is new, it nearly comes between the Sun and Earth, but generally misses by a little, passing either north or south of the line joining the two bodies. Occasionally, however, it does come right between them, and the tip of the lunar shadow may fall across the Earth.

You are used to a shadow much bigger than the object casting it. This happens at night when you enter a large room, holding a candle. Your shadow looms behind you on the wall and ceiling, far bigger than you. This is because you are much larger than the candle flame. Lines of light travel out from it in all directions. Those that pass by your body are spreading; therefore, they are farther apart the longer they have to travel.

The Moon, with its diameter of 2,160 miles, is considerably smaller than the Sun, with its 865,000 miles. Thus, if the Moon's shadow were cast on a surface close to it, the shadow would be practically the Moon's diameter, only a little smaller. But the farther away the screen on which the shadow is cast, the smaller is the shadow, because the light from opposite edges of the Sun can pass around behind the Moon. At an average distance of 232,000 miles the lunar shadow tapers down to a point, and beyond that

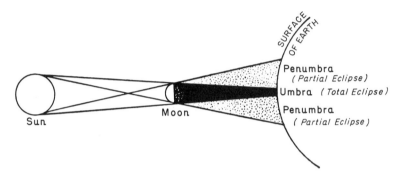

Fig. 16. The umbra and penumbra. A total eclipse of the Sun occurs when the Moon's shadow touches the surface of the Earth. Inside this shadow—the umbra—the Moon completely hides the disk of the Sun. Within the outer part of the shadow—the penumbra—there is a partial eclipse, as the Moon hides only part of the Sun. (By permission from *Astronomy*, by W. T. Skilling and R. S. Richardson. Copyright, 1947, Henry Holt & Co., Inc., New York.)

there is no full shadow. If you happen to be standing there, even though you are exactly in line with the centers of the Sun and Moon, the Moon will fail to hide the Sun. Instead, you will see the dark disk of the Moon surrounded by a ring of light near the Sun's edge; see Fig. 16.

Actually this often happens. The mean distance from the Earth to the Moon is 238,900 miles, or 235,000 from the Earth's surface when the Moon is directly overhead. Thus, under average conditions, when an eclipse occurs, it is of this kind, called an *annular* eclipse. This name comes from the Latin word for ring, *annulus*, and refers to the ring of light seen around the Moon.

But an eclipse may occur when the Earth is nearer the Moon, or when the Moon is farther away than average from the Sun. Its shadow is longer and the full shadow, the *umbra*, reaches the ground. It may have a diameter as large as 192 miles. Then the eclipse is total; the Moon completely hides the Sun. Of course, the Earth is rotating, and the Moon is revolving around the Earth; thus, the shadow does not stay put but sweeps across the Earth from west to east with a speed of 1,000 miles per hour or even more. In this way the shadow traces out a *path of totality* several thousand miles long. If you want to see a total eclipse, you have to go to some point in this path. Over a much larger area there is a partial eclipse, when the Moon passes partly in front of the Sun. And even if you are in the path, the eclipse starts and ends with partial phases.

At *first contact,* the edge of the Moon just begins to encroach upon the disk of the Sun; if you are watching it with some suitable protection for the eyes, a slight nick appears in the edge of the Sun. It resembles a cookie from which someone has taken a very timid bite. But the bite slowly enlarges, for about an hour. Finally the Sun is nearly covered; only a thin crescent remains visible. Then this too disappears, usually by breaking up into a series of bright beads—called *Baily's beads,* after an English astronomer who first described them. They are due to light from the Sun's edge shining through valleys on the edge of the Moon.

With totality, the corona flashes out around the dark Moon. Perhaps one can see some prominences, great flame-like masses of glowing hydrogen and other gases that shoot out from the Sun. Brighter stars and planets may appear in the sky, but it does not get really dark, only like early twilight. Then, with totality over, the Baily's beads appear once more, on the opposite edge from where they were seen at the beginning of totality. The beads join to form a crescent and this enlarges as the Moon moves off the face of the Sun.

How long totality lasts depends on several factors: One is the relative distance of the bodies concerned. With the Moon nearest and the Sun farthest, other things being equal, the eclipse will be longest. It will also be longer the nearer you are to the equator, or at least to the place where the Sun is overhead, for then the bulge of the Earth's curvature brings you appreciably nearer to the Moon. With everything at its most favorable, a total eclipse could last as long as 7 minutes, 40 seconds, but no one knows when, if ever, such an eclipse happened.

SEVEN-MINUTE ECLIPSES

This century, however, has three 7-minute eclipses. The first was on June 8, 1937, when the path went over the Pacific Ocean, just reaching the coast of South America as it ended. Perversely, there were no islands near the middle of the path, where conditions were most favorable, and there was no place for astronomers to set up a temporary observatory. However, John Q. Stewart, of Princeton University, and I were close to the central point, on a U.S. freighter, the S.S. "Steelmaker." There we saw the total phase last for 7 minutes, 6 seconds. We gained 4 seconds because of the ship's eastward motion, which kept us in the Moon's shadow that much longer.

After 18 years and 10 or 11 days (depending on whether there are 4 or 5 leap years in the interval) Earth, Moon, and Sun come back to nearly the same relative positions, and an eclipse is repeated under very similar conditions. This period, known to the ancient Babylonians, is called the *saros*. So, one saros later, there was an eclipse visible in southeastern Asia and the Philippines which lasted even longer at the maximum: 7 minutes, 10 seconds. But the maximum point was in the South China Sea, and no one seems to have beaten our 1937 record. There will be another chance to do so on June 30, 1973. Then the path crosses northern Africa, and totality still lasts more than 7 minutes.

In addition there are eclipses of the Moon (which will be discussed in more detail in a later chapter). These occur when the Moon enters the Earth's shadow, see Fig. 17. While many more people have seen a total lunar eclipse than have witnessed a total eclipse of the Sun, the latter are more common. However, at a lunar eclipse the darkened Moon is visible from more than half the Earth—wherever the Moon is seen at all. With the solar eclipse, as mentioned, one must go to the path of totality to see it.

On the average, there is a total eclipse of the Sun, somewhere on Earth, about every year and a half, while those of the Moon are about two thirds as frequent. However, only once in about 360 years, on the average, will the path of totality of a solar eclipse pass over any particular place.

The twentieth century brings a total of twelve total eclipses visible in some parts of the United States, some much more favorable than others. On July 20, 1963, a path of totality sweeps south-eastward from Canada across Maine. Next, on March 7, 1970, another moves northward from the Gulf of Mexico across northern Florida and the Atlantic Coast of Georgia, South Carolina and North Carolina, then to sea until it reaches Nova Scotia. The Northwest is favored on February 26, 1979, when a path comes eastward from the Pacific Ocean, along the border between Oregon and Washington, then crosses Idaho and Montana as it curves to the northeast across Canada.

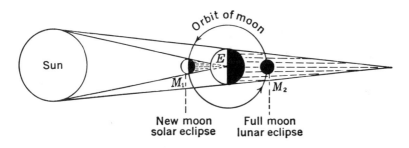

New moon
solar eclipse

Full moon
lunar eclipse

Fig. 17. Solar and lunar eclipses. An eclipse of the Sun can occur only at new Moon, when the Moon is in the same direction from Earth as the Sun. A lunar eclipse must occur at a full Moon, when the Moon is opposite the Sun, so that the Moon may pass into the Earth's shadow. Usually, at either new or full Moon, the three bodies are not exactly in line, and there is no eclipse. (By permission from *Astronomy*, by W. T. Skilling and R. S. Richardson. Copyright, 1947, Henry Holt & Co., Inc., New York.)

With total eclipses so rare, astronomers sought some method whereby they could observe the same effects at any time. It is the glare of the sunlight in the Earth's atmosphere in nearly the same direction as the Sun that keeps you from seeing prominences or corona when you hold your finger in front of the bright solar disk. However, with a device called the *spectrohelioscope*, prominences can now be seen whenever there are any there to see—and the Sun is visible.

Its operation depends on the fact that the glare in the sky is from the white light of the Sun, which has a continuous spectrum; i.e., it includes all the spectral colors, crossed by the dark Fraunhofer lines. But the prominences are part of the Sun's outer layer, which is cooler than the interior, where the white light originates. The prominence spectrum consists of bright lines, with one of the most brilliant in the red and due to hydrogen. Thus, while the white glare consists of a whole range of wave lengths, the light of the prominences consists of only certain particular wave lengths.

If one of these wave lengths could be tuned in the way a radio receiver can be set to receive the signal from one particular station, excluding those on other wave lengths, it would be possible to observe the prominence by itself, since very little of the general white light is in this particular color. That is just what the spectrohelioscope does, by passing the light through a powerful spectroscope. It is used visually, while its counterpart, the *spectroheliograph,* makes a photographic record of the Sun in the light of a single wave length. Not only prominences but many other features on the Sun can be studied with these instruments.

PICTURES BY HYDROGEN LIGHT

Such a record, called a *spectroheliogram,* is very different from a direct photograph of the Sun made at the same time. And even spectroheliograms are different, depending on whether they are taken with hydrogen or calcium light. Sunspots still appear dark, but there may also be many other markings, both dark and bright. In hydrogen light, for example, there appear areas of bright hydrogen vapor from very hot regions. But, curiously, dark areas, called *dark hydrogen flocculi,* may also appear, and these too indicate high temperatures. The dark patch indicates that the gas there is hot, and that it hides the bright interior.

Like sunspots, these dark flocculi are dark only by contrast with the bright background. They shoot up above the main surface of the Sun and, when rotation carries them to the edge, they appear bright against the dark sky. In fact, they are then seen as prominences, for prominences appear as dark flocculi when seen against the solar disk. The bright flocculi, too, are prominences when seen at the edge.

Because the Sun is continually in rapid movement, ordinary spectroheliograms, which are still pictures, catch only an isolated stage of these solar features and fail to show clearly their development. For this reason, Robert R. McMath, of the McMath-Hulbert Observatory of the University of Michigan, devised an improved version that makes movies of the Sun in the light of a single wave length. In these films we can watch huge prominences rising hundreds of thousands of miles above the solar surface, sometimes with speeds of more than 100 miles per second.

More common are the "small" prominences (small, that is, by comparison with the Sun itself). Even a small one may reach a height of several times the diameter of the earth—some 25,000 miles or more. Sometimes they appear as loops, sometimes as vertically rising geysers. Sometimes they shoot out, and then seem to be sucked back. Sometimes a cloud seems to float above the solar surface for days at a time, perhaps with stuff falling down from it for long periods.

Indeed, one very striking feature brought out by these movies is that much more material seems to fall on the solar surface than is shot up from it. It is an old saying that "Whatever goes up must come down," and the converse should be just as true: "Whatever comes down must have gone up." But this seems to be contradicted as we watch the movement of the prominences.

We recall, however, that we never observe rain to go up; we only see it falling, because it ascends as invisible vapor. Not until it is aloft does it condense into liquid water, which descends as visible drops. Perhaps something analogous takes place on the Sun.

Because of the Sun's vast importance to the Earth, and because it is the only star we can see in close-up, it is intensively studied in many aspects. At the McMath-Hulbert Observatory in Michigan, the Mount Wilson Observatory in California, the Arcetri Observatory in Italy, and many others, this research is steadily advancing our knowledge.

While the instruments described have made it possible to study prominences with relative ease, observation of the solar corona without an eclipse proved much more difficult. Indeed, after many unsuccessful attempts, it seemed impossible.

At first glance, it doesn't seem so hard. After all, the corona is approximately as bright as the full Moon. The inner part, near the Sun, is even brighter, and it is easy to see the Moon in the daytime sky.

However, the Moon is then in quite a different part of the sky from the Sun. When you close one eye, and hold up a finger at arm's length so as to cover the Sun, as seen with the open eye, you will find that the glare makes a dazzling bright halo around the Sun. It is so bright that it is hard to look at. But if you try the experiment on top of a high mountain, where the air is extremely clean, the sky is blue, even close to the Sun.

Such a high altitude, with its ultra-clear air, is the first essential for observing the corona without an eclipse, but it is not enough, as the early attempts showed. In addition, the lenses of the instrument must be kept super-clean. Perhaps on some long trip by motor you have driven all day, with no difficulty in seeing the road ahead. But as night comes you find so much glare from the headlights of approaching cars that you can hardly see. When you stop and clean the windshield, visibility is greatly improved. Actually, it was not the oncoming headlights directed at you that made it hard to see. The light that was scattered from the layer of dust and dirt caused the trouble.

Most lenses, even of ordinarily good quality, may have some small bubbles or striations inside them, or scratches on their surfaces. Moreover, the achromatic lens used for astronomical telescopes consists of two different pieces of glass, and light is scattered by reflections between the faces of the elements.

THE CORONAGRAPH

A French astronomer, Bernard Lyot, finally solved the problem with the development of his *coronagraph*. To get the clearest possible sky, he took the coronagraph to an observatory at an altitude of 9,420 feet, on the Pic du Midi in the Pyrenees. In 1930, he was able to observe prominences and in July, 1931, he succeeded in photographing the bright inner parts of the corona.

The construction of the coronagraph was as follows: The main lens was a single one, in order to avoid the reflections between two elements. It was made of very fine glass, free from scratches and other defects, kept scrupulously clean. The tube, made of wood, was 16 feet, 5 inches long and was coated inside with thick oil to collect any dust.

When pointed toward the Sun, a solar image was formed, 134 inches down the tube, on a disk just barely larger. The front of the disk, set at a small angle, was silvered and so reflected the light from the bright solar disk to the side of and out of the tube. Around the disk was the image of the corona and prominences. This image was then picked up by a second lens, also beautifully clean, which then formed a second image on a film still farther down the tube.

A number of improvements have been made since 1931, as the work has continued at the Pic du Midi and as other coronagraph stations were established, notably the Arosa Observatory in the Swiss Alps; one at Wendelstein, in Bavaria; and the High-Altitude Observatory operated by the Harvard Observatory at Climax, Colorado, at an altitude of 11,480 feet. Regular observations, many by motion picture, are made at these stations.

One of the improvements is the use of a special filter, developed by Lyot and, independently, by John W. Evans, of Harvard, and others. This makes use of Polaroid films, which polarize light, i.e., allow the passage of vibrations in only one plane. Ordinary light vibrates in many planes. Each Polaroid film forms the filling of a sandwich between layers of quartz. Each quartz layer is twice as thick as the one before. Such an arrangement has a very curious property; only a very narrow band of color (wave lengths) passes through. By properly choosing the dimensions, the transmitted band can be placed at any desired wave length. In fact, with such a Lyot-Evans filter, it is possible to observe the prominences as with a spectrohelioscope; the assembly being adjusted to transmit only the red hydrogen light. Used with the coronagraph, it adds further to the performance of that instrument.

At an eclipse visible in 1874, astronomers made use of the newly developed spectroscope in their observations. With it they found, in the spectrum from the outer layer of the solar sphere, shining by itself just before the Moon completely hid it, many familiar lines which were then bright instead of dark, as they are in the ordinary solar spectrum. This is called the *flash* spectrum, since it flashes out just at the beginning and end of a total eclipse. But in addition, they saw a yellow line which they did not recognize; it was due to no element they knew. They ascribed it to some element which had not been discovered on Earth, and named it *helium* (from *helios*, the Greek word for the Sun). Twenty years later it was discovered on Earth, forming a small part of the atmosphere. Now we know that it is one of the most common elements in the universe, second in abundance only to hydrogen.

Later some unknown bright lines were discovered, in the green and other colors, in the spectrum of the corona. These likewise were attributed to a hypothetical element, which they called *coronium*. But all the blank spaces in the table of the elements were filled, with no room left for coronium. Evidently, therefore, it was some well-known element shining in a peculiar way under the rather unusual conditions existing in the corona.

DENUDED ATOMS

In 1940 a Swedish physicist, Bengt Edlén, solved the puzzle with a brilliant piece of theoretical work, confirmed by laboratory experiments. He showed that iron, nickel, and calcium were responsible for most of the "coronium" lines. We have seen that atoms become ionized when some of the electrons that normally revolve about their nucleus are lost; under ordinary circumstances only one or two are removed. Edlén demonstrated that the coronal atoms had lost perhaps a dozen or more electrons. One of the most prominent corona lines, green in color, proved to be due to iron XIV, that is, iron atoms from which 13 of its normal quota of 26 electrons were missing (iron I has the normal quota, iron II is missing one electron, and so forth).

As happens so often in scientific research, the solution of this puzzle only led to others. In order to produce such extreme ionization of the iron, nickel, and calcium atoms in the corona, temperatures of about 1,800,000 degrees Fahrenheit would be needed. Other considerations confirm this coronal temperature. At its center the Sun is many times hotter than this, but the surface temperature is around 10,000 degrees. Heat can flow from a hot body to a cooler one but not to one that is hotter; this is a fundamental law of physics. How, then, can the corona get so much hotter than the surface of the Sun below?

The answer to this puzzle has not yet been found, but there are various suggestions. One was that as the Sun moves along it sweeps up interstellar dust, which falls into it at a speed of about 370 miles per second, heating the corona as it goes through. This would heat the corona from the top downward.

But there is doubt whether enough of this material could thus be captured to produce the heating; moreover, there is good evidence that the corona is not heated from above but from below.

HEATING BY SHOCK WAVES

One explanation, proposed by Martin Schwarzschild, has sound waves doing the heating. He suggests that the turbulent motions of the granules in the Sun's surface cause waves like those which carry sounds through the Earth's atmosphere, and that they travel outward at the speed of sound. Even with only a small part of the energy of the moving granules thus carried upward, there still seems to be plenty to give the corona the amount it needs.

Unlike ocean waves, in which water particles move up and down —at right angles to the direction in which the wave is going—sound waves are compressional; that is, the air molecules move back and forth in the direction that the wave is moving. Usually these molecules have a regular to-and-fro motion, something like that of a pendulum. The solar waves start out this way, according to the Schwarzschild theory, but before they have gone more than a couple of hundred miles they have changed their character. They have now become *shock* waves, which travel faster than the normal speed of sound.

Such shock waves are sent out from a large explosion, like that of an atomic bomb, and are responsible for the first damage— knocking over walls and the like. Shock waves are also set up when a jet plane makes a dive at supersonic speed. That is why, when such a maneuver is performed over an inhabited area, there is a rash of broken windows in houses below.

The shock waves differ from the ordinary sound wave not only in speed; the first movement of the molecules along the path of the advancing wave is very sudden. It is more like the motion of a hammer brought down on a nail as quickly as possible, then slowly raised for another blow.

But, as such a wave passes through a gas, it loses the speed and energy which is utilized in heating the gas, i.e., in giving increased speed to the gas molecules or atoms.

In such a manner, energy might be carried through the upper layers of the Sun's atmosphere to the base of the corona, itself so rarefied that the shock waves could not carry through. But they don't need to; the highly agitated atmospheric atoms could themselves transfer energy to the corona as they move up into it.

Although a number of astronomers look with favor on the Schwarzschild theory, it is by no means proved, and there are other theories worth consideration. In fact, there may be more than one mechanism operating to heat up the corona, particularly above the sunspots.

It is known that these spots are huge magnets, and electrically charged particles can be set into motion by a magnetic field that is changing, as the field around a spot would be. An electric current is a movement of charged particles, so this might be regarded as electrical heating of the corona, in somewhat the same way that the tungsten filament of an electric lamp is heated as a current goes through and meets some resistance on the way.

The Harvard astronomer, Donald H. Menzel, in collaboration with a radio engineer, W. W. Salisbury, has developed this general idea somewhat differently. There is one type of atom-smasher, the betatron, in which a stream of electrons is whirled around by the forces of a changing magnetic field until the electrons reach energies of hundreds of millions of volts. These electrons, or the X-rays produced when they strike a tungsten target, have a number of scientific applications, not only for probing into the nucleus of the atom, but for medical and industrial uses as well.

Something analogous may happen in the Sun, by a process which Menzel has described as follows: "The magnetic fields of the Sun change much more slowly than in the betatron. The electrons may thus collide many times with other atoms. Also they can radiate energy in the form of radio waves. So can the electrons in the betatron. To find the ultimate gain in temperature we must allow for both these effects. The indications are that very slow uniform changes of spot fields will not produce enough heating to account for all the observed effects.

"Continuing the analysis, we concluded that small but very rapid fluctuations in magnetic fields were probably responsible. This proposal implies consequences far beyond the Sun itself. Rapid variations of field will produce radio waves, which spread out into space like those from any radio transmitter. The two varieties are similar in every respect but wave length. Where the ordinary broadcast frequencies (say 300 kilocycles) are about a kilometer (0.6 mile) in length, these solar frequencies (about 10 cycles) will be 30,000 kilometers (or 20,000 miles) long.

"The pulsating fields close to the Sun will excite the chromosphere [the upper layer of the Sun's atmosphere, where the absorption which produces the dark lines in the solar spectrum occurs] and corona. The latter, with its lower density, will experience the greater excitation. The electron will move farther and farther and thus can acquire greater speeds between collisions.

"The very long wavelengths of these Sun-induced waves will cause them to whip around the Earth's curved surface. There will be no shadow and the night as well as the daylight hemisphere will receive them. They will cause the Earth's atmosphere to glow. Thus we have a possible explanation of the faint luminosity of the night sky—the permanent aurora. The electrification produced by the waves will have an influence on the ionosphere, or radio roof of the Earth. . . . Near the Earth the waves may produce the so-called 'cosmic rays.' " *

SOLAR FLARES

In September, 1859, two English astronomers, R. C. Carrington and R. Hodgson, were independently observing the Sun through their telescopes when they were surprised to see a huge white area, many times the brightness of the rest of the surface, appear on its face. They made the first recorded observation of a solar *flare*, a phenomenon which has been widely studied in recent years. The flares are best seen with the spectrohelioscope, in hydrogen light. Suddenly an area of perhaps a billion square miles—five times the total area of the Earth—will flash out to some ten times its normal brilliance. At the same time there may be a sudden burst of ultra-violet radiation, which soon reaches the Earth. This may affect the ionosphere, the radio "mirror" high overhead which reflects radio waves so they will travel all the way around the globe. Intercontinental radio transmission may experience a sudden fade-out.

The spectrum of the flare is similar to that of the chromosphere, from which the flash spectrum shines at the beginning and end of a total eclipse; i.e., it consists mainly of bright lines, one of the most prominent being that of red hydrogen light. But some very intense flares have white light, a continuous range of wave lengths, associated with them; these are the ones that have been observed directly by telescopic observers like Carrington and Hodgson.

The smallest flares may be no more than about a hundred million square miles in area (a mere half the total area of Earth) and last about a quarter of an hour. The largest will cover 1 or 2 billion square miles and persist for several hours. And almost invariably they occur close to sunspots.

It seems that flares are not like prominences, in which actual matter moves upward from the Sun; rather are they excitation effects. That is, some sort of radiation from the active region below

* D. H. Menzel, *Our Sun.* Copyright, 1959, Harvard Univ. Press, Cambridge.

seems to excite the solar gases in a particular region, to make them glow and give off intense bursts of ultraviolet light. A familiar example of such excitation is a neon sign: a glass tube from which most of the gases have been evacuated but which contains a little neon. Because the pressure is so low, the gas offers relatively little resistance to a flow of electricity, so, when electrodes at each end are connected to a source of high-voltage electricity, a current passes through the tube in the form of a stream of electrons, exciting the neon gas and resulting in the familiar effect.

Similarly, it seems, according to the ideas proposed by the Italian astronomer R. G. Giovanelli in 1948, that a surge of runaway electrons, impelled by sudden changes in the magnetic field of a sunspot, may excite hydrogen and other atoms, producing a flare. However, the problem is not yet fully settled.

The suddenness of a flare suggests a lightning flash on Earth, and it has even been suggested that they are analogous. However, there is a great difference between conditions in our atmosphere, when a flash occurs, and those which prevail in the Sun's atmosphere. Lightning results when electrically charged raindrops accumulate; those with positive charges at one point, and those negatively charged at another. Finally, when enough have accumulated, a huge spark jumps across to relieve the strain, and this is the bolt of lightning. But the chromosphere of the Sun, unlike our atmosphere, is a good electrical conductor. As soon as positive and negative charges began to accumulate, a current would flow, and so prevent the accumulation reaching any great size. But perhaps other effects, that we do not now understand, may cause a different behavior and some such mechanism might be involved.

RADIO WAVES FROM THE SUN

As noted in Chapter 3, the Sun, like many other astronomical objects, broadcasts radio waves. However, there are a number of solar stations, sources from which these waves are sent.

First of all there is the background radiation from the quiet Sun, the minimum which is always being emitted. This is the *thermal* radiation; the radio waves are really the same as infrared rays given off by a heated body. And from the radio waves we may form an estimate of the temperature of the source, which turns out to be most interesting. For the lowest frequencies, about 10 megacycles, temperatures of nearly two million degrees Fahrenheit are involved. Higher frequency (shorter wave length) waves of about 100,000 megacycles indicate a source temperature of only about 18,000 degrees Fahrenheit. The significance of these data comes from the fact that the low-frequency waves seem to come from the corona, while those of higher frequency are broadcast from the Sun's visible surface, or near it. Actually, this 18,000-degree temperature is somewhat higher than other estimates of the surface temperature—around 10,000 degrees—but the radio waves might well originate a little below the surface, where it is somewhat hotter.

Then, at frequencies higher than about 30,000 megacycles, there is a steady "hum" in addition to the thermal noise. The more spots there are, the stronger is this radiation. When the spots are at their maximum, the radiation may be as strong as the thermal waves of similar length. With the radio telescope, the sources of this hum have been located, and it seems always to come from the vicinity of a spot, or the place where one has recently been.

But this hum is not the only radiation from the spots. Also associated with them are waves about a meter in length (i.e., about 30 megacycles frequency) which may last for hours or days. In fact, they are sent out as a beam from a searchlight, only detected on Earth when the spot is aimed in our direction. This radiation differs from the steady hum, for it seems to consist of two-second bursts, of somewhat lower frequency, superposed on a continual succession of small bursts.

Also there are outbursts of wave lengths of about a meter or more, which may last for something like 10 minutes. Since these come at the frequencies widely used in radar, they sometimes interfere seriously with radar work in locating airplanes. These were what the British radar operators detected during World War II and thought were due to German jamming operations. Often these outbursts are associated with solar flares, but sometimes they occur without a flare; just how, no one yet knows.

Finally there are isolated bursts, of about 30,000 megacycles, apparently originating also in spot areas. These, like the outbursts, seem definitely not to originate as a mere effect of high temperatures. Perhaps there is some sort of activity in a spot whereby masses of ionized gas of both positive and negative charges oscillate back and forth in relation to each other. This could produce radio waves of the kind observed.

These radio observations of the Sun are all so new that only a very tentative and preliminary explanation can be given for them. But, as with many other branches of astronomy, radio has given solar research a valuable new tool. Before many years have passed, we may be learning as much about the Sun from radio techniques as from all the more conventional methods.

Since the Sun through the ages has served as the Earth's powerhouse and heating plant, it seems reasonable to suspect that in some way its variations control our weather. Certainly the great changes in heat received by different regions, depending on whether the Sun is to the north or south, cause the changes in season from the heat of summer to the cold of winter. Why, then, might not smaller changes in its radiation be responsible for variations of weather? Many scientists have thought that the changes are responsible and have long sought for some clear-cut correlation that would enable men to watch the Sun and then, from what they found, tell what earthly weather was going to be next week, next month, or perhaps even next year.

One of these is Charles Greeley Abbot, formerly head of the Smithsonian Institution, who made studies in many parts of the world of the *solar constant*—the rate at which the Sun's total radiation is supplying us with energy. If it were not for the Earth's atmosphere, every square inch of the Earth, at right angles to the direction of the Sun, would be getting about 12.5 calories every minute. This is the solar constant, usually expressed as 1.94 calories per square centimeter per minute, equivalent to about a horsepower and a half for every square yard. Because of the absorption of the Earth's atmosphere, this amount of energy does not reach the ground, but the higher you go the more nearly the energy level approaches the value mentioned. From variations in the solar constant, Abbot has endeavored to make long-range weather forecasts. Despite some measure of success, his ideas have not been generally accepted.

SUNSPOTS AND WEATHER

There does seem to be a correlation between temperature and rainfall, and the solar activity as indicated by sunspots. Trees grow more rapidly, as do many other plants, when the weather is warm and there is a lot of rain. Opposite conditions generally give a poor growing season. It is well known that the trunk of a tree, when sliced, shows a series of concentric rings, one for each year of growth. The more the tree has grown that year, the wider is the ring.

An American astronomer, Andrew E. Douglass, of Tucson, Arizona, used these facts to develop the science of *dendrochronology,* the dating of ancient structures of wood by the arrangement of the annual rings in timbers from which they were built.

He found that timbers from many parts of the world showed an 11-year cycle. That is, approximately every eleventh ring would be a wide one, showing good growth; those between would be thinner, showing that the tree did not do as well in those years. And, when he checked, with wood from a tree cut down recently at a known date, he found that the years of greatest growth were those when the sunspots were at their maximum.

This gave the material for a *tree-ring calendar.* From a tree recently felled, a hundred years old, he could push the record back for a century. Then, perhaps in some old house, built 75 years ago, he would find a beam from a tree that was, presumably, cut down just before it was used. Perhaps it had also been a hundred years old.

On comparing the ring pattern, he would find that the last 25 years of the old log corresponded with the first quarter century of the newer one. In fact, if the date of the old building was not known, he could tell when the building had to be built in order to make the two patterns match, and thus he could tell when the old log was cut. Since it had probably been used soon after, he had a good estimate of the year of building.

By studying logs from many old structures, from trees whose lifetimes overlapped, Douglass has been able to extend the calendar back for thousands of years. Not only does this permit the dating of ancient structures; it has also given us a record of weather variations, and of solar activity, much farther back than the time when systematic observations were started.

Attempts have been made to correlate many other activities with spottedness of the Sun: the price of wheat, the number of rabbits killed in Canada, the fluctuations of the stock market, even the beginning of wars! For the latter it was assumed that, since the

Sun gives off more ultraviolet rays when it is most active and spots are numerous, the rays stimulated people on the Earth, made them more belligerent, so they started wars!

True, there was a maximum in 1937, about the time that the events which led to World War II were coming to a head. There was one in 1860, when the Civil War began, but 1914 was the year after a minimum. So this rule doesn't hold very well!

As for the correlation with the price of wheat, which Sir William Herschel, a famous English astronomer, proposed more than 150 years ago, there is such a correspondence in many years. Really, it is a negative one; high prices come with few spots. Presumably in those years the wheat didn't grow so well and was scarce. In years of maximum the price came down. But in other years, as in 1830, the spots were numerous, and still the prices were up. There is undoubtedly some relationship, but other unknown factors are also involved. Until these are sorted out, and perhaps even more fundamental causes understood, it is not safe to make predictions from solar activity.

6

The Earth

"Solid Earth" is a familiar phrase, even though there are occasions when our planet is not so solid. Sometimes the ground under our feet quivers with an earthquake; there are avalanches and landslides, cave-ins, washouts, and the like. But most of the time the Earth is firm and steady; it seems to be fixed. And once, indeed, people thought the Earth was truly fixed—to think that it was moving seemed a blasphemous idea. The Sun actually moved across the sky from east to west each day, they thought, and the planets did move around the central Earth in a complicated path, sometimes to the east, then backed up for a time, only to resume their eastward movement.

But a revolution in thought began in 1543. Copernicus revived a suggestion made nearly 2,000 years before—that the Earth was one of several planets, all revolving around the Sun. This has given us a better understanding of our place in the cosmos. The Earth is one of nine principal planets that form the Solar System. At its center is the Sun, one of a vast number of stars, many of them far larger. Many of them also have planets, it now seems.

And, of our family of nine planets, the Earth is not the largest— or the smallest—but it is the most important to us, its inhabitants. It is doubtless the only one on which we can survive under natural conditions. This is hardly surprising; man and his ancestors have lived here for billions of years. We have become adapted to our surroundings. If they had been different, we might have adapted ourselves just as well.

What is this planet Earth, the third out from the center of the Solar System?

First, we are 93,004,000 miles away from the Sun. This is the mean distance; we may be as close (early in January) as 91.5 million miles, and in July as far as 94.5 million miles. To make one trip around the Sun takes 365 days, 6 hours, 9 minutes, 9.5 seconds— the period we know as the year. Because of the extra time of about 6 hours over an exact number of days, we must have leap years; otherwise the same calendar day would shift through all the seasons.

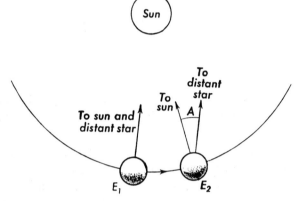

Fig. 18. Solar and sidereal days. On a certain day the Earth is at E_1; the arrow points to the Sun and a distant star beyond. One day later the Earth has turned once on its axis and the arrow again points toward the star. But because the Earth has advanced in its orbit around the Sun, it has to turn a little more to bring the arrow back to the Sun's direction. This makes the solar day about 4 minutes longer than the sidereal day, which is measured from the stars. (Drawing by Felix Cooper. By permission from *The Astronomical Universe*, by W. S. Krogdahl. Copyright, 1952, The Macmillan Co., New York.)

Not only does Earth revolve around the Sun; it also rotates on its axis from west to east, in the period we call the day. Here again there is a complication, for there are two principal kinds of day. If you determine the rotation by watching when a distant star is on the meridian (that is, when it is overhead or directly south or north) and count until it comes back to the same position, you have what astronomers call the *sidereal day*.

But do the same with the Sun and you obtain a period about 4 minutes longer—the *solar day*, the kind that we generally use; see Fig. 18.

The reason for the difference is that during the time that the Earth rotates, as measured from the distant stars, it has moved about 1/365 of its circuit around the Sun. We have moved, but it seems as if the Sun has changed its position; as if it had moved a little to the east against the starry background. To bring the Sun back to the meridian—to the moment called noon—our planet must turn for about 4 minutes more.

The day (both sidereal and solar) is divided into 24 parts called hours, these into 60 parts called minutes, and they, in turn, into 60 subdivisions termed seconds. Mechanical devices—clocks—are made to indicate the passage of these periods and, just as there are two kinds of days, there are two kinds of clocks: sidereal and solar.

The astronomer generally is observing the stars and other similarly distant bodies, so he uses sidereal time. With its aid he can set his telescope to point to a particular object, whether he can see it or not. On September 23 (the beginning of autumn in the Northern Hemisphere), the sidereal clock is in step with its solar counterpart. Six months later, when spring commences, the sidereal clock has gained half a day; by the following September they are again in step. But in this time there have been 366 sidereal days and only 365 solar days. Thus a certain time on the sidereal clock comes during daylight at one time of year and during the night 6 months later. Therefore, in our ordinary reckoning, we use solar time, so we know, regardless of the month, whether a particular clock reading is in day or night.

EARTH'S AXIS TILTED

Another important feature of the Earth's rotation has to do with the direction of its axis. It so happened, as the solar system evolved, that the Earth's axis became stabilized at an angle of 67.5 degrees from the plane in which we go around the Sun, known as the plane of the ecliptic. That is, it is tilted 23.5 degrees from the vertical, as referred to this plane.

This is the cause of our seasons. Over the years, or even a lifetime, the direction of the axis remains the same, pointed approximately to the star Polaris. The axis, at any time of year, is parallel to its position at any other time. Thus it is that in June the North Pole is tilted toward the Sun; in the Northern Hemisphere the Sun rides high in the sky each day. Its rays fall nearly vertically and are most concentrated, so their heating effect is greatest. Therefore we have summer—a time of warm weather.

But the South Pole now tilts away from the Sun, which is low for regions in the Southern Hemisphere. With a reduced heating effect they have winter, beginning in June.

Six months later conditions are reversed. The North Pole is slanted away from the Sun, which is low in Northern Hemisphere skies, so that part of the world experiences winter. But south of the Equator, people are enjoying their summertime.

Over the years men have tried to determine the exact size—and shape—of the Earth. The idea that it is spherical did not originate, as many believe, with Columbus. As early as 500 B.C., in ancient Greece, Pythagoras taught that it was a sphere, suspended in space without support. And about 200 B.C. another Greek, Eratosthenes, measured it and arrived at 252,000 stadia for its circumference. This corresponds to 24,662 miles, a figure surprisingly close to the one used today. In view of his crude methods, it must have been partly good luck that led him to so good a value!

The Earth's mean diameter is 7,917.78 miles, which makes its mean circumference 24,874 miles. But the diameter is not the same in all directions. From pole to pole it is 7,900 miles; at the Equator it is about 7,927 miles. In other words, there is a bulge around the Equator. The reason is the centrifugal force caused by the turning of the Earth. At the Equator its rotational speed is about a third of a mile per second, and this pushes that part of the planet's surface 13 miles farther from the center than the poles.

Until recently, it was thought that the Earth was approximately symmetrical about the Equator, and that its shape was that of a doorknob, an *oblate spheroid*. However, one of the first results from the work of the International Geophysical Year, which ended at the beginning of 1959, showed that it is pear-shaped. Variations in the Earth's shape have an effect on satellites moving about it. Conversely, variations in a satellite orbit can be used to determine the Earth's figure. Studies of the Vanguard satellite, launched by the United States in March, 1958, showed that the distance from the center to sea level at the North Pole is not the same as it is to the South Pole sea level. The North Pole is about 50 feet higher than previously supposed, and the South Pole 50 feet lower. Thus, there is a little more bulge south of the Equator than north of it.

Not only can the size of the Earth be measured; it can also be "weighed." It is, however, not correct to talk of the "weight" of the Earth; rather we should refer to its *mass,* which is a measure of the amount of matter that it contains. Weight is the force with which the Earth attracts an object at its surface, and it becomes less the higher the object is—the farther it is away from the Earth's center.

Take an object that weighs 10 pounds at sea level. Then raise it to a height equal to the Earth's radius—about 4,000 miles— that is, it is twice as far from the center as before. Its weight will then be only a quarter as much, or 2.5 pounds. At a height of two radii (three radii from the center) it will be a ninth and at four radii a sixteenth as heavy. (On the surface of the Moon it would weigh about 1.6 pounds, and on Mars about 3.7 pounds.)

Thus, the weight of an object depends on where it is. Much more fundamental is its mass, which has not changed as we raised it to the skies. We measure mass in the same units that we use for weight. That is, at the surface of the Earth, a mass of one pound weighs one pound.

WEIGHING THE EARTH

But how are we to find the mass of the Earth? We cannot put it on the scales or a balance. Yet there are several rather simple methods that make use of an ordinary balance, with considerable accuracy. One of these is explained in Fig. 19. Still more accurate measurements have been made with the torsion balance. This consists of a pair of small spheres on the ends of a light rod, which is hung on a long quartz fiber. The twist is measured as a heavy mass is brought near the little balls. In this way, the mass of the Earth has been determined at about 5×10^{21} (five sextillion) tons.

But how can we determine the structure of the Earth, with the center nearly 4,000 miles down, when the deepest hole is only about 4 miles?

If you have ever tapped a melon to tell whether it is ripe, you have used the basic method. This depends on vibrations passing through the melon. No artificial tap—not even a hydrogen bomb —provides vibrations in the Earth strong enough to be used, but an earthquake does. When the center of the tremor is sufficiently far away, the waves it sets up will travel through the core of the Earth and tell much about its nature.

The essential instrument in such studies is the seismograph— the earthquake detector. To illustrate its principle, lay a sheet of newspaper on a table, and a plate on the newspaper. Pull the paper away with a quick jerk. The plate doesn't move but stays where it was. This is an effect of inertia, which keeps the plate stationary unless you pull the paper slowly, and then the plate moves along with it.

Basically the seismograph consists of a large steady mass, which has inertia and remains stationary even when the ground moves beneath it. In one form, the mass is suspended like a pendulum.

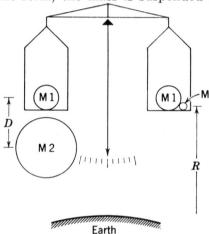

Fig. 19. The Poynting balance, used to determine the mass of the Earth. The scale is exactly balanced by having equal masses, M 1, on each side. Then a very large mass, M 2, is brought under M 1 and pulls it down slightly. This is balanced by adding additional mass, M', on the other side. Now the attraction between M 1 and M 2 is exactly the same as that of the Earth for M'. From the known masses of M 1, M 2, and M', and the distances (D and R) involved, the Earth's mass may be calculated. (By permission from Astronomy, by T. G. Mehlin. Copyright, 1959, John Wiley & Sons, Inc., New York.)

When an earthquake wave comes along there is a relative movement between the weight and the ground. This movement, however, may be only a small fraction of an inch and so it must be magnified.

In early forms of seismograph, this was accomplished with a system of levers; now it is done electrically. The mass may consist of a coil of wire, with a magnet close to it on the ground, so that the coil is in the magnetic field. When such a coil is moved in a magnetic field an electric current is generated. This is the principle on which an electrical generator works.

Even though the current is small, a sensitive detector can measure it and make a record, usually by a spot of light on a moving strip of photographic paper. When this is developed, there is a line that remains straight when the ground is still; but when the Earth moves the line shows waves, their size indicating the extent of the motion. One pendulum may move in a north-south direction, another east and west. A third mass is often hung on a spring, so it is sensitive to up and down motion. From the study of three such records the exact movement of the ground at the station is determined.

EARTHQUAKE WAVES

Fig. 20 shows a typical record of a distant earthquake, and you can see several main phases. The first wave arrived at P, and caused a small jog in the line. A few minutes later, at S, there was a larger movement, as the first of the next group of waves arrived. Still later (not shown on the figure) came some very large waves which may have continued for an hour or more.

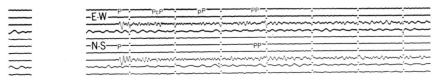

Fig. 20. Seismograph record. Record of an earthquake in Brazil on July 9, 1950, as recorded by a seismograph in Tucson, Arizona. The upper record (E–W) shows the vibrations from east to west, and the lower (N–S) shows those in a north-south direction. Various wave types are indicated by P (the first to arrive), PcP, $_pP$, PP, and S. The long surface waves appear in a later portion of the record. (Courtesy U.S. Coast and Geodetic Survey.)

When an earthquake occurs, it may be centered far below the ground. It is usually due to a strain which has been building up for some time and is then suddenly relieved as the Earth gives way. From the center a number of waves, of various kinds and speeds, travel outward in all directions.

The fastest are similar to sound waves in the air. The particles of the ground move forward and backward in the direction in which the waves travel; their speed varies from about 3 miles per second near the surface to 8.5 miles per second at a depth of 1,800 miles. They cover the first hundred miles in about 27 seconds and the first thousand in 3 minutes, 20 seconds. They travel nearly straight from the center of the quake to the observer; that is why they may go so deep. These, called the primary waves, make the first record on the seismograph.

With the next group, the secondary waves, the movement is from side to side, like light waves. Also traveling in a nearly direct line, their speed is about two-thirds of that of the primaries; they take 47 seconds to travel the first hundred miles, and 6 minutes for the first thousand. Slowest are the *L*, or long, waves, which go

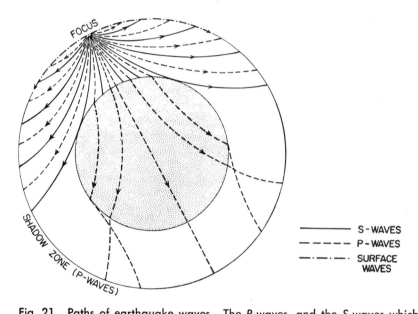

Fig. 21. Paths of earthquake waves. The *P*-waves, and the *S*-waves which follow, both travel through the Earth's interior, while the surface waves travel along or near the surface. The *S*-waves are stopped at the discontinuity between the mantle and the core (shaded); the *P*-waves are transmitted through the core but they are bent (refracted) at the discontinuity. Thus shadow zones are produced at certain places on the surface. (By permission from *Introduction to Astronomy*, by Cecilia Payne-Gaposchkin. Copyright, 1954, Prentice-Hall, Inc., Englewood Cliffs, N.J.)

only about two miles a second and travel through the crust of the Earth. They take 7 minutes, 20 seconds to cover a thousand miles.

On a seismograph that is close to the center of the tremor, all these waves would arrive at practically the same moment; but the farther away it is, the more they are separated. It's as if, at a certain signal, three messengers started off together: the first in an airplane, the second in an automobile, and the third on horseback. The aviator would be first to reach a distant point, and the delay in arrival time of the other two would be greater the longer their journey. If you knew the exact speed of each one and timed their arrival with a stop watch, you could tell the distance to the place where they started.

This is similar to the way that the distance of an earthquake is determined; see Fig. 21. The seismograph record not only shows the waves themselves, it also gives the times at which they arrive. When P and S can be identified (often more difficult than in the record shown in Fig. 20) the time between them can be measured. The seismologist has tables and charts that give the distances corresponding to various values of S minus P. If the difference is 8 minutes, for example, he knows that the *epicenter* (the point on the Earth's surface directly above the center of the disturbance) is 4,000 miles distant. An S minus P value of 11 minutes, 49 seconds would show the distance to be 7,000 miles. And to cover this the P and S waves follow a path which takes them to a depth of 1,800 miles.

But if the epicenter is more than 7,000 miles away, the record changes character considerably. P comes in later than it should— and S doesn't come at all! Something at the depth they reach, deeper than 1,800 miles, slows up the first and eliminates the second.

This something is the Earth's core, about 4,320 miles in diameter. When waves go deep enough to enter it, they are greatly altered. The core is more dense than the material above, so the waves are bent as they enter and leave it, as light waves are bent, or *refracted,* by a lens. Thus, when the primary wave comes out of the core, its direction is different from what it would have been if the core hadn't been there. At a distance just over 7,000 miles from a quake there is a shadow zone, where the direct wave cannot reach and neither can the one that has passed through the core.

A LIQUID CORE

Compressional waves, with the material first being pushed ahead and then falling back as the disturbance moves on, can travel through both solids and liquids. That is why sound waves travel well through water. But the lateral waves, with the material shaking from side to side, do not go through water or other liquids;

they can only go through solids. This indicates that the core, in part, at least, is liquid.

It is also known that the core must be very dense. With the Earth's mass determined and its size known, the average density may be found, and this is a little over 5.5 times that of water. Yet the density of the crust, which can be directly studied and measured, is less than 3. This means that the core must be many times more dense than the average. Indeed, at the center it may get up to as much as 18 times the density of water. With all the overlying material of the Earth's mantle, the pressures in the core are enormous—1⅓ million times ordinary atmospheric pressure (15 pounds per square inch) at the top and as much as 4 million atmospheres at the center. This would be 60 million pounds per square inch—no wonder the density is high!

The composition of the core is still uncertain. Many geophysicists have supposed that it consisted mainly of iron, perhaps mixed with nickel. This is the composition of most meteorites that fall on the Earth, and these are believed to be remains of an exploded planet that may have been similar to Earth. However, other studies suggest that the core may be a modification, of high density, of the rocky material of the mantle just above. As the pressure increases with depth, according to this view, it reaches a critical value at about 1⅓ million atmospheres and then there is a sudden jump in density. But perhaps the core is not entirely liquid; the inner core, about 1,720 miles in diameter, may well be solid.

At a depth of about 20 or 25 miles from the Earth's surface, there is also a change in the properties of material. This is called the *Mohorovicic discontinuity,* after the Yugoslavian seismologist who discovered it in 1909 from a study of the waves from an earthquake in the Balkans. Below mountain ranges it is deeper, while it is less below ocean beds. The region of the Earth above it is often termed the crust; see Fig. 22. However, it is not a crust in the same sense as the crust of a loaf of bread, enclosing softer material within. Actually, through the underlying *mantle* of silicates and nickel-iron, the Earth's rigidity increases, all the way down to the upper part of the core where it is nearly four times as rigid as steel.

A leading Australian geophysicist, K. E. Bullen, has estimated that just below the crust the density is about 3.3 times that of water; going deeper in this region, the mantle, the density increases to 5.5 at the bottom. Then it suddenly jumps to 9.5 at the top of the core and increases to 11.5 just before the inner core is reached.

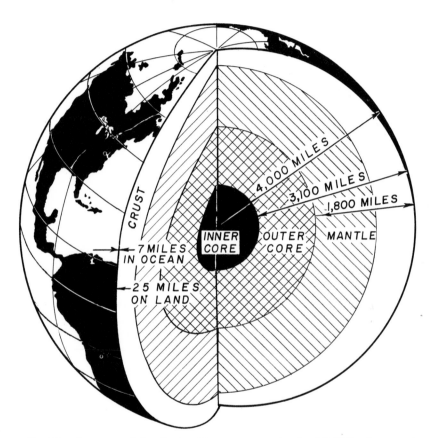

Fig. 22. Structure of the Earth. The core, at a depth of 1,800 miles, consists mainly of nickel-iron. The outer core is probably liquid, and the inner core solid. (Redrawn from a diagram in *Scientific American*.)

He has also calculated the pressure at various depths. It is about 800 times that of the atmosphere, at the bottom of the Pacific Ocean. Passing into the mantle, the pressure reaches some 100,000 atmospheres at 200 miles; and 1,800 miles down, at the bottom of the mantle, it is 1,130,000 atmospheres. At the center of the Earth, he estimates, it is nearly 4,000,000 atmospheres.

COMPOSITION OF THE CRUST

But let us return to the crust, which is, after all, the one part which we can see and study directly. It seems to be made mainly of heavy basalt under the ocean beds, and of granite, which is lighter, under the continents. It has been extensively analyzed, so we can find the average composition. By weight there is more oxygen than any other element: nearly 47 per cent. Then come: silicon, 28 per cent; aluminum, 8 per cent; and iron, 5 per cent; followed by small amounts of calcium, sodium, potassium, magnesium, titanium, phosphorus, hydrogen, and manganese. However, it is somewhat misleading to give the composition by weight, since iron weighs some 56 times as much as hydrogen. If we count the number of atoms, then oxygen, silicon and aluminum are still the first three, but with proportions of 60, 20, and 6 per cent respectively. Hydrogen is now in fourth place, with nearly 3 per cent, while iron drops to seventh place with 1.9 per cent, less than sodium and calcium.

Much knowledge of the structure of the crust has come from measurements of the strength of gravity in various parts of the Earth. As we have seen, there is a variation due to the bulge of the Earth at the Equator, so objects there are farther from the center and pulled less. Also, at the Equator, centrifugal force neutralizes a little of the pull. From these two effects, a person weighing 180 pounds at the North Pole would weigh only 179 pounds at the Equator. This would have to be measured with a spring balance. If he were to use ordinary scales, in which his own weight is balanced by standard weights on the other side, there would be no difference in weight at the two places because the weights themselves would weigh less.

Perhaps this has some slight effect in athletic records. Athletes competing in the 1956 Olympic games at Melbourne, Australia, were considerably nearer the Equator than those who competed in the 1952 games in Helsinki, Finland, and had less pull of gravity to overcome. They should have jumped higher, and thrown the javelin farther. Actually, at the Melbourne games, new records were set in every field event except the broad jump. However, the difference in latitude could account for only a small fraction of the gain, for example, of nearly 3 inches in the high-jump record, or of more than 17 feet in the javelin throw.

In addition to this general variation in the pull of gravity between Equator and poles, there are local variations. A difference of only one part in 50 million can be detected with modern instruments, the chief of which is a swinging pendulum.

If a clock pendulum swings in exactly 1 second, its length is about 39 inches. But the time of the swing depends not only on its length; the force of gravity is also a factor. If the force is less, the pendulum swings more slowly, while a stronger pull speeds it up. It would be impossible to measure accurately the difference in a single swing, but from the total time required for, perhaps, several million swings, the difference becomes apparent. Thus gravity stations have been set up in many parts of the world to plot variations in gravity over a wide area. However, with land covering only about a quarter of the total area of the Earth, this left a large blank area—until a Dutch geophysicist, F. A. Vening Meinesz, found how to operate a gravity pendulum at sea.

The pendulum, of course, requires a firm foundation, and even when the ocean is at its calmest, there is usually some swell, so that a ship could not be used. Some gain is secured in a submarine, for, at a little depth, it is out of reach of surface movements. But even this is not steady enough for an ordinary pendulum.

What Vening Meinesz did was to use three pendulums together. Each has a slightly different period, so they slowly come into step and then out of step with each other. While all three are affected equally by water motion, the relative movements with respect to each other are not and the gravity can be measured. His first experiments were made in the twenties by a Dutch submarine. Later the U.S. Navy made one available for similar measurements in the Caribbean and the Gulf of Mexico.

While the pendulum is standard for absolute measures of gravity, a simpler instrument called the gravimeter is widely used. This is really an ultra-sensitive spring balance. On a thin wire (of silica or invar, an alloy of nickel and steel that does not change appreciably with temperature) a small weight is hung, and, from the extent to which the wire stretches, a gravity reading can be obtained in a few minutes. Since the gravimeter weighs only a few pounds, it is easy to transport, but its indications are only relative. It has to be calibrated by using it at a base station where the force of gravity is accurately known from pendulum measurements.

From these gravity determinations, made at many locations over land and sea, has come much new knowledge of the structure of the Earth's crust, which can actually bend to a considerable degree. For example, the ice in the arctic and antarctic would make some 6 million cubic miles of water if it were all melted. This much water, added to the oceans, would raise the sea level well over 200 feet, provided that the bottoms remained the same. However, they would not remain the same, and the actual rise of sea level would only be about two-thirds as much as we should expect.

COMPOSITION OF THE MANTLE

The mantle of the Earth (the region under the crust) is composed of apparently solid rock to a depth of 1,860 miles. But actually it is not solid; it is a very viscous fluid, something like pitch. Take a lump of pitch and hit it with a hammer. It is brittle, and shatters much like glass. But leave it for a long time, even at room temperature, and it slowly flows and assumes the shape of its container, with a level surface on top.

Similarly the mantle may seem to be stronger than steel to forces acting for days, or even years. But over periods of thousands of years, the rock—or *magma*—slowly adjusts itself and changes in form. This is well shown in Scandinavia, where the ice of the last glacial period, that once covered northern Europe, melted about 9,000 years ago. It had been more than a mile in thickness, so a tremendous load was removed when it melted. An unloaded ship rides higher in the water than one with a heavy cargo, and similarly the crust under Scandinavia has been slowly rising, pushed up by the flowing magma beneath it. At Stockholm the ground is still rising, about a foot and a half per century. Northern Sweden, where the ice was thickest and remained longest, is rising about 4 feet in a century. The complete adjustment of the crust takes from 20,000 to 30,000 years, with about half of the total rise taking place in the first 8,000 years. Thus for many centuries Sweden will experience this uplift.

This principle, that the crust of the Earth floats on the fluid magma below, and adjusts itself to changing loads, just as a ship does in water, is called *isostasy*.

The parts of the crust that make up the continents are formed of lighter materials; they float high on the magma, like a block of cork or balsa wood on water. At the ocean bottom, however, the crust is heavier, or more dense, and that is why it does not float as high. In general, under any point on the Earth's surface, there is almost an equal weight of material in the crust. Under high mountains, the crust not only rises higher to the top; it also penetrates deeper into the mantle. Under the Rocky Mountains, for example, the crust goes down to a depth of about 35 miles, but under the

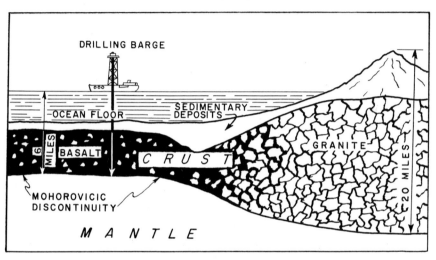

Fig. 23. Drilling to the mantle. The crust of the Earth is thickest under land masses and thinnest under the oceans. Plans for a *Mohole* through the crust to the mantle call for operations from a drilling barge at sea, to take advantage of this fact.

central plains of the Midwest, the depth to the mantle is about 27 miles. And under the sea it is still less, only 7 miles at some places in the Atlantic Ocean; see Fig. 23. Thus the crust under the oceans is considerably denser than that under the land areas, and even more so than that under the mountains.

A space explorer from some distant system who observed us from his rocket ship would probably report that the Earth was mainly a watery planet, for the oceans cover about 70 per cent of the surface. Of the land area, about 10 per cent is covered with ice, mostly in Antarctica, perhaps 10 per cent in Greenland, and the rest on mountains in temperate zones in the form of glaciers. The Earth has a total of about 350 million cubic miles of water. Of this about 97 per cent is in the oceans, about 2 per cent is in the atmosphere as water vapor, and only about 1 per cent in the form of ice or snow.

Originally the oceans were not salty; but, through the ages, rivers and streams passed across the land, dissolved small amounts of salts from the rocks and soil they encountered, and carried them to the sea. As the Sun's heat caused evaporation, water turned into vapor, to be carried over land areas again, to fall as rain, and supply the rivers with more water to repeat the process and so take more salts to the sea. Thus the saltiness of the ocean has been slowly increasing.

Because of the constant circulation in the oceans, these salts are rather generally distributed. The average, by weight, is about 3.5 per cent. When sea water is evaporated, they appear as a white residue, mostly ordinary salt, or sodium chloride. However, in the ocean the dissolved materials are largely in the form of ions, electrically charged units which form pieces of molecules. Of the total solids, some 30 per cent is sodium and more than 55 per cent is chlorine, and if these were combined, we would have nearly 86 per cent of ordinary salt. But there are also smaller proportions of magnesium, calcium, and potassium, which might also combine with chlorine to form their respective chlorides. Thus, in speaking of the composition of sea water, it is better to talk of the elements that are present, rather than of the compounds.

GOLD IN THE SEA

Of natural sea water, chlorine constitutes nearly 1.9 per cent and sodium slightly more than 1 per cent. Magnesium is a little more than a tenth of a per cent, and sulfur a little less. Calcium, bromine, potassium, carbon, and strontium are all present, each to a proportion of more than a thousandth of a per cent. About 45 different elements have been identified in sea water, in addition to the hydrogen and oxygen of which water itself is composed.

There is even some gold, about six parts in a trillion—enough that many efforts have been made to extract it. Some have been successful, to the extent that gold has been produced, but they have not been economical. In every case the cost of extraction was greater than the value of the gold obtained. But with magnesium, the third most abundant element in sea water, the situation is different, and the sea is one of the main sources of this useful metal.

It is also the principal source of bromine, used in making high-octane gasoline.

Actually there are differences in the salinity of the oceans. In the North Atlantic it is about 3.5 per cent but in the Red Sea, where the hot Sun causes increased evaporation, it is about 4 per cent. And in a landlocked sea, like the Dead Sea or Great Salt Lake, it is six to eight times higher. In the Baltic Sea, because of dilution by fresh water from melting ice and many rivers, it is only about .7 per cent. Even in the Atlantic, as in the Pacific, there is a variation between summer and winter, as low temperatures slow down evaporation and decrease the saltiness.

Such differences would be much greater were it not for the ocean currents, which produce a fairly complete mixing. These currents are great rivers in the seas, including the Gulf Stream, which flows from the Gulf of Mexico in a northeasterly direction across the Atlantic toward the British Isles and Scandinavia; the Kuroshiwo Current, which flows in a somewhat similar manner in the Pacific off the coast of Japan; and the equatorial currents and counter currents.

Currents, in the Northern Hemisphere, tend to curve toward the right. Thus, the Gulf Stream feeds into the North Atlantic Drift, and this current curves southward, past the northwestern coast of Africa, and then to the west in the North Equatorial Current. Finally it comes back to the Gulf Stream. There is a similar effect in the Pacific as the Kuroshiwo Current (also called the Japan Current) curves toward the east and then to the south in the North Pacific Current. There the water joins the North Equatorial Current to flow west again and return to the Kuroshiwo. In all cases, in the Northern Hemisphere, these circular patterns are in a clockwise direction.

But in the Southern Hemisphere the circulation is counterclockwise, for the currents are deflected toward the left. This is due to what are called *Coriolis forces,* caused by the rotation of the Earth.

An ice skater starts spinning, with his arms outstretched. Then he pulls them in close to his body, and spins more rapidly. This is due to the *conservation of angular momentum.* Instead of the skater, imagine a vertical shaft with a rod at the top, and two weights balancing at the ends of the rod. Now the shaft turns, and there is a certain amount of angular momentum, which is made up both of the speed of the rotation around the axis and the distance of the weights from that axis. If the weights are suddenly moved toward the center, the distance is less and the speed of rotation increases to compensate for the change and to maintain the same angular momentum.

Because the Earth is rotating toward the east, each particle of matter, whether in the land or the sea, has a certain angular momentum. If a mass of water is moved north from the Equator, as in the Gulf Stream, it comes closer to the Earth's axis. It is already turning toward the east, because of the rotating Earth, so this motion is increased. That is, it moves to the east even more rapidly than the Earth itself, so it really goes toward the northeast, just as we find the Gulf Stream to do. A movement from north to south produces a slowing of the rotational speed, so then there is a shift toward the west, and we also find this occurring. For example, the California current, which moves southerly off the coast of California, swings to the west to join the North Equatorial Current.

But in the Southern Hemisphere, a movement from the Equator toward the south brings material closer to the axis, so a southerly movement is accompanied by a swing to the east. Similarly, to the north, the movement will swing to the west. The circulation is counterclockwise, opposite to the clockwise movement in the Northern Hemisphere.

Coriolis forces also affect the movement of air currents, and of projectiles fired from large guns. Artillery men and sharpshooters long ago learned that in the Northern Hemisphere they had to aim a little to the left of their target. In the Southern Hemisphere they have to change their practices and aim to the right. It is said that at the time of the Boer War, when British soldiers suddenly found themselves shooting in South Africa, their marksmanship was very poor until they realized what was wrong.

SHIFTING CURRENTS

Currents in oceans are unlike rivers because they do not stay put. For example, the captain of a freighter, following a path which, according to the climatic charts, would put him right in the Gulf Stream, helping him along on his way to Europe, may find that he is a hundred miles away from that current, and may even be bucking a countercurrent moving the other way!

In 1950, five ships from the U.S. Navy's Hydrographic Office were sent out to study the Gulf Stream. They found that the stream had meandered from its usual path and had formed a 250-mile-long loop. Two days later this loop broke away from the stream and formed a separate eddy, which gradually disappeared. But while it was operating, this eddy injected some 10 million tons of cool water from the subarctic into the ordinarily warm subtropical Atlantic. In this way important effects may be produced. The cooler water would bring many more living organisms into the more southerly regions, where, ordinarily, life is not so prevalent.

The bed of the ocean forms a valuable record of its past history, for there, over the ages, are collected the remains of plants, animals, and rocks which have gradually filtered down, to remain practically undisturbed. Many years ago, scientists studying the oceans would scoop up samples of the ocean floor, but these were only the top layers, the parts that had been most recently formed. But in recent years, corers have been developed which can be lowered even in depths up to 24,000 feet. Then they penetrate as much as 70 feet into the ocean bed, bringing up a core that long, and 2½ inches in diameter, which shows a record for many thousands of years. And by means of the remaining activity of radioactive carbon in these cores, the age of successive levels is accurately determined.

Scientists from the Lamont Geological Observatory of Columbia University made such studies in the Atlantic Ocean and in equatorial regions, the Caribbean and the Gulf of Mexico. They found, like others before them, that the top foot of each core was salmon pink in color; below, the core was gray. Examining them more closely in the laboratory, they found that the pink sediment contained shells of warm-water animals, whereas the gray part was made of animals that had lived in cold water. The radiocarbon measures showed that the sharp dividing line corresponded to a period 11,000 years ago. Something happened at that time—all over the Atlantic—to make the ocean considerably warmer than it had been before.

Maurice Ewing, director of the Lamont Observatory, and his associate, William Donn, a meteorologist, finally decided that the freezing of water or the melting of ice were the only effects that could produce a sudden change in the temperature of a large body of water. Ordinarily, oceans do not freeze, because the currents redistribute the warm and cold water before freezing can occur. There is ice in the Arctic Ocean, however, because this body of water is almost wholly surrounded by land. Only through the narrow Bering Strait and through the wide but shallow sill between Norway and Greenland does the Arctic Ocean open into others, and it is hard for its waters to interchange with those to the south.

AN ICE-FREE ARCTIC OCEAN

It has generally been assumed that in the glacial periods, when much of North America and Europe was covered with ice, the Arctic Ocean had even more ice than it does at present. But Ewing and Donn decided that this idea was wrong. Instead, during the last glacial period, they suggested, the Arctic Ocean was free of ice. Its waters could interchange with the warmer waters from the Atlantic over the Norway-Greenland sill. The Arctic would be warmer—and the Atlantic colder.

With a warm Arctic Ocean, plenty of moisture would have been put into the air, moisture which would fall as snow on the northern lands, building up deeper and deeper, year after year, to form the glaciers which pushed far to the south. But finally so much water would have been transferred to the glaciers that the level of the Arctic Ocean would be lowered, some 300 or 400 feet. With the supply of warm water from the Atlantic cut off, the Arctic Ocean would freeze over. No longer would it supply moisture in the form of snow to feed the glaciers. With the warming rays of the Sun during each successive Arctic summer, some of the glacial ice would melt, and the water would flow back to the oceans. The sea level would rise, until once again warm Atlantic water flowed over the sill in sufficient quantity to melt the ice covering the Arctic Ocean. Then again snow would start falling, and another glacial cycle would be under way.

Several other bits of evidence indicate that the last ice age ended about 11,000 years ago and thus tend to confirm the Ewing-Donn hypothesis. Moreover, anthropologists have found that men were living on the shores of the Arctic Ocean 11,000 and more years ago. The ocean must have been open, or else they could not have found the fish and game they needed for survival. And the anthropologists also found that these early settlers suddenly started migrating south, again about 11,000 years ago!

As the story has been reconstructed, these men came to North America, from Siberia, across a land bridge that existed where the Bering Straits are today. To the south were great glaciers, so they could not go in that direction. Instead, they settled on the Arctic shores. But then, as that ocean began to freeze, food became scarce. They could not go back to Siberia, because the rising water had closed the passage across the land bridge. But to the south the glaciers were melting, and they found routes through the ice. So they penetrated farther and farther south, eventually reaching even the southernmost tip of South America.

During the past million years there has been a regular succession of glacial and interglacial periods but prior to that, geologists believe, the whole Earth was warmer. Palms grew in Greenland, and subtropical plants thrived even at 79 degrees north latitude. At that time the North Pole was not in the Arctic Ocean, but in the middle of the Pacific, with plenty of water around it to dissipate the cold, and keep water and ice from accumulating. A shift in the Earth's crust, for which there is other evidence, started perhaps 30 million years ago. About a million years ago, the North Pole was carried to the landlocked Arctic Ocean and the South Pole to the Antarctic Continent, again a place where no ocean currents could dissipate the cold. Thus arose our present pattern of climate with great contrasts between the Frigid, Temperate, and Torrid Zones.

And now, it seems, the arctic is getting warmer, as ocean levels are rising again and our winters are generally getting less severe. In the future, there will be open water in the arctic, but it is impossible to set a time scale. Then the snows will start falling in northern countries and glaciers will form. A few thousand years thereafter, much of North America and Europe may again be covered with ice—as much as two miles thick. If he hasn't been able to do anything to stem their progress, man may have to move to tropical regions—or to the shores of the Arctic Ocean.

QUADRILLIONS OF TONS OF AIR

Surrounding the solid—and liquid—Earth is the atmosphere, which accounts for about a millionth of its total mass. This may seem small—until we recall that the Earth "weighs" some 5 sextillion tons. Thus there are 5 quadrillion (that is, some 5×10^{15})

tons of air, a very respectable amount. Its normal composition is about 78 per cent nitrogen, 21 per cent oxygen, 1 per cent argon, with small amounts of other gases.

The atmosphere is in several layers. At the bottom is the troposphere, the part in which we live and move, even when flying in most varieties of aircraft. At a height of about 4 miles at the poles, 6.5 in middle latitudes, and some 10 miles at the Equator, is the tropopause. This is the boundary between the troposphere and the next layer—the stratosphere—extending upward to about 50 miles; see Fig. 24. In the stratosphere is the ozone layer. Like the lower regions this layer contains oxygen, not the ordinary kind in which two atoms are combined to form the molecule, but in the form of ozone, with three oxygen atoms to each molecule. This layer absorbs the shortest ultraviolet rays, which are quite lethal. Without this protective cover, our kind of life would be quite impossible on Earth.

As atoms of the upper atmosphere absorb ultraviolet rays, electrons are torn off, producing ions. These form the ionosphere, which begins at about 50 miles, and is in several layers that vary from night to day. It makes possible long-distance radio transmission, for radio waves travel in straight lines and cannot bend around the curving globe. But, by successive reflections from the ionosphere, they can travel completely around, once or even several times. Shorter waves pass through the ionospheric layers without reflection, but some are scattered, in much the same way that a small portion of the light energy in a searchlight beam is scattered to the side, thus making the beam visible.

Utilizing this effect, long-distance communication is conducted, even with very short waves, by *scatter propagation*. That is, the message is projected high into the sky on a radio beam. Most of the energy passes out into space, but some is scattered. A sensitive receiver far away from the transmitter picks up this scattered radiation, and the message is clearly received.

The upper part of the ionosphere goes up to about 400 miles, and the uppermost part is called the mesosphere. And above this is the exosphere, the beginning of outer space.

In general, the density of the atmosphere decreases with altitude. About three-fourths of the atmosphere is in the troposphere, and a quarter in the stratosphere. The ionosphere contains about 1/3,000 of the total while there is less than 1/100,000,000,000 in the

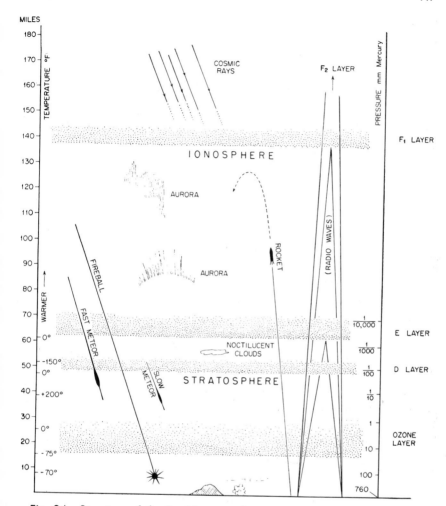

Fig. 24. Structure of the Earth's atmosphere. From the bottom to a height of 5–10 miles (depending on latitude) is the troposphere, in which all our weather occurs. Then comes the stratosphere, to a height of about 50 miles. Above this is the ionosphere, in which there are several layers (D, E, F_1, and F_2) of ionized atoms which reflect radio waves downward. (By permission from *Introduction to Astronomy*, by Cecilia Payne-Gaposchkin. Copyright, 1954, Prentice-Hall, Inc., Englewood Cliffs, N.J.)

exosphere. Actually this is a very good vacuum, for its density is a trillionth of that at ground level, or less.

It used to be thought that the temperature of the atmosphere dropped uniformly as altitude increased. At heights to which people traveled when climbing mountains, or flying in ordinary aircraft, this was true, but some curious phenomena indicated that it might not be true at greater altitudes.

When Queen Victoria died in 1901, a cannon was fired every minute in London. The people there heard it, and so did others up north, near the Scottish border. But those in between didn't hear it. Similarly, when the Pacific fleet held target practice off Catalina Island, windows were broken in Bakersfield, California, but no sound was heard in Los Angeles, about halfway between.

At first, it was supposed that winds caused such an effect. But, when it was proved that there was a circular area around the source of sound where the sound wasn't heard and another farther out where it was, this idea was disproved. The winds couldn't blow in all directions at once. Another idea was that there was a layer of hydrogen and helium up in the stratosphere. This might cause such an effect, but, even though there is some hydrogen up there, it isn't enough.

And then in April, 1947, the British blew the first syllable out of Helgoland, the heavily fortified island the Germans had built in the Baltic. About 5,000 tons of TNT were used to destroy it. To study the effects of this great explosion, American scientists set up a string of stations equipped with microbarographs—instruments to measure air waves—in a 660-mile line from north of Bremerhaven, Germany, to Gorizia, in Italy. Some of the most interesting records were obtained near the Pied Piper's home town of Hamelin, 150 miles from Helgoland. There they recorded sound waves which had gone up into the stratosphere.

INVERSION LAYERS

Possibly you live a number of miles, perhaps 5 or 10, from a railroad. Ordinarily you can't hear the trains, but sometimes at night you hear them very clearly. The reason is that there is a temperature inversion, a layer of warmer air above the cooler air near the ground. Usually sound waves travel outwards from the source in an ever-enlarging hemisphere, so that only those moving near the ground reach a point a few miles away. But in warm air, sound travels faster than in cold air. In the inversion layer, the air is warmer, so here the sound overruns the lower part of its wave and starts downward again. Then you can hear the train.

A warmer layer up in the stratosphere would produce the same effect. Moreover, there is other evidence for increased temperatures high overhead, from shooting stars, or meteors, small bits of iron or stone which come into the vicinity of the Earth from outer space. When they enter the atmosphere, there is a great deal of friction, and the meteor burns up in the flash of light commonly called a shooting star. (These will be described in more detail in Chapter 10.) Astronomers plot the paths of meteors from widely separated points on the ground, and thus determine their height, generally between 45 and 60 miles.

But, if the temperature of the atmosphere continued to fall steadily as it does near the ground, it would reach absolute zero— the coldest anything can be, about 460 degrees Fahrenheit below zero—at 30 miles. The atmosphere would suddenly stop at this altitude. Meteors prove that there is some atmosphere at greater heights. Therefore at considerable altitudes it must be warmer than people used to suppose. From about 60 degrees Fahrenheit, a typical temperature at sea level, it drops to about minus 65 degrees at the tropopause. It remains at about that temperature up to about 15 miles, then starts to get warmer, and reaches about 60 degrees at 34 miles. Then it falls again, and at a little over 50 miles is down to about minus 100 degrees. After this, it starts to get warmer again and continues in this trend as long as any atmosphere is left. At 115 miles it is over 700 degrees, and at 300 miles nearly 2,000 degrees!

We are now up in the region where artificial satellites travel, and it might seem that these would get red hot and their sensitive equipment would not operate. But, in this case, high temperatures do not mean great heat. At this height the density of the air is so low that air molecules are widely scattered. True, they are moving about very rapidly, and temperature is measured by the speed of molecular motion. But there are so few molecules that they would have no appreciable heating effect on a satellite, or rocket ship, in that region.

Sometimes at night, as you look toward the northern sky, you may see a faint greenish glow close to the horizon. Then the glow may brighten and form an arc, from west to east, which climbs higher into the sky. Other arches may appear below; then they may break up into rays, extending upward like beams from a battery of great searchlights. Or they may form luminous curtains, apparently waving back and forth in the breeze. Usually they are apple-green, but purple or even red may appear. The whole northern sky, and even part of the southern section, may be filled with these weird and fascinating lights.

CAUSE OF THE AURORA

While there are still many puzzling features, the aurora seems to result from particles shot out from the Sun. Formerly they were supposed to be mainly electrons, but now it seems that some, at least, are protons, which, after they enter our atmosphere, combine with electrons and form hydrogen atoms. As an electron falls into place in its orbit around a proton, hydrogen light is emitted. But later phases of an auroral display, when the continuous arch breaks up into rays, may be caused by electron beams. These electrons knock off the electrons that are revolving around the hydrogen atoms, but the hydrogen electrons soon fall back into place, and more light results.

During 1958–59, when scientists around the world were intensively studying the Earth in connection with the International Geophysical Year, the Sun reached a higher stage of activity than ever recorded before. There were many brilliant displays of the aurora; observers in northern countries saw the aurora borealis, and their co-workers in Antarctica enjoyed fine exhibitions of its southern counterpart, the aurora australis.

As these particles arrive close to Earth, they are caught by the terrestrial magnetic field and spiral in toward the magnetic poles. It is for this reason that in Alaska and Canada, where the north geomagnetic pole is located, these displays are most common. Farther south, toward the equator, they become less frequent. When the Sun is at the minimum of its cycle of activity, auroras generally are seen less often. At College, Alaska, the Geophysical Institute of the University of Alaska is an important place for aurora study. There, even in 1953–54, when solar activity was near its minimum for that cycle and the Earth's magnetic field was quiet, some auroral displays were observed.

Even when the aurora cannot be seen, there is a faint light in the sky called the airglow. The spectroscope shows that it consists mainly of four different colors, or wave lengths. Some of it is green light, from excited oxygen atoms. Some is red, also resulting from oxygen atoms, which have been excited to a different level. There is also yellow light, from atoms of sodium. Actually there is not much sodium in the atmosphere at these heights of 55 miles. However, sodium atoms release their typical yellow glow very easily, and even with one to a trillion of the other atoms, the sodium light in the airglow is as intense as the green and red from the far more abundant oxygen atoms.

Then also there are molecules made of an oxygen atom attached to one of hydrogen, known as hydroxyl. This is what is called a radical, a combination of atoms that can exist only briefly under ordinary conditions at sea level. But in the highly rarefied conditions at these great altitudes, they can last for a considerable time, because they seldom encounter another atom with which they can combine.

The hydroxyl light of the airglow is considerably stronger than that from sodium and oxygen; indeed hydroxyl light is as bright as a moderately brilliant aurora. However, its wave length is too long for the eyes to detect; the wave length is in the infrared. If we could see infrared, it would make the night sky as bright as the middle stages of twilight.

The exact mechanism by which these atoms are excited in the airglow is not fully understood, although, like the aurora, the mechanism certainly seems to be connected with the Sun. Airglow formed an important area of research during the International Geophysical Year; when these data are studied and analyzed, our knowledge may be greatly enlarged.

ULTRAVIOLET RAYS THE CAUSE

During the day, it seems, ultraviolet rays from the Sun disrupt oxygen molecules, releasing the two atoms of which they normally consist. During the night, oxygen atoms rejoin to form molecules, but a third atom or molecule is also involved. If one free oxygen atom hit another one, they would not stick together as a molecule but would bounce off each other. They will join, however, if, at the same time, they hit a third atom or molecule, which may not be affected.

The infrared hydroxyl light, it is thought, results when ozone (an oxygen molecule made of three atoms) hits a hydrogen atom. One of the oxygen atoms attaches itself to the hydrogen, thus forming hydroxyl, and leaves ordinary two-atom oxygen behind. Then the oxygen atom in the hydroxyl joins an odd oxygen atom that happens along, and the hydrogen atom is set free again.

By the use of rockets, the sodium airglow was produced artificially. In a cubic mile of the upper atmosphere, there is less sodium than could be placed on the head of a pin. But sodium radiation is so strong that it occurred to scientists studying these effects that, if they could release a few pounds of sodium vapor at that altitude, they should be able to make a glow that would be easily visible. The experiment was performed, in 1955, with a rocket sent up fom White Sands, New Mexico, and the yellow glow was seen clearly even at great distances. In a later experiment, U.S. Air Force scientists released nitric oxide gas at about 60 miles, and this produced a spectacular glow that lasted about 10 minutes.

Another form of airglow, about 100 times as strong as the nighttime variety, occurs at twilight, when the Sun has set for an observer at the ground but is still shining on the upper atmosphere. Because of the greater brightness of the sky, this airglow is invisible. In the same way, the Sun produces a dayglow, quite impossible to study from the ground because of all the sunlight scattered by the lower levels of the atmosphere, giving the daytime sky its blue color. From rockets fired high above these levels to regions where even the daytime sky is dark, this effect may be studied.

RADIATION BELTS DISCOVERED IN IGY

Although years will pass before the full scientific results of the International Geophysical Year will be known, it has already revealed important new knowledge. Among the most important is the presence, around the Earth above the equatorial regions, of two belts of intense radiation. One, at a height of about 1,200 to 3,100 miles, extends from about 20° north to 20° south latitude. The other is at an altitude of 8,500 to 13,000 miles and extends to about 50 degrees to the north and south.

Prior to the opening of the IGY in July, 1957, there had been some hints of unusually intense radiation at great altitudes above the Earth. In 1952–53 a group of scientists from the State University of Iowa, under James A. Van Allen, were studying cosmic rays by *rockoon*. This is a combination of a rocket and a balloon. The latter rises to some 12 to 15 miles, carrying a small rocket, which then climbs, with a modest payload of instruments, to some 60 or 70 miles. Van Allen explained that the object was to "develop a profile of the cosmic-ray intensities at high altitudes and latitudes." Thus, he hoped, they would learn more about low-energy cosmic rays which do not reach the ground at lower altitudes and latitudes, because they are either deflected by the magnetic field of the Earth or absorbed in the atmosphere.

Most of the results were quite as expected, but two rockoons, sent up from a naval vessel near Newfoundland, showed that at 30 miles the radiation was far more intense than they had anticipated. This was in the zone, extending around the Earth some 23 degrees south of the North Magnetic Pole, where visible auroras are most frequent, so they thought at first they were picking up the showers of particles from the Sun which stimulate the aurora. But then they found the radiation present even when no auroras were visible.

At first the instruments had detected X-rays. Later it proved that the radiations were largely electrons. They generated X-rays when they hit the casing of the instrument package or some of the nearby atoms in the upper atmosphere. When the IGY began, the work was continued both with rockoons and two-stage rockets. It was then found that the radiation included protons of high energy as well as electrons.

Satellite observations were needed for additional data, so the first Explorer, launched January 31, 1958, carried a cosmic-ray detector and a radio to relay its findings to the ground. First reports showed that the radiation increased with altitude as expected. Then records came from South America and South Africa, where the Explorer passed at much higher altitudes than it did over northern countries. These results were very surprising, for they indicated that over the Equator, at 500 to 1,000 miles, the radiation seemed to fall off greatly and even disappear for part of the satellite's path. No theory seemed able to explain this.

Similar instruments, which had been very carefully tested, were aboard Explorer III when it was launched March 26. They, too, showed that at 200 to 300 miles the counting rate was low. At 500 to 600 miles the rate went up rapidly, then dropped almost to zero.

By now the researchers realized what had happened. The counter had been designed for only a moderate intensity of radiation. When it went far above this value it "jammed" and failed to count at all. So instead of no radiation at these heights, it was actually enormously strong!

In May, 1958, Van Allen reported to the National Academy of Sciences the discovery of this radiation belt (now named the *Van Allen layer*) and advanced the idea that it consists of "charged particles—presumably protons and electrons—trapped in the magnetic field of the Earth." Such particles would probably originate in the Sun.

HOW THE BELTS ARE FORMED

Later (in an article in *Scientific American* for March, 1959) he gave this picture of the trapping mechanism: "When a fast-moving particle is injected into the Earth's magnetic field, it describes a corkscrew-shaped trajectory, the center line of which lies along a magnetic line of force. The turns of the helical path are quite open over the equator, but become tighter as the particle reaches the stronger magnetic field toward the poles. At the lower end of its trajectory the particle goes into a flat spiral and then winds back along a similar path to the other hemisphere, making the transit from one hemisphere to the other in a second or so.

"During this time its line of travel shifts slightly, so that the particle drifts slowly around the Earth as it corkscrews from hemisphere to hemisphere. An electron drifts from west to east; a proton, in the opposite direction. At each end of its path the particle descends into regions of higher atmospheric density; collisions with the atoms of atmospheric gases cause it gradually to change its trajectory and to lose energy. After a period of days or weeks the particle is lost into the lower atmosphere." *

On July 26, 1958, Explorer IV went into orbit, carrying improved instruments that could measure the radiation accurately over a much greater range of intensity. For nearly 2 months this sent back its data, from altitudes up to 1,300 miles and from 50° north to 50° south latitude. The magnetic-trapping theory seemed fully confirmed.

So far the Explorers had only penetrated the lower boundary of the Van Allen layer. How high did it extend? And was there only one layer or, as some thought, two?

On October 11, Pioneer I, the first lunar probe, was fired. It failed to reach the Moon, but did get to a distance of 70,000 miles from Earth. It too carried radiation instruments, and even though

* James Van Allen, *Scientific American*, vol. 200, no. 3. Copyright, 1959, by Scientific American, Inc., New York.

the readings were spotty, they showed that the Van Allen belt extended outward for many thousands of miles, with the height of maximum intensity no more than 10,000 miles.

After Pioneer II fizzled, the third was launched successfully on December 6. It, too, failed to reach the Moon but did yield excellent data on the radiation belts, as high as 65,000 miles, both on the ascent and descent. These showed clearly that there are two belts. The inner one reaches its maximum about 2,000 miles high, and the outer at about 10,000 miles. Beyond this the intensity diminishes gradually and vanishes almost entirely beyond 40,000 miles; see Fig. 25.

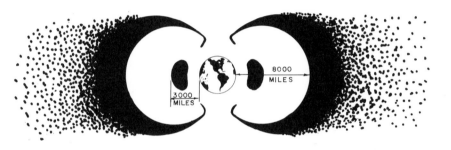

Fig. 25. The Van Allen Belts. Shown in black around the Earth, they are regions of intense radiation, revealed by space probes and satellites.

"Most of us," writes Van Allen in his *Scientific American* article, "believe that this great reservoir of particles originates largely in the Sun. The particles are somehow injected into the Earth's magnetic field, where they are deflected into corkscrew trajectories around lines of force and are trapped. In this theoretical scheme the radiation belts resemble a sort of leaky bucket, constantly refilled from the Sun and draining away into the atmosphere.

"A particularly large influx of solar particles causes the bucket to 'slop over,' mainly in the auroral zone, generating visible auroras, magnetic storms and related disturbances. The normal leakage may be responsible for the airglow which faintly illuminates the night sky and may also account for some of the unexplained high temperatures which have been observed in the upper atmosphere."

However, as Van Allen points out, there are difficulties to this theory. It is hard to explain the exact mechanism whereby the charged particles from the Sun can get into the Earth's magnetic field in the first place. And the observed energies of the particles in the belts seem to be far greater than the energies which particles from the Sun are believed to have. But as further studies are made, these difficulties may be overcome.

An alternative theory (proposed by a Russian physicist, S. N. Vernov, and Nicholas Christofilos of the University of California) relates the belts to cosmic rays, which may or may not have some fundamental connection with the Sun. Such rays, which come in continuously from outer space, hit atoms in the upper atmosphere and release neutrons. These have no charge, so they can travel freely through the magnetic field. But some decay into protons and electrons. These, according to this idea, are then trapped, to produce the radiation belts.

Perhaps both of these effects occur, and may have something to do with the presence of two belts. Another problem is whether there are always two. After all, the original observations were made at the time of great solar activity. It will be of interest to study them through the 11-year solar cycle, when activity greatly diminishes, then comes to a maximum again.

PROJECT ARGUS

Closely related to these effects was an experiment suggested by Christofilos, performed in August and September, 1958, using the Earth itself, and three atomic bombs, not to mention three-stage high-altitude rockets, etc., as part of the equipment.

In October, 1957, long before the discovery of the Van Allen layer, Christofilos proposed that an atomic bomb be exploded high above the Earth. It would produce large numbers of electrons, he suggested, which would be trapped in the magnetic field in the manner described above. So would other products of the explosion —the fragments resulting from the fission of the uranium used in the bomb—and the electrons produced by their decay. Thus, he said, these particles would travel back and forth along lines of force from one hemisphere to another, and might persist for days or even longer.

When discovery of the actual radiation belts was announced by Van Allen in May, 1958, new attention was given to the Christofilos proposal. The Advanced Research Projects Agency of the Department of Defense was authorized to proceed to carry out his experiment, which was dubbed "Project Argus."

From the deck of the U.S.S. "Norton Sound," a ship especially fitted for launching missiles, rockets with atomic warheads were sent aloft and exploded at heights of more than 300 miles, on August 27 and 30, during early morning hours, and shortly before midnight on September 6. The ship was in the Atlantic Ocean off the coast of Africa, at about 45° south latitude. An official White House statement on Project Argus says:

"A fascinating sequence of observations was obtained. The brilliant initial flash of the burst was succeeded by a fainter but persistent auroral luminescence in the atmosphere extending upward and downward along the magnetic line of force through the burst point. Almost simultaneously at the point where the line of force returns to the Earth's atmosphere in the northern hemisphere—the so-called conjugate point—near the Azores Islands, a bright auroral glow appeared in the sky and was observed from aircraft previously stationed there in anticipation of the event, and the complex series of recordings began. For the first time in history, measured geophysical phenomena on a world-wide scale were being related to a quantitatively known cause—namely, the injection into the Earth's magnetic field of a known quantity of electrons of known energies at a known position at a known time."

Explorer IV was in orbit at this time, and relayed back its observations of the shell of radiation, formed as the line of electrons drifted eastward around the world. Fortunately, as it turned out, the latitude that had been selected for the experiment was such that this artificial shell of radiation was in the gap between the inner and outer Van Allen belts. From a more northerly, or more southerly, position, it would have coincided with the natural belts, and detection would thereby have been much more difficult.

The official report says that "Explorer IV continued to observe the artificially injected electrons from the Argus tests, making some 250 transits of the shell, until exhaustion of its batteries in latter September, though by that time the intensity had become barely observable above the background of natural radiation. . . . It appears likely, however, that the deep space probe, Pioneer III, detected a small residuum of the Argus effect at very high altitudes on December 6, 1958. But the effect appears to have become unobservable before the flight of Pioneer IV on March 3, 1959."

7

The Moon

Other than the Sun, the Moon is the most prominent celestial object; it has probably been appreciated the more because it is not continually visible. During periods when it shone at night, men had a source of illumination for their nocturnal travels and labors. Perhaps this was one reason why the Moon was the basis of many early calendars, such as that of ancient Rome before Caesar introduced the Julian calendar, that of the Mohammedans, and also the one used by the Jews.

The motion of the Sun across the sky from rising to setting, regularly repeated, gave one unit, the day. The changing seasons, along with the varying height of the noon-day Sun, gave another: the year. But one of intermediate length was also desirable, and the cycle in which the Moon passed through its phases gave such a period. After a series of moonlit nights, it disappeared for a time. Then, one evening, just after sunset, the narrow crescent Moon could be seen low in the west, ready to start on another cycle. Thus, the priests of many ancient nations, who were also the astronomers, would carefully watch for its appearance, and thus were able to proclaim the start of a new month.

Such a month would last about 29½ days. At the beginning the crescent was visible only briefly after the Sun went down in the west; at the end it was seen, again as a crescent, in the east just before the Sun rose. Then came a couple of days when it could not be seen at all. But in the middle of such a month, the Moon would be full or nearly so. It would shine most of the night. If you wanted to travel at night, with the benefit of its illumination, you knew what days of the month to do so.

Unfortunately, the lunar month does not go evenly into the year, and complicated systems were needed to fit them together, by having a year sometimes with 12, sometimes with 13 months. When Caesar introduced the Julian calendar, he abandoned the tie with the Moon, but even today our months, of 28, 29, 30, or 31 days, still are roughly the same length as the period in which the Moon goes through its phases. Moreover, the first three letters of the word *month* come from the Anglo-Saxon name of our satellite: *mona*.

The Moon has been the subject of superstitious beliefs about its supposed effects on crop growth, on weather, on mental disease, as shown by the old word, "lunatic," no longer used by psychiatrists. And there are real effects: particularly the tides which are so important to sea-faring peoples. But the Moon is assuming even greater interest as we approach the time of its direct exploration; what was considered "science fiction" a few years ago is rapidly becoming a reality.

The Moon is Earth's only natural satellite, one of 31 such bodies that revolve around six of the planets. It is not the largest; its diameter of 2,160 miles is exceeded by the 3,000 miles of Titan, largest of the nine moons of Saturn; by Triton, 2,500 miles, the larger of the two encircling Neptune; and by Ganymede and Callisto, two of the 12 which accompany Jupiter. The diameters of the latter are 3,000 and 2,800 miles.

But measured in proportion to the planet it attends, the Moon far exceeds any other. Titan, for example, is about 4.2 per cent of the diameter of Saturn's ball, while Triton's diameter is 9.3 per cent of that of Neptune. Ganymede and Callisto, respectively, are 3.5 per cent and 3.2 per cent of Jupiter's diameter. As for the Moon: its 2,160 miles represents more than 27 per cent of the Earth's diameter of 7,918 miles. It would take the material in 750 Tritons to equal the mass of Neptune, 4,150 Titans to equal Saturn, and more than 19,000 Callistos to duplicate Jupiter's mass. But our Earth is only about 81.25 times as massive as the Moon.

As seen from Venus, where, of all the other planets, the best view would be obtained, the Earth and the Moon would look like a double planet. When most favorably placed, the Earth would shine with about six times the brilliance of Venus in our sky when most prominent. The Moon would oscillate back and forth, first to one side of the Earth, then to the other. It would get about as far from Earth, in the sky of Venus, as the Moon's diameter appears in our sky; and it would shine as brightly as we see Jupiter. There would be a noticeable difference in their color; our planet would be bluish-white, and the Moon yellowish.

DARK BROWN MOON

Brilliant though the Moon appears when it is full and shines high in the night sky of winter, it is really dark brown in color. About 7 per cent of the sunlight falling upon it is reflected, which is comparable with that of dark-colored rocks on Earth. If it were really white, perhaps made of magnesium carbonate which reflects more than 97 per cent of the light falling upon it, the Moon would be about 14 times as bright as it is now!

While we often say that the Moon revolves around the Earth, an observer who watched from outside the Solar System would see both bodies revolving around the Sun. The movement of the Moon around the Earth would be but a very small part of its general motion, since the distance of the Moon from the Earth (238,857 miles) is only about 1/390 of the distance of the Earth-Moon system from the Sun. Drawing a map on the scale of an inch equal to a million miles, we could represent the Earth's orbit by a circle 93 inches in radius. The Moon's path would deviate from it by less than a quarter of an inch. Sometimes it would be on the inside, sometimes on the outside. It would cross the circle 24 or 25 times in each trip around the Sun, i.e., in a year.

The most obvious feature of the Moon is its change of phase; see Fig. 26. This period, which established the month in the ancient lunar calendars, is about 29½ days, or, more precisely, 29 days, 12 hours, 44 minutes, 2.78 seconds. This is only one of several kinds of month recognized by astronomers, but the others need not concern us.

When the Moon is precisely *new*, we cannot see it; it is in the same direction as the Sun, and its sunlit half is turned away from us. Generally, at new, the Moon is a little north or south of the Sun; although sometimes it comes directly between Sun and Earth. When it does, we have a total solar eclipse.

A couple of days after new, the Moon has moved eastward from the Sun, and follows that body in its daily motion across the sky. After the Sun has descended behind the western horizon, the Moon is still visible. Moreover, a narrow sliver of the sunlit hemisphere is turned to our view, and we see a narrow crescent. The horns of the crescent always point away from the Sun; a fact not always recognized by artists.

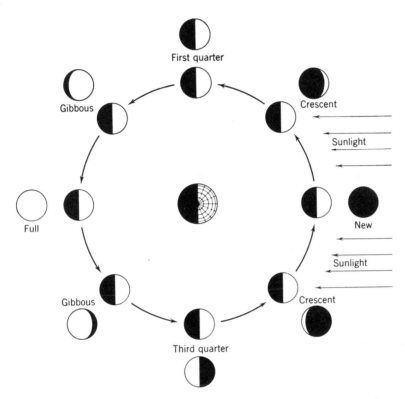

Fig. 26. Phases of the Moon. In the inner circle you are looking down on the Earth-Moon system, with sunlight coming from the right. Only the half of the Moon, or the Earth, toward the Sun is bright. As the Moon revolves around the Earth we may see all the sunlit half (full Moon), none (new Moon), or part (first and last quarters). These various phases are indicated in the outer circle. (By permission from *Astronomy*, by T. G. Mehlin. Copyright, 1959, John Wiley & Sons, Inc., New York.)

About a week after new, the Moon has moved a quarter of the way around. Hence, as the Sun sets, the Moon is high in the south. We then see half of the sunlit hemisphere, or a quarter of the complete Moon; this is the phase called *first quarter*.

Another week passes; the Moon has gone half way around, to the part of the sky opposite the Sun. Now the sunlit side is completely toward us, and we see the complete circle—the *full Moon*. Of course, if the Moon is exactly opposite the Sun, it will enter the Earth's shadow and we will have a lunar eclipse. Occasionally this occurs, but generally, as at new Moon, it is either north or south of the straight line passing through the centers of Sun and Earth. At full, of course, the Moon rises in the east just as the Sun is going down in the west. Here again artists—and writers—sometimes err by having a full Moon appearing in the *western* evening sky; it cannot get there until early morning hours. Or they may have a crescent Moon rising in the east at midnight!

With the passing of about another week, the Moon has completed three-fourths of its journey. Now it does rise around midnight, and is in the south at sunrise. Again only half of the hemisphere toward us is illuminated; the phase is *last quarter*. And then—29½ days after the beginning of the cycle—the Moon is back in the Sun's direction, new again, and the process starts over.

The time the Moon takes to go around the Earth is also the time that it takes to rotate once on its axis—in other words, its "day." As a result, it always keeps approximately the same hemisphere toward Earth. This sometimes puzzles people, who do not understand how it can maintain the same face toward us if it is turning. Perhaps a little experiment will clear up any such difficulty.

Stand in the middle of a room, with another person facing you, say at arm's length and to your north. Now, you pivot toward the left and the other person moves also, in a circle around you, maintaining his distance and continuing to face you. Finally the circle is completed; he is once more to the north, and, as before, he is facing south. But, as he went around, he successively faced all points of the compass—east, north and west—then south again. In order to do this he must have turned once, on his "axis," yet as he went around he was continually facing you, so you never saw the back of his head.

THE MOON ROCKS

Exactly the same thing happens with the Moon, although we do see a little more than half of the surface. There are several kinds of *librations* or "rockings." One of these enables us to see alternately over the north pole or the south pole, to the other side. Also, we can see varying amounts of surface around to the east or west. All told, in the course of a period of nearly 30 years we can see about 59 per cent of its total area. The other 41 per cent was perpetually hidden from our view, until the fall of 1959 when the Soviet Lunik III photographed the far side and transmitted the picture back by radio. (One of these is shown in Plate 5b.) Crude though these pictures are, compared with lunar photographs through powerful telescopes, they show that the far side is not essentially different from the side turned earthward. Further studies from artificial satellites will soon be giving us important additional information.

The part we do not usually see, of course, receives the same two weeks of sunlight and two weeks of darkness as the half that is turned earthward. At new Moon, the "other side" is fully lighted; at full, it is dark.

Our eyes have such extraordinary powers of accommodation to extremes of illumination that in winter, when the full Moon is high in the sky and the ground is covered with snow, the landscape seems almost as bright as during daylight hours. Actually, the full Moon is only about 1/400,000 as bright as the Sun.

You might suppose that the full phase would be twice as bright as the quarter, for we see twice as much of the illuminated surface as we do of the quarter phase. But the full Moon is nine times as bright, which indicates the roughness of its surface.

When the sunlight falling on the Moon is from behind us, as it is at full, we see no shadows. If you look at a rock, for example, from the same direction as that from which the light is shining, its shadow is hidden behind it. But if the light is off to one side, the shadow is at least partly visible. It is thus with the Moon. At the quarter phase, much of the surface that we can see is covered with shadows—not only shadows of the high mountains, but also those of small irregularities, no larger than boulders, or even pebbles.

Looking at the Moon with the naked eye, you can see dark areas which form the familiar features of the "man in the Moon" as well as the other figures: the donkey, the rabbit, and the lady reading the book, which human imagination has pictured around the markings. Early lunar observers thought that these dark regions were bodies of water, so they called them *maria,* or seas. They gave them fanciful names, such as Sea of Darkness, Sea of Serenity, Sea of Rains, and Sea of Tranquility. The last two form the eyes of the "man in the Moon."

It is now known that there is no water on the Moon, so these "seas" are merely dark areas, perhaps hardened lakes of lava, which would explain why they seem to be smoother than other parts.

There is no atmosphere on the Moon; at least none comparable with what we have above the Earth's surface, though there might be one that is very rarefied, perhaps comparable with that of our planet at a height of many miles. Proof of the lack of atmosphere is shown at an occultation, when the Moon passes in front of a star. The star shines with undiminished brilliance until it goes behind the lunar disc, and then it vanishes instantly. If the Moon had an atmosphere like ours, there would be a gradual diminution of the star's light. As it came nearer the Moon's edge, the light beam would pass through an ever-increasing thickness of the lunar atmosphere, and it would begin to fade sometime before it disappeared.

GRAVITY WEAK ON MOON

The reason the Moon has lost any atmosphere it may once have possessed, is tied up with the force of gravity on its surface. The same force holds people, buildings, oceans, and the atmosphere itself, to the Earth. Gravity is an effect of gravitation, the attraction between two masses. The greater the mass, the greater the attraction; the intensity diminishes with the square of the distance. (At twice the distance, it is reduced by the square of 2, or 4; at three times, by the square of 3, or 9, etc.) And with a planet—or a satellite—gravity acts as if the whole planetary mass were concentrated at the center. Jupiter's mass is nearly 320 times that of Earth, but on the surface of Jupiter you would be 11 times as far from the center as you are now from the Earth's center. You divide 320 by 121 (the square of 11) and get 2.6. This is the ratio of surface gravity on Jupiter to that on Earth. A mass of 1 pound, which would weigh 1 pound on Earth, would weigh a little over $2\frac{1}{2}$ pounds on Jupiter.

Now consider the Moon. Its mass is about one-eightieth of Earth's. But its radius of 1,080 miles (which is the distance of its surface from the center) is about 0.27 of the Earth's radius. The square is 0.0729. Dividing 0.0125 (which is $\frac{1}{80}$ expressed as a decimal) by the square, you get 0.17, or somewhat more than a sixth. So a pound on Earth weighs about a sixth of a pound on the Moon.

In these days of satellites and space probes, it is well known that an object moving upward with a speed of about 7 miles per second, or more, will be able to escape from the Earth's gravity. This is true not only for large objects, like rockets; it applies equally to molecules and atoms, such as those of nitrogen and oxygen which constitute the bulk of our atmosphere. These air molecules are moving rapidly, with a mean speed of about a third of a mile per second, at the temperature at which water freezes. At the boiling point, the speeds are about 17 per cent higher.

Note that these are *mean*, or "average," speeds and that many molecules would be moving considerably faster. On Earth, a few even have velocities as great as 6.5 miles per second, and these might leave Earth entirely if they were headed in the right direction. Fortunately, such high-speed molecules are so rare that there is no appreciable loss of our atmosphere.

But on the Moon, with its lower surface gravity, escape velocity is only 1.5 miles per second, and a considerable number of molecules might reach it. Once escaping, they would never return, so there would be a gradual loss of any lunar atmosphere, particularly if it was hotter than it is now, for higher temperatures increase the speed of the molecules. Even though hundreds of millions of years might be required before the bulk of an atmosphere would thus depart, the Moon's age is probably numbered in billions of years, so very little is left today.

One argument that has been used to support the idea of a very thin lunar atmosphere is the following: Every day, millions of meteorites strike the Earth's atmosphere; most burn up due to friction with the air, making a "shooting star." Very few get below an altitude of 50 miles, where the air is about 1/4,000 of its density at sea level. Despite all the years that men have been observing the moon through telescopes, there is no known case of anyone ever having seen a meteor strike its surface. Therefore, it would seem that the Moon does have a slight atmosphere, comparable at the surface with that of ours 50 miles high, which destroys the meteors before they hit.

But R. B. Baldwin, an American astronomer who has made a detailed study of the Moon, points out that only the larger meteors, many of which do survive passage through the atmosphere and land on the Earth as meteorites, would be visible by the explosive flash produced when they hit the Moon. He assumes that it would take at least a 10-pound meteorite, hitting the lunar surface, to be visible from here.

Perhaps 6,000 meteorites of this size or larger hit the Earth every year. The Moon, with its smaller dimensions, would get about 450. When you consider the time that the Moon is invisible, either below the horizon or hidden by clouds, as well as other factors, possibly no more than four or five would produce a flash that could be seen from Earth, even if an astronomer happened to be looking at the right place and the right time through his telescope.

Moreover, says Baldwin, it is questionable "whether or not a person seeing a brief flash of light on the Moon would believe it real, would report it if he did believe it, or would be believed if he reported it." Thus, the probability of seeing the flash made by a meteorite hitting the Moon is very remote.

"The best that can be said for the existence of a lunar atmosphere," he concludes, "is that none exists which is observable by present techniques, and that even the maximum permissible atmosphere [which he puts at about an eight millionth of the density of ours] is a very poor shield against meteoritic bombardment."

BOMBARDED BY METEORITES

But while few large meteorites seem to be hitting the Moon today, the Moon must have experienced an intense bombardment in past ages, for meteorites seem to have been responsible for some of the most important lunar features.

Besides the seas, some 30,000 craters have been charted on the visible area of the Moon. The largest are as much as 150 miles across, while others are only a few miles in diameter. Following a system introduced, in 1650, by the Italian astronomer Riccioli, the craters have been named after famous astronomers and philosophers of Earth. Plato, Copernicus, Kepler, and Aristotle are there. As more modern lunar maps were drawn, their makers took the opportunity to perpetuate the names of later, and even contemporary, scientists, but it is doubtful whether all of these will be generally accepted.

With the largest telescopes, combined with the very best observing conditions, the Moon can be seen as it would appear from less

than 100 miles. Structures the size of some of the largest buildings on Earth, such as the Pentagon, could be detected if they were
on the Moon. Thus, with the most powerful telescope, hundreds
of thousands of tiny craters, less than a mile in diameter, which
have never been charted, much less named, can be seen.

Also there are lunar mountains, of which the heights can be
determined by measuring the lengths of their shadows. Some are
as high as Mount Everest. There is a great circular range that
partially bounds the Sea of Rains, which rises about 4 miles above
the plain.

From some of the craters, bright streaks radiate. Called *rays,*
some are as much as 1,500 miles in length and 10 miles in width.
And there are *rills,* narrow and sharply defined lines extending
across some of the seas. Perhaps they are cracks or wrinkles in
hardened beds of lava.

To explain these varied lunar features, many theories—some
quite bizarre—have been proposed. Most of them start with the
craters, many of which have central humps that seem similar to
those in many terrestrial volcanoes. It was formerly assumed that
lunar craters also had been a product of volcanic action. Although
as long ago as 1873, a British astronomer, Richard A. Proctor, proposed that they were scars left from the impact of meteorites, the
volcanic hypothesis persisted.

The early advocates of the meteoritic theory held that the Moon
had once been in a semi-plastic condition, so that when meteorites
hit, they would produce a splash which would harden. One apparently fatal objection to this theory was that a majority of meteorites
would hit at a grazing angle rather than vertically, so gouges,
rather than circular craters, would be more common.

Study of aerial bomb craters during World War I brought a
new idea as to what would happen when a meteorite hit the Moon.
Herbert E. Ives, an American physicist who had done photographic
research for the U.S. Army Air Corps, studied such bomb craters
at Langley Field, Virginia, and published an account of his researches soon after the war.

He demonstrated that a large meteorite, striking the Earth or
Moon at high speed, would possess a large store of energy by virtue
of its motion—what the physicist calls kinetic energy. When it
struck solid ground and its movement was arrested, something

would have to be done with this energy, to convert it into heat. So much heat would be released, in fact, that the meteorite itself, and much of the ground around it, would be completely vaporized. The vapors would take up considerably more room than the solid matter, so there would be a violent explosion, quite comparable with that of an aerial bomb. Thus, as Ives pointed out, bomb craters represented "large scale experiments imitating the craters on the Moon."

The force of such an explosion, whether from TNT in a bomb or the sudden release of kinetic energy in the meteorite, is upward, whether it enters the ground vertically or at an angle. Thus the resulting crater is round. Ives suggested that this was the mechanism by which lunar craters were formed.

SCHROETER'S RULE

There is an interesting relationship known as Schroeter's rule (named after the late eighteenth-century astronomer who measured the dimensions of lunar craters and so discovered the rule) which states that for every crater the amount of material above the surface, in the surrounding wall or the central peak, is approximately equal to the volume of the interior depression below the surface.

Fig. 27. A lunar crater, shown in cross-section. According to Schroeter's rule, the material in the wall, above the surface level is approximately equal in volume to the excavated space below this level. Thus, if a huge bulldozer were to push the wall back into the hole, the surface would be level. This rule also holds for bomb craters on Earth.

Bomb craters follow the same rule. This, of course, is exactly what you would expect with a meteoritic impact. The wall of the crater is made up of material which has been blasted out of the center, and has fallen down again. Consequently if you ran a huge bulldozer over the crater and pushed the stuff of the walls back into the hole it would just be filled; see Fig. 27. No additional material was supplied, except for the negligibly small amount in the original meteorite.

A volcanic crater, on the other hand, is built up entirely of lava which has welled up from beneath the surface. Consequently it rises much higher than the bomb crater, and generally the bottom of the interior of such a crater is higher than the surrounding plain.

When the meteoritic theory began to be considered, people asked: How, if the Moon suffered such a severe bombardment of meteorites as to produce these thousands of craters, did its neighbor, the Earth, escape?

The answer is very simple: We didn't escape. There is, on the Earth, many a crater which seems to have been caused by the impact in past ages of a huge meteoritic mass. The best known is near Winslow, Arizona, the Barringer Crater, nearly a mile across. Others are in Africa, Siberia, Arabia, Australia, northern Canada, and many other parts of the globe. True, the terrestrial craters are not nearly as numerous as on the Moon, but that is easily explained.

On Earth, with its atmosphere, its winds and rains, we have erosion. Over the ages, mountains are smoothed down, valleys are filled up by sedimentation. Perhaps, when the lunar craters were formed, an equivalent number were carved in the Earth as well. They would remain on the Moon, but those on Earth would long since have been obliterated. Only those formed relatively recently remain.

Although many—perhaps all—of the craters on the Moon seem to have been caused by explosions of high-speed meteorites, volcanic action may also have occurred there. There may have been some combined action, such as a meteorite impact releasing lava from below. One crater, Wargentin, is flat on top. Apparently it was filled to the brim with lava, which then hardened. A few other craters of similar nature are known. The seas may also have been formed in this way, for they are generally circular and surrounded, in part at least, by circular mountain ranges. Since these are so large—hundreds of miles across—it seems likely that they represent the impact of meteoritic masses far larger than those that caused the craters. Such impacts may have been followed by upwelling of lava, which spread over the surface and hardened to form the dark areas now visible.

There have been many reports of changes on the Moon, but few have stood up under close scrutiny. However, an interesting observation was made in November, 1958, by a Russian astronomer, N. A. Kozyrev, with the 50-inch reflecting telescope at the Crimean Astrophysical Observatory.

Kozyrev had been studying the lunar surface, making use of a spectrograph to analyze the light from various regions. In the early morning hours of November 4, he was making a series of spectrograms of the central peak in the crater Alphonsus, shortly before the Sun set on that portion of the Moon. Each exposure lasted for half an hour—from 2:30 to 3:00, 3:00 to 3:30, 3:30 to 4:00, etc. In order to keep the telescope accurately aimed, he was guiding it by watching the central peak, reflected on the polished jaws that formed the slit of his spectrograph.

A CLOUD ON THE MOON

A little after 3:00 A.M., Kozyrev noticed the outlines of the peak were blurred. It seemed to be covered by a reddish cloud, which moved a couple of miles toward the direction of the setting Sun. After a few minutes the cloud had vanished.

A possible explanation came when he developed the spectrographic plates and examined them. Ordinarily, the spectrum of light from the Moon is the same as that from the Sun since it is really reflected sunlight. But on the 2:30-3:00 A.M. exposure, the violet part of the spectrum was noticeably weakened, while the red part was normal.

On the one made between 3:00 and 3:30, when he observed the red cloud, the spectrum was very different. Instead of the normal dark and sharp lines of the solar spectrum, he saw what are known as *Swan bands*. These are broader than the normal lines, and are the result of light radiated from glowing carbon molecules. The next spectrogram—made between 3:30 and 4:00— showed the normal solar spectrum.

Apparently a large cloud of gas, largely carbon, puffed out from the central peak. The gas glowed, because it was very hot or was excited to luminosity by ultraviolet rays in the sunlight. This cloud would not cause the diminution in violet light in the earlier spectrogram, but, as it puffed out, it may have stirred up a cloud of dust. Through such a cloud, red light might penetrate easily while violet rays would be absorbed. The red cloud that Kozyrev saw was probably the one that contained the glowing carbon.

Since volcanoes that men have studied on Earth do send out masses of hot gases, it would seem that this observation is good evidence that volcanoes on the Moon are not yet quite extinct.

This observation took place just as the Sun was setting on Alphonsus, and it was two weeks later before it rose again and astronomers could take another look. On November 19, H. P. Wilkins, a leading British lunar observer, noticed a reddish patch about a mile and a half across in Alphonsus. In addition, there was previous evidence that strange things may happen inside this crater.

An American astronomer, Dinsmore Alter, photographed it in 1956 with the 60-inch reflector of the Mount Wilson Observatory, making exposures alternately in blue and infrared light. On some pictures taken October 26, a marking that is quite familiar to lunar observers, a rill at the foot of the western inner slope of the crater, was distinct in the infrared exposures but invisible in those taken with blue light. Other areas, in the next-door crater Arzachel, showed no such difference in the detail shown in the two colors. Here again there must have been some temporary obscuration, such as a cloud, which hid part of Alphonsus, at least in blue light.

Probably the Moon is covered with a layer of dust, perhaps several inches thick or even more. Part of this would be meteoric dust, slowly settling from space, made up of very small meteorites. In addition, the fragments produced by the larger ones that hit and explode would also add to this dust layer.

Moreover, although there is no erosion on the Moon from effects of wind and rain, the great temperature changes may well result in a process which gives somewhat similar results.

This process is known as *exfoliation*. It occurs on Earth with rock surfaces, for example, on mountains, where alternate heating and cooling produce expansion and contraction and cause flakes of rock to break off. Exfoliation is aided by the presence of moisture, which expands as it freezes and so speeds the process. Since the Moon is completely dry, the rocks there would exfoliate much more slowly. However, over millions of years a very considerable amount of flaked fragments of rock may have accumulated on the lunar surface. In many places on Earth there are what the geologists call talus slopes, where piles of these fragments accumulate on the sides of mountains. Perhaps the lunar mountains may be of a similar nature.

In the 2 weeks it takes from lunar noon to midnight, the rocks would change temperature very slowly. They would have time to adjust internally, and exfoliation, as a result purely of expansion and contractions between day and night, would be very slow.

However, an American astronomer, Fred L. Whipple, director of the Smithsonian Astrophysical Observatory, has suggested that lunar eclipses may produce a much greater effect. When the Moon, always full at the time of an eclipse, enters the Earth's shadow, the temperature drops in an hour from about +160° F. to −110° F. Total eclipses of the Moon occur about four times every 5 years, on the average. In the past billion or two years there have been nearly that many eclipses, so the quick cooling has occurred a great many times.

This theory leads to a surprising corollary. The invisible other side of the Moon would never experience an eclipse by the Earth; consequently exfoliation may not occur there, and it may be much rougher than the side we see! This will be one of many things that the first lunar explorers will have to check. The photographs made from lunar space probes are still too crude to answer the question.

COVERED WITH DUST

Additional evidence for a layer of dust on the Moon comes from radio observations. As mentioned above, the Moon does not radiate light of its own, but sends out invisible waves that are considerably longer than those which our eyes can detect. Those just too long to be seen are the infrared rays, while those of still greater wave length—as much as an inch or so—are in the region of radio, what are termed *microwaves*. Even at temperatures well below the melting point of ice—indeed at any temperature higher than the absolute zero of −460° F.—any object is giving off at least a little of both infrared and microwave radiation.

Using the thermocouple—a sensitive detector of infrared waves —attached to large telescopes, astronomers have measured these heat waves at various stages in the Moon's cycle of phases. The variations in the infrared rays follow quite clearly the changes in brightness of visible light.

In 1948, from April to July, two radio astronomers in Australia, J. H. Piddington and H. C. Minnett, made similar measurements of the strength of microwave radiation of 1.25 centimeters (about half an inch) in wave length. This radiation also changed with the changing phases, but not in the same way as the visible and infrared radiation. The microwave maximum came not at full Moon, but nearly 4 days later. In addition, they found, the range was not nearly as great. Infrared measurements, as made by Edison Pettit and S. B. Nicholson at the Mount Wilson Observatory, indicated surface temperatures above the boiling point of water (+212° F.) when the Sun was overhead to −243° F. in the middle of the dark side. But, the changes in microwave intensity showed a range only about 39 per cent as great. From about 40° F. at the maximum, it cooled to about 100 degrees below zero.

This could be explained, Piddington and Minnett pointed out, by a layer of meteoritic debris, dust, etc., about 15 inches deep. Such a layer would be opaque both to visible and infrared rays. Therefore the Mount Wilson measurements would be of radiation that came from the top of the surface layer, where cooling and heating would be rapid.

On the other hand, this dust layer would be quite transparent to 5-inch microwaves, and they would come from a deeper level. Such a layer provides excellent heat insulation; because there is no air between the particles, the layer would act like the vacuum walls of a Thermos bottle. This explains why, at 15 inches below the visible lunar surface, it never gets as hot—or as cold—as it does on top, even after a couple of weeks. During a total eclipse, there is practically no change in the output of microwaves, as shown by other microwave observations made by W. W. Salisbury, an American physicist. At a depth of 15 inches, the Moon doesn't have time to cool at all during the hour it is shaded by Earth.

The Moon has been the subject of many superstitions, some still quite prevalent despite the astronomer's debunking efforts. One of these concerns the "wet" and "dry" Moon. When the crescent appears with the horns pointing upwards, it is said, the crescent is like a bowl that will hold water and is wet. Therefore rainy weather will follow. But when the horns of the crescent point toward the left, the bowl cannot hold water, so it is dry and the weather will be the same.

In other places, however, people say the crescent with the up-pointing horns is dry, because the water will not spill out. With the horns to the side it is wet, for then the water will spill onto the Earth below!

The horns of the crescent always point away from the Sun, so their direction is merely a matter of the time of year. In the spring, after sunset, you always see the young crescent Moon well above the Sun's position, so then it is always dry (or wet). In the fall, on the other hand, it is always well to the side of the Sun, with the horns more nearly parallel to the horizon, and is always wet (or dry). But despite this, we may have both wet and dry weather in the spring as well as the autumn.

Another common superstition holds that certain crops grow better if planted in certain phases of the Moon. For example, a calendar that is widely distributed (and no doubt widely believed in) says that asparagus, cabbage, corn, oats, onions, and seeds of flowering plants (among others) should be planted between new Moon and first quarter. Beans, peas, pumpkins, and tomatoes are plants that grow best when planted between first quarter and full Moon. Then, as the Moon is decreasing, from full to last quarter, you should plant your artichokes, beets, carrots, potatoes, etc. During the final week, as the Moon returns to new, you shouldn't plant anything; however, this is a good time to turn the sod, pull weeds, and destroy noxious growths. And above all, we are warned, we should avoid the first day of the new Moon for any planting; also the days on which the phases change!

Although many careful studies have been made of the various factors that influence plant growth, there is no scientific evidence that the Moon has anything to do with it. However, it is impossible to prove absolutely that a thing *never* can happen, particularly to someone who likes to think that it can!

CAUSE OF THE TIDES

But in one respect, the Moon does affect the Earth in an important manner, and also the lives of many people. This is by the tides in the oceans, due mainly to the Moon's gravitational pull and, to a lesser degree, that of the Sun as well.

We have seen that the force of gravitation, which any body exerts to some extent on any other, becomes smaller as the square of their distance apart becomes larger.

The mean distance of the Moon from the Earth is about 240,000 miles, and the diameter of the Earth nearly 8,000 miles, or about 3.3 per cent of the distance. When you are on the part of the Earth nearest the Moon, you are about 8,000 miles (the Earth's diameter) nearer our satellite than when you are on the opposite side. This difference is only about a thirtieth of the Moon's distance, but, because the variation is with the square and not with the distance itself, there is about 7 per cent difference in the Moon's pull at the two positions. The solid globe responds slightly to this difference, but the main effect is on the waters of the oceans since these are free to flow as the Moon draws them toward it.

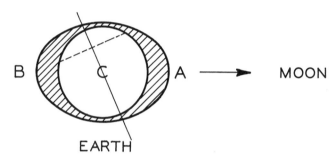

Fig. 28. Cause of the tides. The Moon's gravitational attraction pulls on the Earth and the oceans, shown here completely covering the planet. Water at A, nearest the Moon, is pulled hardest, so it rises into a bulge, toward the Moon. But the water at B, farthest from the Moon, is pulled least, even less than the Earth itself, at C. Thus the Earth is pulled away from the water at B, where there is another bulge, away from the Moon. As the Earth rotates, a particular place is carried around (dotted line). When it passes the bulges there are high tides, with low tides in between.

Thus, the water directly under the Moon is pulled most and tends to pile up at that position. Directly opposite, the pull on the water is weakest, even less than on the Earth itself. The effect, therefore, is that the globe is pulled away from the waters on the far side, while the waters on the side nearest the Moon are pulled away from the globe. The result: A bulge of water toward the Moon, and another bulge in the opposite part of the Earth; see Fig. 28. As the Earth makes its daily rotation, coastal areas, and mid-ocean islands, are carried past the bulges, to produce high tides at these points. Between the bulges they go past the low-water regions; then come the low tides.

Although the Sun is many times more massive than the Moon, it is so much farther away that its gravitational effect in raising tides is only about $5/11$ of that of the Moon. When Sun, Moon, and Earth are in line, as they are at new or full Moon, the two bodies act together, the high tides are extra high, and the low tides extra low, so the range between them is at a maximum. These are the *spring* tides, a term which has no reference to the season since they may occur at any time of year.

At first or last quarter, Moon and Sun are 90 degrees apart in the sky. The bulge from the Sun comes at the low part of the lunar tides. The result is the *neap* tides, with the least range from low to high.

Each month the Moon goes through a regular change in its distance from the Earth, and this is another factor. When closest (at *perigee*) it may be as near as 221,463 miles. At its farthest position (*apogee*) it may recede to as much as 252,710 miles. At perigee, the tide-producing force of the Moon is about 30 per cent greater than at apogee. Thus, the greatest range of all, from high to low tides, comes when the Moon is new or full at the time of perigee; this happens twice a year.

TIDES DELAYED

If the solid Earth were perfectly smooth and completely surrounded by water, there would be one high tide directly under and another directly opposite the Moon, and they would average about 2 feet higher than the low tides 90 degrees away. But actually the ocean bottoms are not smooth, and the Earth is not completely covered, so the tides are delayed in their response to the pull of the Moon and Sun. They may be late by several hours; for a particular place, the time by which they are retarded is called the *establishment of the port*. It is helpful in predicting the times of high or low tides. However, the accurate prediction of tides is most important for a coastal city and is a complicated process. Elaborate computing machines are used by the U.S. Coast and Geodetic Survey, as well as by similar bureaus in other governments, to forecast tides, and tide tables are published more than a year in advance.

In some places, notably the Bay of Fundy in Nova Scotia, the daily range of tides is extreme, perhaps 50 feet or more. The reason is that the shoreline is shaped like a funnel. As the tide comes in, the water is squeezed and has to rise many times higher than it would normally.

Tides also occur in inland lakes, but are much smaller, since much less water is available to respond to the Moon's pull. At Chicago, for example, the tide in Lake Michigan has an average range of less than 2 inches. Weather effects produce much greater changes in height.

Even the solid Earth responds, rising and falling by about 9 inches at the time of spring tides. This would not happen if the Earth were perfectly rigid, for then it could not yield to the distorting forces of the Moon and Sun. Consequently, the waters of the ocean would give all the response. If it were completely elastic, the Earth would respond as much as the water, and there would be no change in height with the tides.

Some years ago a Chicago physicist, Albert A. Michelson, made very careful studies of tides in a level pipe, 500 feet long and provided at each end with windows through which he could measure the height of the water, which half filled the pipe. Tidal differences in the water level were less than 1/1,000 of an inch, but by observing with a microscope, they could be measured with high accuracy. All the usual tidal phenomena were beautifully shown.

But the range of these pipe tides was only about 70 per cent of what it should theoretically be, since the response of the Earth itself canceled out some of the expected effect. This shows that the Earth has great rigidity, even greater than steel. However, it responds instantly to the tide-lifting forces, and returns immediately to its original shape once they are removed. Thus does the study of the tides give us valuable information about our own Earth and its behavior.

EARTH SLOWING DOWN

Another effect of the tides is that they act as a brake on the Earth, very gradually slowing down its rotation. This was first shown by a study of ancient eclipses of the Sun, recorded in old writings. Of course, in those days there were no accurate clocks, but the records show the place where the Moon's shadow crossed the Earth and the Sun was hidden. This itself gives us a good idea of the time when it happened.

But there are discrepancies between the times that these ancient eclipses should have occurred, as figured back from current data, and when they did happen. This can be explained by a lengthening of the day by nearly a thousandth of a second in a century.

Such slowing results (to a considerable extent at least) from the friction of the tides, as the water flows over shallow areas and through narrow channels, particularly in the Bering Sea, which accounts for much of the total braking action.

Not only does the Moon act on the Earth—the Earth acts on the Moon. The effect of this mutual relationship is that as the Earth slows down the Moon draws farther away, by about 5 feet in a century. As this happens, its orbital speed around us is lessened, and the month is gradually becoming longer.

George Darwin (son of Charles Darwin) traced backward the history of the Earth-Moon system, on the basis of these ideas. He found that the Moon was once less than 10,000 miles from us and went around in slightly more than a day. This may have been about 4 billion years ago.

Then the Moon rotated faster on its axis as well, and did not keep the same face toward the Earth as it does now. But, with enormous tides on Earth because of the Moon's proximity, there would have been large tides on the Moon, which may then have been somewhat plastic. Thus there would have been tidal friction, which would have slowed down its rate of rotation. Finally, it was slowed so much that day and month became identical. Then the tides would no longer flow, even if the Moon were still plastic or had oceans. With friction stopped, the Moon has kept the same hemisphere earthwards ever since.

But what of the future? Many, many billions of years from now—no one seems to have been able to figure out exactly how many—the Earth's rotation will have slowed so much that we will keep the same face toward the Moon, which will then go round us in about 47 of our present days. This, however, may not be the final state. If there are still oceans on the Earth at that remote era (and that is very doubtful), there will still be tides from the Sun, and these will slow the Earth's rotation even more. Our day will then become longer than the month and the effects of previous ages will be reversed. The Moon will start to approach the Earth. After an inconceivably great length of time, it will come so close that tidal forces produced will become so great that they will tear it apart. Its debris, except for what may shower on the Earth, will form a ring around our planet much like the rings now surrounding Saturn. Indeed, Saturn's rings may have been formed by a similar breakup of a moon that ventured too close.

Of course, if this happened there would be enormous tides here as well, and, while the Earth would probably not break up, like the Moon, it would doubtless suffer huge and devastating earthquakes. If any life remained on Earth at that time, it would certainly be completely destroyed. However, long before this comes to pass, the Sun itself may well have ceased to shine, and our Earth would have become a completely dead planet.

8

Earth's Neighbor Planets

In early March, 1940, an unusual sight could be seen in the western sky at dusk. There, in a row, parading toward the horizon, were Mercury, Venus, Mars, Jupiter, Saturn—the five planets that are visible to the naked eye. Not for many years will there be another opportunity to see them all at once in this manner. However, you will have ample opportunity to see each of them to good advantage, if you watch the skies, month after month.

The stars we see at night are bodies like our Sun but are many times farther away, and they are arranged into groups called *constellations*. A thousand years ago these constellations had much the same appearance to the naked eye as they do today; they will look much the same a thousand years in the future. These constellations are shown for typical evenings in winter, spring, summer, and autumn on the maps constituting Plates XVII through XX. The maps show the appearance of the northern and southern evening skies in winter, spring, summer, and autumn from approximately 40° North Latitude. The time for each pair of maps is given in standard time for your own zone. The names of stars of the first magnitude (i.e., the brightest) are given in italics. No planets are shown, but they appear close to the dashed line marked "Ecliptic." Each year, at the same time, the constellations are back to the same positions. But the planets are wanderers; in fact, that is the origin of the name. Ancient peoples called them *stellae planetes*—wandering stars—to distinguish them from the *fixed stars*.

These early observers found the planetary motions hard to explain. At first glance, it seems as if the Earth stands still and all the other heavenly bodies move around us, so they thought this actually happened. First of all, it seemed, the whole sky with Sun, Moon, planets, and stars, turned around us every day, causing these objects to rise in the east and set in the west some hours later.

The Moon steadily progresses eastward among the stars, night after night, making a complete circuit in about a month; but the movement of Jupiter, while generally eastward, is more irregular. Once each year it seems to retrograde, to go backward toward the west for about four months.

According to the Ptolemaic theory, which held sway for many centuries, the basic path of each planet was a circle around the Earth called the *deferent*. But the planet itself did not move in this circular orbit. It moved in a smaller circle—the *epicycle*—of which the center traveled around in the deferent at uniform speed. Sometimes the motion in the epicycle was opposite to—and counteracted—the movement in the deferent; then the planet's direction was retrograde. At other times the two movements were added and the motion of the planet was direct, toward the east; see Fig. 29.

Some of these early theorists thought that the planets were literally attached to crystal spheres, concentric with the Earth, to which the epicycles, as smaller spheres, were attached. In their motions, they believed, these gave off beautiful music, the "music of the spheres."

With more careful observations, they found that one epicycle was not enough to explain the way the planet moved. More and more epicycles were added, the center of each moving in the one next larger. Finally this whole mechanism became so complicated that, as Sir Arthur Eddington once observed, "The music of the spheres was lost in the whir of machinery."

Aristarchus, a Greek astronomer who lived on the island of Samos about 200 B.C., had a different notion. None of his actual works have survived, but, from references by other writers, we know he proposed that the Sun, and not the Earth, was the center around which the planets revolved. The Earth, he said, was a planet. Thus, the movement of a planet in the sky would be a combination of its own motion and ours. Jupiter seems to go backward when we, traveling at higher speed, overtake it.

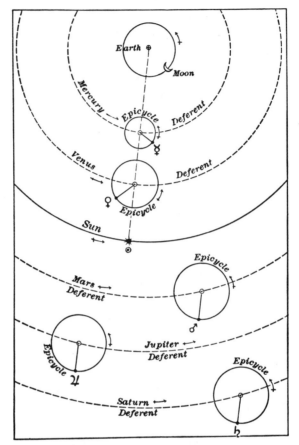

Fig. 29. The Ptolemaic System of the planets. This system placed Earth at the center, with the Sun, Moon, and the other planets all revolving around the Earth. Each planet moved in a small circle, called the epicycle. The center of each epicycle, in turn, moved around a larger circle—the deferent—centered at the Earth. Smaller epicycles were placed on the larger ones. (By permission from *Astronomy*, by H. N. Russell, R. S. Dugan, and J. Q. Stewart. Copyright, 1927, Ginn & Co., Boston.)

THE SUN IS THE CENTER

These ideas were not accepted in Aristarchus' time, but they were revived in 1543 by a Polish astronomer, best known as Nicolaus Copernicus, the Latinized form of his name. He shifted the center of the solar system from Earth to Sun, but he could not get away from the idea that the heavenly bodies all moved in circles.

He had to retain the epicycles to explain the movements, but the machinery was considerably simplified; see Fig. 30.

Then came the German astronomer, Johann Kepler. As assistant and then successor to Tycho Brahe, who served the Emperor

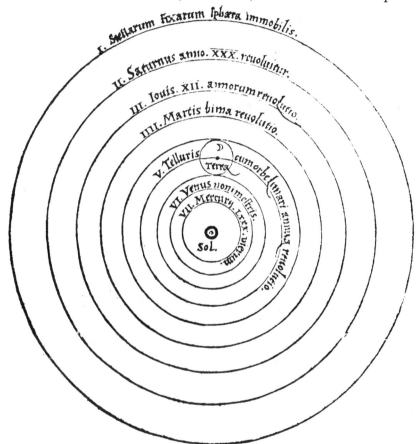

Fig. 30. The diagram of the solar system published by Copernicus in his great work, *De Revolutionibus*, in 1543. The Sun is at the center; the planets all revolve around it, and the Moon revolves around the Earth. Actually, because Copernicus thought the planetary orbits had to be circular, he retained most of the Ptolemaic epicycles, and even added some new ones.

Rudolph in Prague, he inherited the highly accurate observations that Tycho had made at his earlier observatory at Hven, an island in the Sound between Denmark and Sweden (and within sight from the ramparts of Elsinore Castle, where Hamlet chatted with his father's ghost).

In 1609, Kepler published the first—and most fundamental—of his three laws of planetary motion: that the planets move not in circles, but in ellipses, with the Sun at one focus. (An ellipse is the curve that you can draw if you put two thumb-tacks on a piece of paper on a drawing board; put a closed loop of string around both tacks and then, with a pencil held tight in the loop, draw a curve on the paper. Each tack is a *focus* and, when they are placed closer together, the ellipse becomes more and more circular. A circle, in fact, is an ellipse in which the two foci coincide.)

Kepler's second law showed that a planet moves faster when close to the Sun than when it is out at the most distant part of its orbit. The third law described the way in which the period that the planet takes to go around the Sun decreases with its mean distance from that body.

When he propounded these laws, Kepler had no idea why the planets moved so; his laws were purely empirical—they fitted the observed facts. But in 1681, in England, Sir Isaac Newton published his great work, the *Principia Mathematica*, in which he gave his law of gravitation—that every body in the universe attracts every other, with a force proportional to its mass and inversely proportional to the square of the distance—and showed that Kepler's laws followed.

These laws gave no explanation why the planets were placed at their particular distances. In searching for some relationship among them a German astronomer, named Johann Elert Bode, found a rule which he published in 1772. This is known as *Bode's law*. However, it is not truly a "law" like those of Kepler and Newton, merely an approximate numerical relationship. Moreover, the name of another German astronomer, J. D. Titius, should really be attached to it, for he had announced it some years earlier than Bode.

BODE'S LAW

Write a series of 4's, and under them a series starting with zero, then three, then 2×3 or 6; then 2×6 or 12; and so on, doubling the number each time. Then add these numbers to the fours, like this:

4	4	4	4	4	4	4	4	4
0	3	6	12	24	48	96	192	384
4	7	10	16	28	52	100	196	388

Then divide by 10, by inserting a decimal point before the last figure in each number:

0.4   0.7   1.0   1.6   2.8   5.2   10.0   19.6   38.8

This represents roughly the relative mean distances of the planets from the Sun, with the Earth's distance (93,000,000 miles) as the unit. Here are the actual distances:

Mercury	Venus	Earth	Mars	Jupiter	Saturn
0.39	0.72	1.0	1.52	5.20	9.54

Thus the agreement is fairly good, except that there is no planet at the fifth position: 2.8. However, as we shall see presently, a vast horde of tiny planets—the asteroids, which may be the remains of an exploded planet—move between Mars and Jupiter at approximately this distance.

When Uranus was discovered, in 1781, its distance from the Sun turned out to be 19.19, close to the 19.6 from Bode's law. But when Neptune was located later, it proved to be only 30.07 astronomical units from the Sun instead of 38.8. Then in 1930, Pluto was discovered at 39.46, which agrees pretty well.

Despite its inaccuracies, Bode's law is a convenient means of recalling approximate distances of most of the planets from the Sun. Remember "Bode" and "law," with four and three letters. This gives the figures you start with: the row of 4's and the 3 in second place below, after the zero.

One of the striking features of the solar system is the dominance of the Sun; in it is concentrated 99.886 per cent of the system's total amount of matter. And, among the planets, Jupiter alone accounts for about 70 per cent of the total mass. The planets move around the Sun in nearly the same plane as that of the Earth's orbit, known as the plane of the ecliptic. The elliptical paths of the larger planets, and most of the asteroids as well, are nearly circular. It seems unlikely, however, that this regularity occurred originally. Over the billions of years since the solar system was formed, there have been many forces—the great pull of Jupiter may have been one—which tended to bring them to this state.

While astronomers have long discarded the old idea of real spheres to which the planets and stars are attached, they still speak of the celestial sphere. For some purposes, when you are not concerned with their distances, it is a convenient simplification to think of the Earth as being surrounded by a great sphere with the stars and planets on it. As with the Earth, there are various imaginary lines on the celestial sphere. One is the equator, directly over the Earth's Equator. Another, of considerable importance, is the ecliptic, the line where the plane of the Earth's orbit would cut the celestial sphere, if extended out far enough.

The ecliptic also is the path of the Sun around the sky. And since the Moon and the planets move nearly in the plane of the ecliptic, they remain close to this line. Pluto can get as far as 17 degrees away from the ecliptic but, of the naked-eye planets, none can get farther than the 9 degrees of Venus. Thus, a band 18 degrees wide, with the ecliptic marking its middle, is the part of the sky in which the planets may be seen.

THE ZODIAC

This band is called the *zodiac*, which means the "zone of animals." Such a name was given because most of the constellations through which it passes are representative of animals: Aries, the ram; Taurus, the bull; Gemini, the twins; Cancer, the crab; Leo, the lion; Virgo, the virgin; Libra, the scales; Scorpio, the scorpion; Sagittarius, the archer; Capricornus, the sea-goat; Aquarius, the water-carrier; and Pisces, the fishes.

The zodiac also passes through parts of other constellations, especially Ophiuchus, the serpent-bearer; as well as Orion, the warrior; Cetus, the whale; and Auriga, the charioteer; but the twelve first mentioned are zodiacal constellations. In fact, the band is arbitrarily divided into twelve sections of equal length, known as signs of the zodiac. These are named after the constellations that corresponded to these regions several thousand years ago, before a celestial movement called *precession of the equinoxes* shifted them out of step. At present, when a planet is in the sign of Aries, it is actually in the direction of the constellation of Pisces.

The planets have a variety of periods in which to go around the Sun, ranging from 88 (terrestrial) days for Mercury, to 29.5 years for Saturn, and 248 years for Pluto. These are their *sidereal* periods, the times they take to make one orbital circuit, and stand in the same direction from the Sun, that is, toward the same distant stars.

Plate 1a. From Mount Palomar the 200-inch Hale telescope peers at the heavens on a moonlit night (see page 32).

Plate 1b. In using the 200-inch Hale telescope, an astronomer rides at the top of the instrument to aim and guide it.

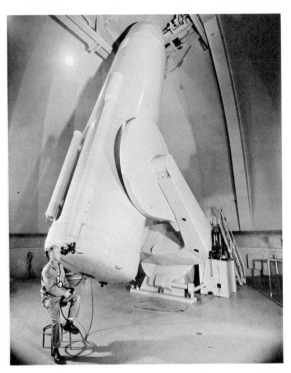

(Courtesy Mount Wilson and Palomar Observatories.)
Plate 2a. The 48-inch Schmidt telescope at Mt. Palomar (see page 34).

(Courtesy British Information Service.)
Plate 2b. The 250-foot "dish" of the Jodrell Bank radio telescope in England can be pointed toward any part of the sky, despite its weight of 750 tons (see page 51).

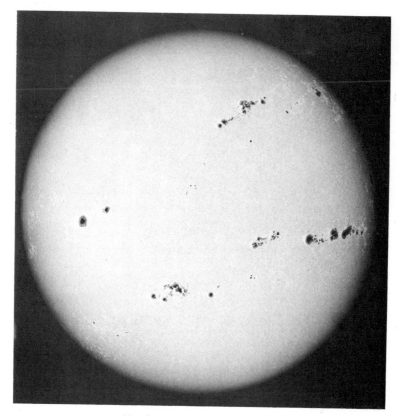

(Courtesy Mount Wilson and Palomar Observatories.)
Plate 3a. The Sun, photographed at the time of sunspot maximum, on December 21, 1957 (see page 73).

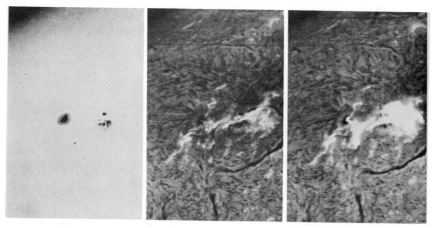

(Courtesy Mount Wilson and Palomar Observatories.)
Plate 3b. Solar flare of August 8, 1937. At left is an ordinary photograph of the sunspot group; in the middle is the same region taken in the red light of glowing hydrogen, and at the right the same area 5 minutes later when the flare reached its maximum intensity (see page 89).

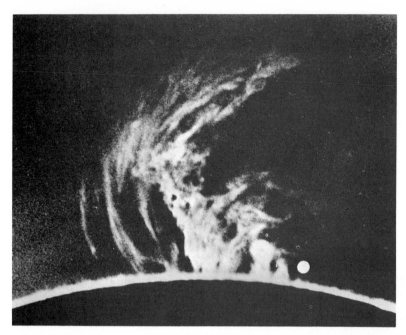

(Courtesy Mount Wilson and Palomar Observatories.)
Plate 4a. A solar prominence, rising from the Sun's edge to a height of 140,000 miles, photographed in the light of calcium, on July 9, 1917. The small white disk represents the size of the Earth on the same scale (see page 81).

(Courtesy Mount Wilson and Palomar Observatories.)
Plate 4b. The Sun's corona, photographed at the total eclipse of June 8, 1918, from Green River, Wyoming (see page 79).

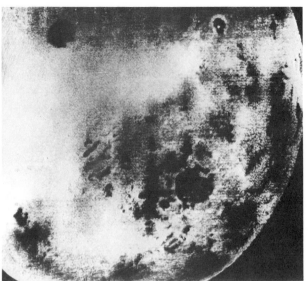

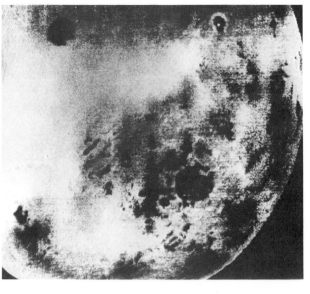

(Sovfoto.)

(Courtesy Mount Wilson and Palomar Observatories.)

Plate 5a (left). The full Moon in a photograph made with the 100-inch Hooker telescope at Mount Wilson.

Plate 5b (right). The back of the Moon. Part of the "other side" of the Moon, photographed by the Soviet lunar probe, Lunik III, on October 7, 1959, from a distance of about 41,000 miles. The black spot toward the upper right is the Sea of Moscow; underneath, toward the lower right, is the crater Tsiolkovsky. The features at the left are visible from Earth. Toward the upper left is the Humboldt Sea, on the boundary between the visible and invisible hemispheres. So is the Smyth Sea, the large dark spot about halfway from the center of the picture to the lower left-hand edge of the Moon. Near the edge at this point is the Sea of Fecundity and partly visible, at the left side of the picture, is the Sea of Crises. Both of these seas are in the visible half (see page 258).

(Courtesy Mount Wilson and Palomar Observatories.)
Plate 6. The great lunar crater Clavius, about 150 miles in diameter, is shown in this photograph by the 200-inch Hale telescope. On its rim and within its boundaries are many smaller craters. The smallest shown are only a few miles across (see page 136).

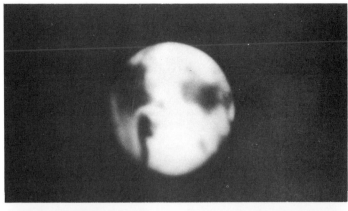

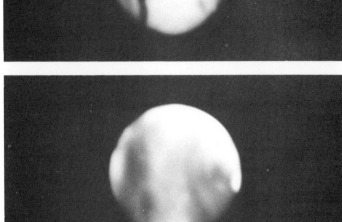

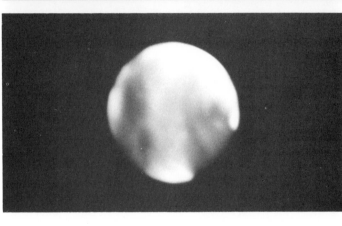

(Courtesy Mount Wilson and Palomar Observatories.)

Plate 7a (left). The planet Venus (in crescent phase), photographed with the 200-inch Hale telescope. Only the tops of the clouds covering it are visible (see page 184).

Plate 7b (right). The planet Mars, photographed (left) in blue light and (right) in red, with the 200-inch Hale telescope (see page 187).

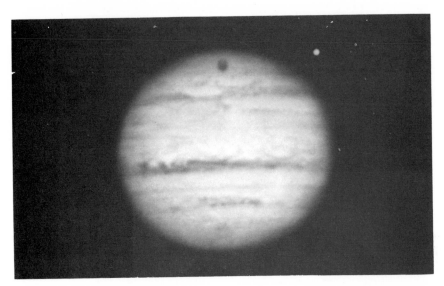

(Courtesy Mount Wilson and Palomar Observatories.)
Plate 8a. The planet Jupiter, photographed with the 200-inch Hale tele-scope. Above, and right, is its satellite Ganymede, casting a shadow on the planet's surface (see page 206).

(Courtesy Mount Wilson and Palomar Observatories.)
Plate 8b. The planet Saturn with its ring system, photographed from Mt. Wilson with the 100-inch Hooker telescope (see page 214).

(Courtesy Mount Wilson and Palomar Observatories.)
Plate 9a. The head of Halley's Comet, photographed with the 60-inch telescope of the Mount Wilson Observatory, May 8, 1910 (see page 244).

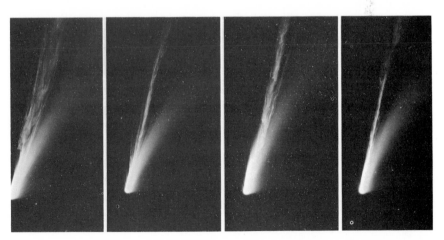

(Courtesy Mount Wilson and Palomar Observatories.)
Plate 9b. Four photographs of comet Mrkos, which was prominent in the evening sky in the summer of 1957, taken with the 48-inch Schmidt telescope at Mount Palomar on August 22, 24, 26, and 27 (see page 243).

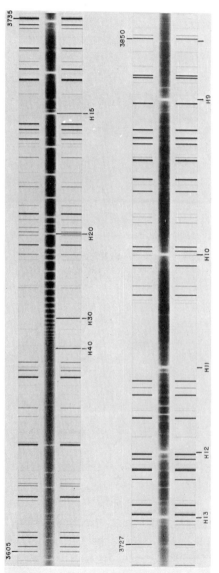

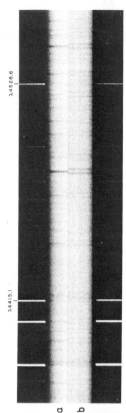

Spectral Type A2

λ4415.1   λ4528.6

Period 20.5 days

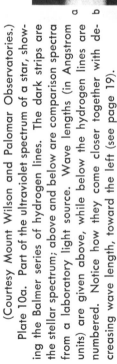

a

b

(Courtesy Mount Wilson and Palomar Observatories.)

Plate 10a. Part of the ultraviolet spectrum of a star, showing the Balmer series of hydrogen lines. The dark strips are the stellar spectrum; above and below are comparison spectra from a laboratory light source. Wave lengths (in Angstrom units) are given above, while below the hydrogen lines are numbered. Notice how they come closer together with decreasing wave length, toward the left (see page 19).

(Courtesy Mount Wilson and Palomar Observatories.)

Plate 10b. Part of the blue region of the spectrum of the star Mizar, in the great dipper. Notice how the lines that are single in the upper spectrum are double in the lower, taken about two days later. Mizar is a double star, and the lower spectrum shows it when one component was moving away and the other toward the Earth. Thus the lines from each

166

(Courtesy Mount Wilson and Palomar Observatories.)
Plate 11a. The "Great" nebula in Orion, photographed with the 100-inch Hooker telescope (see page 318).

(Courtesy Mount Wilson and Palomar Observatories.)
Plate 11b. The "Horsehead," a dark nebula in Orion, photographed with the 200-inch Hale telescope (see page 319).

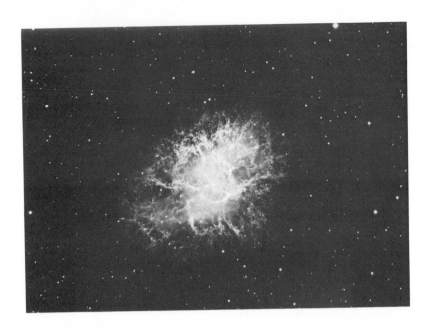

(Courtesy Mount Wilson and Palomar Observatories.)
Plate 12a. The "Crab" nebula in Taurus, photographed with the 200-inch Hale telescope. This is the remains of a supernova which flashed into view in 1054 A.D. (see page 308).

(Courtesy Mount Wilson and Palomar Observatories.)
Plate 12b. A typical planetary nebula, called "The Dumbbell" on account of its shape, photographed with the 100-inch Hooker telescope (see page 319).

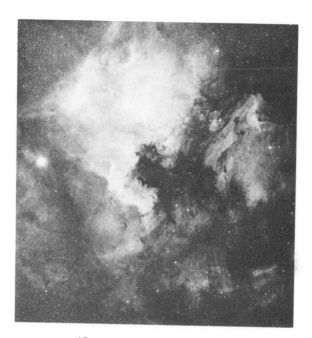

(Courtesy Mount Wilson and Palomar Observatories.)
Plate 13a. The "North America" nebula in Cygnus, photographed with the 48-inch Schmidt telescope (see page 318). (Copyright National Geographic Society—Palomar Observatory Sky Survey.)

(Courtesy Mount Wilson and Palomar Observatories.)
Plate 13b. The globular star cluster in Hercules, photographed with the 200-inch Hale telescope (see page 330).

(Courtesy Mount Wilson and Palomar Observatories.)
Plate 14a. One of our neighbor galaxies, in the constellation of Andromeda, photographed with the 48-inch Schmidt telescope (see page 331).

(Courtesy Mount Wilson and Palomar Observatories.)
Plate 14b. Another galaxy in the constellation of Ursa Major, photographed with the 200-inch Hale telescope.

Plate 15a. A galaxy in Virgo, seen on edge and showing the surrounding dark material, taken with the 200-inch Hale telescope.

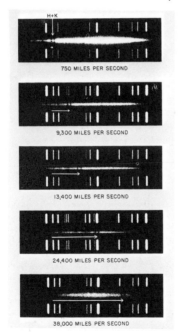

Plate 15b. The red shift in the spectra of outer galaxies, which seems to indicate that the universe is expanding. The farther away the object (given in light-years), the farther the calcium lines, H and K, are shifted toward the right, to the red end of the spectrum. Assuming that these shifts are due to the Doppler effect, these objects must be receding at speeds up to 38,000 miles per second, for the most distant (see page 335).

(Courtesy Mount Wilson and Palomar Observatories.)
Plate 16a. The radio source *A* in Cygnus, apparently two galaxies in collision, photographed with the 200-inch Hale telescope (see page 335).

(Courtesy Mount Wilson and Palomar Observatories.)
Plate 16b. The farthest reaches of space, photographed with the 200-inch Hale telescope. The faint cluster of galaxies at the center of the picture is more than a billion light-years away, and near the limit of the observable universe.

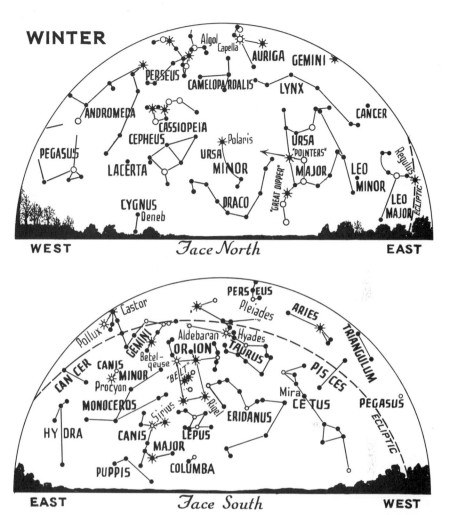

WINTER

WEST   *Face North*   **EAST**

EAST   *Face South*   **WEST**

☼ ✳ ○ ●   SYMBOLS FOR STARS IN ORDER OF BRIGHTNESS

Plate 17. Winter. These show the skies at about midnight, December 1; 10 p.m., January 1; and 8 p.m., February 1 (also 4 a.m., October 1 and 2 a.m., November 1). The brightest star is *Sirius* (stars of the first magnitude are given in italics) in Canis Major, the great dog, in the southeast. High in the south is Orion, the warrior, with two first-magnitude stars, *Betelgeuse* and *Rigel*. Between them is a row of three fainter stars that form Orion's belt. Higher and to the right is Taurus, the bull, with *Aldebaran*, distinctly red in color. Overhead is Auriga, the charioteer, with *Capella*. High in the east are the twins, Gemini, with first-magnitude *Pollux* and second-magnitude Castor. Below is the lesser dog, Canis Minor, with *Procyon*. *Deneb* is in Cygnus, the swan, low in the northwest, and *Regulus* in Leo, the lion, is toward the east. Both are so low that atmospheric absorption makes them unusually faint. The familiar "great dipper," part of the great bear, Ursa Major, is in the northeast, the handle pointing downward. Two stars in the bowl are the "pointers," which show the direction of Polaris, the pole star, to the north. In the northwest is Cassiopeia, the queen, shaped like a letter W or M. (Science Service, Inc.)

SPRING

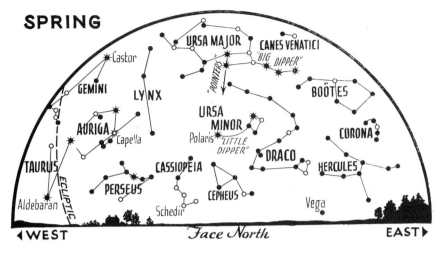

◀ WEST — *Face North* — EAST ▶

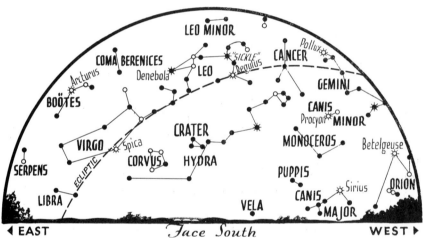

◀ EAST — *Face South* — WEST ▶

☆ ✳ ○ ● SYMBOLS FOR STARS IN ORDER OF BRIGHTNESS

Plate 18. Spring. These show the skies at about midnight, March 1; 10 p.m., April 1; and 8 p.m., May 1 (also 4 a.m., January 1 and 2 a.m., February 1). Leo, the lion, is high in the south. In this constellation is a smaller group, the "sickle," with *Regulus* at the end of the handle. Virgo, the virgin, is in the southeast, with *Spica;* above it is Boötes, the bear driver, with *Arcturus*. Toward the west some of the brilliant stars of the winter evening are still visible. *Sirius,* in Canis Major, is low in the southwest, and to the right is Orion, with *Betelgeuse* remaining in view. Farther to the right is Taurus, with *Aldebaran,* dimmed by reason of its low altitude. Above stands Auriga, with *Capella,* and to the left of this group is Gemini, with *Pollux*. Greatly dimmed, just above the northeastern horizon, is *Vega* in Lyra, the lyre. Ursa Major, with the great dipper, stands high in the north, above Polaris. (Science Service, Inc.)

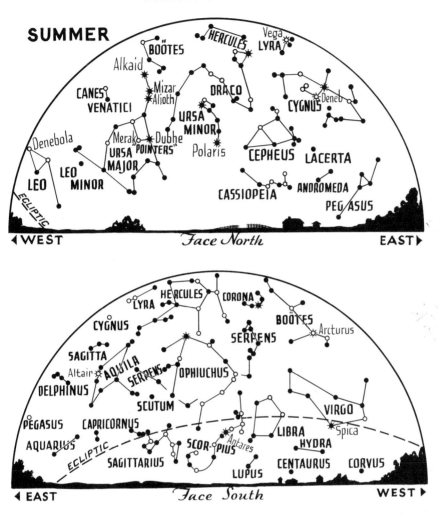

☼ ✳ ○ ● SYMBOLS FOR STARS IN ORDER OF BRIGHTNESS

Plate 19. Summer. These maps show the skies at about midnight, June 1; 10 p.m., July 1; and 8 p.m., August 1 (also 4 a.m., April 1 and 2 a.m., May 1). One of the most conspicuous and characteristic constellations is Scorpius, the scorpion. You can see it in the south, with *Antares* quite red. *Spica*, in Virgo, is now in the southwest, while *Arcturus*, in Boötes, is above it. *Vega*, in Lyra, is high in the east. Below it, toward the right, is *Altair* in Aquila, the eagle, and, to the left, *Deneb* in Cygnus. The great dipper is now in the northwest, handle upward, to the left of the pole star. Cassiopeia is low in the northeast. (Science Service, Inc.)

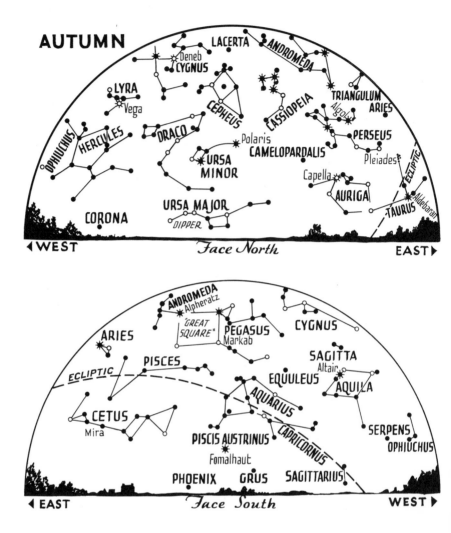

☼ ✸ ○ ● SYMBOLS FOR STARS IN ORDER OF BRIGHTNESS

Plate 20. Autumn. These show the skies at about midnight, September 1; 10 p.m., October 1; 8 p.m., November 1; and 6 p.m., December 1 (also 4 a.m., July 1 and 2 a.m., August 1). Now *Deneb,* in Cygnus, is high in the west. Below it, to the right, is Lyra, with *Vega,* and, to the left, *Altair* in Aquila, the eagle. Low in the south is Piscis Austrinus, the southern fish, with the star called *Fomalhaut.* Dimmed by its low altitude, it is now about as high as it ever gets in these latitudes. Low in the northeast is Auriga, with *Capella,* and, to the right, Taurus, with ruddy *Aldebaran.* Pegasus, the winged horse, is high in the south, with the "great square." This is a prominent figure, even though it contains no stars of the first magnitude. The star in the upper left-hand corner of the square is Alpheratz in the neighboring constellation of Andromeda, the chained princess. The great dipper is now low in the north, while Cassiopeia is high in the northeast. (Science Service, Inc.)

But more important to earthly observers is the *synodic* period, which tells us where a planet will be in relation to Earth and when we can observe it. When a planet is in opposition, i.e., in the opposite direction from the Sun, we can see it best, for then it is visible through the entire night.

Because the Earth itself goes around the Sun in a sidereal period of 365¼ days, oppositions occur when we catch up to the planet. Take Mars, for example, which was in opposition September 10, 1956. A year later the Earth was back in the same part of its orbit, but Mars takes nearly two years (607 days) for one circuit, so it was far around in the opposite portion of its path. Thus on July 29, 1958 (687 days after the opposition), Mars had returned to the same position but the Earth was well behind. Not until November 8, did we catch up to Mars, so it was again in opposition. The elapsed time was 780 days; this is the synodic period for Mars. With different figures, similar stories might be told for Jupiter and Saturn.

But for the inner planets, Mercury and Venus, it is a little different. The Earth cannot come between them and the Sun, consequently they cannot get to opposition. There is another term, *conjunction,* used to designate the time when a planet is in the same direction as the Sun. The outer planets come to conjunction about half way between oppositions. Mars reached this position September 21, 1957. But for Mercury and Venus there are two conjunctions. One is called *superior,* when the planet is out far beyond the Sun. *Inferior* conjunction occurs when the planet is on the same side of the Sun as Earth. Then, for an observer on one of these planets, the Earth would be in opposition.

For these planets, the synodic period is the time between inferior conjunctions, when the planet catches up to us. At either conjunction the planet is not visible; it is so nearly in line with the Sun that it is lost in its glare. But between superior and inferior conjunction, when the planet is east of the Sun, the planet follows that body across the sky each day and sets after sunset. Thus, it remains visible for a little while in the evening, as the *evening star.* Between inferior and superior conjunction, however, it precedes the Sun and sets before sunset. But it then rises before sunrise, and is visible in the early morning hours as a *morning star.*

One striking feature of the solar system is that it is mostly empty space. This makes it quite impractical to construct an accurate model. If you make the ball representing the Sun of reasonable size, those balls representing the planets are microscopic, and they spread over too large an area to handle.

MODELS OF THE SOLAR SYSTEM

Of course models have been made. One type is called an *orrery*, named after one constructed for the Earl of Orrery a couple of centuries ago. A ball, or in modern examples, an electric lamp, stands for the Sun. The planets are attached to rods, and a system of gearing moves them around the Sun in circular orbits in the proper relative periods. But any such model gives the idea that the solar system is much more crowded than it actually is; see Fig. 31.

Suppose we wanted to make a true scale model. Washington, D.C., would be a good place for it, and the dome of the Capitol might represent the Sun. The maximum outside diameter of the dome is slightly over 135 feet. Where will the planets be placed, and how large are the balls for the planets?

For Mercury, we would take a ball about 5½ inches in diameter and place it slightly over a mile away, which might be in the Department of Justice building at 9th and Pennsylvania Avenue. Venus would be a ball about 14¼ inches in diameter, possibly reposing on the desk of the President at the White House, 2 miles distant. The Earth? A ball about 15 inches in diameter, over in Arlington in front of the Pentagon! Mars is out in the Washington Zoo, about 4¼ miles from the Sun. Its diameter: 7¾ inches.

The Jupiter ball is considerably bigger, 13 feet, 7 inches; it is located down the Potomac at Fort Belvoir, just below Mount Vernon, somewhat more than 14 miles from the Capitol. Saturn, 11 feet, 2 inches in diameter, must be placed about 26 miles away. The Naval Academy at Annapolis is at this distance. Uranus is about 55 inches in diameter, 53 miles away, in Fredericksburg, Maryland. Neptune is a little smaller, 52 inches in diameter. It is 82½ miles distant, which would place it a little south of Harrisburg, Pennsylvania. Pluto, for its mean distance, is 109 miles away. This puts it, a 6¾-inch diameter ball, in Chester, Pennsylvania, below Philadelphia. The asteroids might be represented by a truckload of sand and pebbles, scattered around a circle about 8 miles from the Capitol.

The total area within the circle of Pluto's orbit would be about

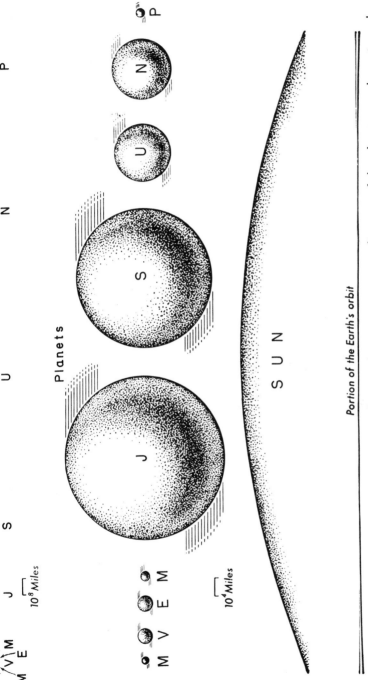

Fig. 31. The scale of the Solar System. At the top, the respective mean distances of the planets are shown to scale. Below, on a much larger scale, are the planets themselves, an arc of the Sun's surface, and a small arc of the Earth's orbit, compared with a straight line. (Drawing by Felix Cooper. By permission from *The Astronomical Universe*, by W. S. Krogdahl. Copyright, 1952, The Macmillan Co., New York.)

37,000 square miles. With only these nine balls, ranging in diameter from a few inches to about 14 feet, plus the sand and pebbles, and the Capitol dome, within that area, you can appreciate the emptiness of the solar system.

In some books on astronomy, published in the 1860's, there is a description of the planet Vulcan which, supposedly, travelled around the Sun in a period of 19 days, at a distance of 13 million miles. This planet was "discovered" in 1859 by a provincial French physician and amateur astronomer, named Lescarbault. He thought he saw a dark object move across the face of the Sun, and that it moved too fast to be a sunspot.

Now it happened that there had been a mysterious discrepancy in the motion of Mercury (since explained by the theory of relativity). Urbain Joseph LeVerrier, director of the Paris Observatory and one of the greatest astronomers of that period, had been responsible a few years earlier for the discovery of Neptune, after Uranus had inexplicably departed from its predicted path. He suggested that either Venus was about a tenth more massive than had been supposed, or that there was another planet, revolving in a smaller orbit. Either, by its added gravitational pull, might account for the discrepancy.

So, when Lescarbault wrote to LeVerrier of what he had seen, the astronomer had reason to be receptive although he was, in fact, rather skeptical. But he paid the doctor a visit, prepared to demolish his claims. Instead, he came away convinced of the reality of the new planet, and named it Vulcan.

No one else was ever able to see it. Perhaps it was a sunspot that the good doctor saw—or something else. For a number of years, at solar eclipses when the Sun's glare was hidden by the Moon and a planet close to it might be seen, astronomers made special observations in searching for an intra-Mercurial planet, but none was ever found. It now seems certain that there is no such planet, although one as small as 25 or 30 miles across might have escaped detection.

MERCURY, INNERMOST PLANET

Next we come to Mercury, the innermost planet. This little body is about 3,100 miles in diameter, although this may be slightly in error as the exact size is quite difficult to measure. It revolves

TABLE 1

The Solar System

	Mean Distance from Sun (miles)	Period of Revolution around Sun (sidereal period)	Synodic Period (days)	Diameter (miles)	Period of Rotation on Axis	Weight of 200-lb. man	Number of Moons
Sun............				864,000	24.7 days		
Mercury	36,000,000	88 days	116	3,010	88	76 lbs.	
Venus	67,200,000	224.7	584	7,610	30 (?)	152	
Earth	93,000,000	365.3	—	7,918	23 h. 56.1 m.	200	1
Moon	238,857 (from Earth)	27 d. 7.7 h. (around Earth)	—	2,160	27 d. 7.7 h.	32	
Mars	141,500,000	687 d.	780	4,140	24 h. 37.4 m.	78	2
Jupiter	483,300,000	11.86 yrs.	399	86,900	9 h. 50 m.	530	12
Saturn	886,000,000	29.46	378	71,500	10 h. 2 m.	234	9
Uranus	1,783,000,000	84.01	370	29,500	10.8 hrs.	210	5
Neptune	2,791,000,000	164.8	367.4	26,800	15.8 hrs.	246	2
Pluto	3,671,000,000	248.4	366.7	3,600	6.39 days	32	

about the Sun every 88 days (the sidereal period) and passes Earth every 116 days (its synodic period). Its orbit is more eccentric (i.e., it differs more from a circle) than any other planet except Pluto. When nearest the Sun its distance is 28,600,000 miles; when farthest, 43,400,000 miles. Its mean distance is 36,000,000 miles. Its mean speed around the Sun is about 30 miles per second, but its actual velocity varies, in accordance with Kepler's second law, depending on the distance from the Sun. When nearest, the gravitational pull of that orb is so great that Mercury has to rush around at 35 miles per second; but when out at the maximum distance, it slows to a more leisurely 23 miles per second.

Occasionally, for a few days at a time, Mercury may be seen; either low in the west at dusk, or in the east at dawn. The former occurs when it is at its greatest angle in the sky to the east of the Sun, or at *greatest eastern elongation.* Dawn visibility comes when it is at *greatest western elongation,* and rises a little ahead of the Sun. The best time to see it in the evening is in the spring, while the most favorable morning visibility occurs in the fall. About 44 days after its evening appearance it comes into the morning sky, having been at inferior conjunction between the two dates. Generally it passes north or south of the Sun, but once in a while—sometimes after 7 years but more often 13 years later—it comes directly between Sun and Earth. This is called a transit of Mercury. With telescopic aid, you could then see it as a tiny dot on the bright solar disk.

With the clear skies that frequently prevail around the Aegean Sea, the ancient Greeks often observed Mercury both in evening and morning, but they didn't realize that they were looking at the same object on both occasions. They thought there were two planets and they called it Mercury, when seen in the evening, and Apollo in the morning.

When Mercury is near inferior conjunction, most of the bright, sunlit hemisphere is turned away from us, like the Moon when almost new. Consequently, as with the Moon, it then appears (through a telescope) as a crescent. On the other hand, when near superior conjunction, and out on the far side of the Sun, its illuminated half is turned toward us, and it appears like the Moon when almost full. Unlike the Moon, it shows a marked change in size with the phases. The full Mercury is always far out beyond the Sun, some 136 million miles away from Earth. When in the crescent shape, it is much closer than the Sun, perhaps not more than 50 million miles from us.

Planets are best studied through telescopes when they are high in the sky but Mercury is never in such a position at night. Consequently most of the telescopic observations are made in broad daylight; it is not very difficult to screen the lens from the direct rays of the Sun. In this way some permanent dark markings have been observed on the planet's face.

Observing such markings, astronomers have found the length of the Mercurian "day," i.e., how long it takes to turn once on its axis, and this turns out to be 88 days—the same time that it takes to go around the Sun. Recall that the Moon behaves the same way in its revolution around the Earth, thereby always keeping approximately the same hemisphere toward the Earth. Similarly, Mercury always keeps the same face toward the Sun. No doubt, as with the Moon, this is a result of tidal friction. Once Mercury was probably in a plastic state, and the Sun's attraction raised great tides. These caused friction and acted as a brake, gradually slowing down the rate of rotation. Finally day and year were equal, as they have been ever since.

As with the Moon, there are librations, whereby a little section of one side, then a little of the other, swings toward the Sun. From these areas, if you could live at all on Mercury, you would see the Sun rise, and then drop below the horizon again. Over a much larger region, the Sun always shines, and over a similar area, opposite the Sun, it never appears.

This causes an enormous difference in temperature between the opposite hemispheres. The one which faces the Sun is about 700° F.—hot enough to melt tin or lead. This is the highest surface temperature found on any planet. But the other side, even though near the Sun, never receives any of the warming rays, and the temperature there is probably close to the absolute zero of −460° F., at which an object has no heat at all. There is no atmosphere on Mercury—with its small mass, its gravitational attraction is not strong enough to hold one—so air currents cannot carry heat around to the dark hemisphere. For this reason, Mercury is both the hottest and coldest of all the planets. Even Pluto, which is more than a hundred times farther from the Sun, does not get as cold, for its rotation exposes all parts of the planet to the solar warmth, feeble as it is at that distance.

VENUS

The next planet, out from the Sun, is Venus. Moving in the most nearly circular of all the planetary orbits, it is 67,200,000 miles from the Sun, or a little less than three-fourths of our mean distance. It takes Venus just under 225 days to complete one circuit of its orbit, while it passes Earth every 584 days.

Because, like Mercury, Venus has an orbit inside the Earth's, the way Venus appears to us is similar. It, too, appears alternately in the evening, after sunset, and in the early morning before sunrise. And also, like Mercury, the ancients thought it two planets: Hesperus, they called it in the evening; Phosphorus in the morning.

However, Venus becomes much more prominent than Mercury ever does. With its larger orbit at its eastern and western elongations, Venus gets much farther away from the Sun, sometimes as much as 45 degrees. Thus it may remain in the sky for several hours after sunset—or appear as long before sunrise—so it is frequently prominent in the night. In fact, when at maximum brightness, it is more brilliant than any other planet or any star.

As with Mercury, and for the same reasons, Venus undergoes changes in phase as it passes through its cycle of alternate evening and morning appearances. After superior conjunction it begins to shine in the west after sunset. At this time it is in the full phase. Then, 220 days after conjunction, it is at its greatest eastern elongation and in a phase like the Moon at first quarter. Because it swings in closer and closer to Earth, it rapidly increases in brightness. Although rapidly narrowing into a crescent, with most of the sunlit hemisphere turned from us, its decreasing distance more than compensates and it continues to brighten. Maximum brilliance is reached 36 days after elongation. Then as the crescent becomes still narrower, it draws closer to the Sun, and after 36 more days is in line with that body, i.e., at inferior conjunction. Around this time, for a few weeks, it is invisible. Then it reappears in the east at dawn and goes through a cycle just the reverse of what it had followed in the evening during the preceding months.

The changing phases of Venus, of course, cannot be seen with the naked eye, but they are visible through even a small telescope. Indeed, they were discovered, in 1610, by Galileo in Italy, using an instrument very small and crude by modern standards.

This discovery, incidentally, was a very important bit of evidence in favor of Copernicus' idea that the Earth goes around the Sun. Under the older Ptolemaic concept, Venus and the Sun both revolved about the Earth, but Venus moved in a circle completely inside that in which the Sun travelled. Consequently, it could never get out beyond the Sun and show a full phase. The fact that it went through a complete change, from crescent to full and back to crescent, demonstrated clearly that it shifted back and forth from our side of the Sun to the other side: in other words, it revolved around it.

In size, Venus is very much like the Earth, 7,700 miles in diameter compared with 7,918 miles for our planet. From the effect that its pull has in distorting, or perturbing, the movements of Mars and the Earth, the mass of Venus can be calculated. This proves to be about 82 per cent of Earth's mass. With both slightly smaller size and smaller mass, the pull of gravity on Venus is only 88 per cent of Earth's. Thus, if you weighed 200 pounds here, on Venus you would weigh only 166.

But, even though Venus becomes so prominent in the sky and comes closer to Earth than any other planet, we know nothing about the nature of its surface, which is perpetually hidden; all we can see are the tops of the clouds. Sometimes hazy markings have been reported but they are not very definite. This makes it difficult to determine the planet's rate of rotation. Some authorities have supposed that, like Mercury, Venus always maintains the same face to the Sun.

Temperature measurements of Venus have been somewhat discordant. At one time it seemed that the sunlit side might get as warm as 110° F., or more, but newer measures made at Mount Wilson have indicated that temperatures are the same—about −38° F.—both where the Sun is shining and where the planet is in darkness. This would hardly be the case if the same half always faced the Sun.

THE ATMOSPHERE OF VENUS

At first glance, it may seem surprising that Venus should be so cold when it is so much nearer the Sun than we are, but remember that this is the temperature at high altitudes, above the clouds which continually veil its surface. Above high clouds on Earth it is much colder than on the ground. And indeed it seems likely that the temperature on the surface of Venus is considerably higher than here. Not only is it nearer the Sun but, as spectroscopic studies have revealed, there is considerable carbon dioxide in Venus' atmosphere. Thus, as on the Earth, there may be a marked "greenhouse" effect, whereby the solar heat can enter but not escape. Measurements of radio waves from Venus indicate that the surface temperature is around 580° F.

While the spectroscope reveals carbon dioxide above Venus, it fails to show any water vapor. The method is believed to be sensitive enough to show vapor, if the Venus atmosphere, above the clouds, contained 2 to 5 per cent as much water vapor as there is in our atmosphere over Mount Wilson. On this basis, it has been suggested that the clouds of Venus could not be clouds of water droplets like those that we know.

However, two Harvard astronomers, Donald H. Menzel and Fred S. Whipple, have pointed out that there may be water on Venus after all. The light with which we observe Venus is reflected from the tops of the planet's clouds at great altitudes above its surface. Here, as we have seen, the temperature is −38° F., and when air is this cold the moisture is squeezed out—very little can remain.

Not only may there be clouds of water droplets on Venus; underneath them an ocean of water may completely surround the planet, uninterrupted by land masses. With land there would doubtless be rocks, probably made largely of silicon-containing compounds, and these would combine with the carbon dioxide from the atmosphere to form carbonates. Then the proportion of carbon dioxide in the atmosphere would probably not be as high as it seems to be.

Sometimes when the Moon is in a narrow crescent phase, we can faintly see an illumination on the Moon's dark portion. This effect—the ashen light—is due to sunlight falling on the Earth and reflected to the Moon. A similar effect is observed sometimes with Venus when it, too, forms a crescent, but it could not be explained by earthlight—the distance is too great. Perhaps this may be an aurora in the Venus atmosphere, similar to northern lights on Earth.

When Venus is out on the far side of the Sun, at superior conjunction, it may be at a distance of 160 million miles. When it comes between us and the Sun at inferior conjunction it may be only 26 million miles away. Except for the Moon, an occasional comet, and a few of the asteroids, no other celestial body ever comes so close to us. Unfortunately, this proximity does not give us a good view of the planet, for we cannot see it at such a time. Not only is it hidden by the solar glare, but, even if this could be overcome, the illuminated hemisphere is turned completely away from us.

MYSTERIOUS MARS

Although Mars, the next planet out from Earth, does not come as close as Venus does, we can observe it much better. When Mars is closest, it is in opposition, i.e., directly opposite the Sun. It is then visible throughout the night, and its entire sunlit half is presented to our view. While Mars revolves around the Sun every 687 days (1 year, 10½ months), and the Earth catches up to it every 780 days (nearly 2 years, 2 months), there are great variations in the oppositions that occur when we overtake it.

Its mean distance from the Sun is slightly more than one and a half times the Earth's distance, about 142 million miles, but the orbit of Mars is quite eccentric. When nearest the Sun (at perihelion), Mars is only 129 million miles away. When farthest (at aphelion), the distance is about 155 million miles. Thus, if opposition occurs close to perihelion, Mars may be only 34,500,000 miles from us; with an opposition at the Martian aphelion, on the other hand, its distance will be nearly 63 million miles. A very favorable opposition occurred in August, 1924, when it was nearly at the minimum distance.

Another good one occurred in September, 1956, with a distance of about 35 million miles. At this time, astronomers all over the world made a concerted effort to observe the planet, especially from the Southern Hemisphere where it was high in the night sky. For northern observers it was rather low in the south, as it always is, unfortunately, at times of closest approach. This happens because Mars is nearest the Sun when we are in the latter part of the Northern Hemisphere summer. Hence, the Northern Hemisphere of Earth is tilted toward the Sun and away from that opposite part of the sky where Mars is located. But at the same time the Earth's Southern Hemisphere is in late winter, so it is tilted toward Mars, and Mars is seen higher in the sky.

Fig. 32 illustrates the way the distance of Mars varies at opposition. On September 11, 1956, we overtook that planet near its perihelion, and it was a little over 35 million miles away. The next time around we caught up to it on November 16, 1958, and its distance was somewhat less than 46 million miles, a little better than average.

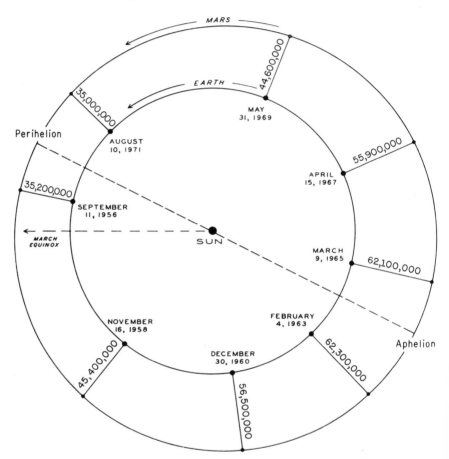

Fig. 32. Approaches of Mars to Earth from 1956 to 1971. When Mars was in the same direction from the Sun as the Earth (i.e., in opposition), in 1956, it was only 35,200,000 miles away. The next opposition came in November, 1958, when the planets were 45,400,000 miles apart. After the 1963 opposition, with 62,300,000 miles, they will come closer, until August, 1971, when Mars will be even nearer than it was in 1956. (By permission from *Sky and Telescope*.)

This is followed by a series of unfavorable oppositions: 57 million miles at the end of December, 1960; about 62 million in February, 1963, and March, 1965. But then an improvement will begin. April, 1967, will be an approach of 58 million miles, and then comes a still better one, with only 46 million miles at the end of May, 1969. Since this comes in the northern spring, it will be a good one for Northern Hemisphere observatories. Its greater altitude in the sky will compensate to some degree for its distance. Then, in early August, 1971, comes a very favorable approach to within 35 million miles.

TABLE 2

OPPOSITIONS OF MARS—1960-2000

Year	Opposition	Nearest Earth	Millions of Miles	Magnitude
1960	Dec. 30	Dec. 25	56.5	−1.3
1963	Feb. 4	Feb. 3	62.3	−1.0
1965	March 9	March 12	62.1	−1.0
1967	April 15	April 21	55.9	−1.3
1969	May 31	June 9	44.6	−1.9
1971	Aug. 10	Aug. 12	35.0	−2.6
1973	Oct. 25	Oct. 17	40.5	−2.2
1975	Dec. 15	Dec. 9	52.5	−1.5
1978	Jan. 22	Jan. 19	60.7	−1.0
1980	Feb. 25	Feb. 26	62.6	−0.9
1982	March 31	April 5	59.1	−1.1
1984	May 11	May 19	49.5	−1.6
1986	July 10	July 16	37.6	−2.4
1988	Sept. 28	Sept. 22	36.6	−2.5
1990	Nov. 27	Nov. 20	48.1	−1.7
1993	Jan. 8	Jan. 3	58.2	−1.2
1995	Feb. 12	Feb. 11	62.9	−0.9
1997	March 17	March 20	61.3	−1.0
1999	April 24	May 1	53.8	−1.4

SOURCE: *Sky & Telescope*, XVI, 256.

Even when Mars is closest, its distance is about 160 times that of the Moon; therefore if you looked at Mars through a telescope magnifying 160 diameters, it would look about as large as the Moon does to the naked eye. And with a pair of six-power binoculars, the Moon looks as big as Mars does with a magnification of 950 diameters, which is about the largest that we can use on Mars, on account of the atmospheric irregularities through which we must look.

However, there are well defined markings on Mars which were seen even through the crude telescopes used by the early observers. Christian Huygens, the Dutch astronomer who pictured it in a book published in 1659, showed a feature which can easily be identified today. From these markings the period of rotation of Mars—its "day"—can be accurately determined. This is 24 hours, 37 minutes, so an Earth-dweller transported to Mars would not notice a great difference in the alternation of day and night. There are also seasonal changes, from winter to spring, then summer and autumn; like the Martian year, these are considerably longer than our seasons.

The diameter of Mars is 4,200 miles, little more than half the Earth's. Its mass is about 11 per cent of Earth's but, because its smaller size brings objects on its surface closer to the center, the surface gravity is 38 per cent of that on our planet. This means that a 200-pound man would weigh only 76 pounds on Mars.

THE SURFACE OF MARS

The dark markings cover about a third of the Martian surface, while about two-thirds is covered by bright markings, orange in color. This is what gives Mars its characteristic ruddy hue when seen with the naked eye. Probably the light areas, somewhat similar to earthly deserts, are covered with sand, or dust, containing compounds similar to iron oxide, or iron rust, which as you know is red in color. Since there seems to be little oxygen in the atmosphere of Mars, it therefore seems that, if much oxygen had formerly been present, it has entered into combination with other elements to form these oxides—in other words, Mars has literally rusted!

Sometimes yellow clouds appear over Mars and last for several days, obscuring the details beneath. On the dusty desert hypothesis, these are explained as sandstorms, similar to those occurring over terrestrial deserts.

One means of checking this idea is by observations with polarized light. Whereas ordinary light waves vibrate at random and in all directions around the line along which they travel, polarized light consists of vibrations confined to one plane. Any materials which reflect or scatter light may produce some polarization, often quite small. By measuring the extent to which it occurs, and the various angles, a characteristic curve may be obtained, which is different for different materials and even for the same materials in different forms.

At the close approaches of Mars in 1922, 1924, and 1926, a

French astronomer, Bernard Lyot, made such observations through the 33-inch refractor at the Meudon Observatory near Paris. Such curves, he found, greatly resembled those for the Moon. So, he stated: "It looks as though there exists, on the surface of the Martian continents, a dusty cover analogous to that which colors the lands of the Moon."

To determine the nature of this "dusty cover," Lyot, in the laboratory, determined the polarization curves for a variety of terrestrial materials that might possibly be found on Mars. With a mixture of gray and brown volcanic ash, there was an exact correspondence with the lunar curves, as well as with that of Mars as far as it could be observed. Thus it seems as if both Mars and the Moon are covered with ashes and dust of this sort, says Gerard de Vaucouleurs, of the Lowell Observatory, a leading authority on Mars.

In 1948 and 1950, using the 24-inch refracting telescope at the Pic du Midi Observatory in the French Pyrenees, A. Dollfuss, who was a pupil of Lyot, again observed Mars by polarized light. He also measured terrestrial substances—several hundred of them—and found that only powdered limonite, a brown iron ore, matched the Martian curves. Commenting on this, de Vaucouleurs has stated: "The exact agreement between the two highly peculiar curves, those of Mars and of limonite, make the method 'very specific' and the identification 'most critical' so that other possibilities seem excluded."

In spite of this positive opinion, however, there is some evidence to the contrary from another type of observation. Gerard P. Kuiper, using the 82-inch reflecting telescope at the McDonald Observatory in Texas, measured the intensity of infrared radiation reflected from Mars, as well as from the Moon. The two were quite similar, although they did not match exactly.

He also measured terrestrial substances and found that a brown rock, called *felsite* (chemically a mixture of aluminum and potassium silicate), duplicated almost exactly the curve for Mars, which led Kuiper to say that "We may tentatively assume that the bright desert regions of Mars are composed of igneous rocks, similar to felsite." (An igneous rock, it may be noted, is one formed by volcanic action or some similar process.)

So here we have a problem. Is Mars covered with felsite or limonite? It will take further work to resolve the dilemma.

THE POLAR CAPS

Even brighter than these areas are the polar caps which are seen around both the north and south poles of Mars. In fact, they are the most obvious of all the Martian markings, and they vary in size during the Martian year. Since the poles of the Earth are also covered with white areas, of ice and snow, which change with our seasons, it is now generally accepted that the polar caps on Mars are some form of frozen water, although probably not deposits of snow many miles thick like those in Antarctica. The variations of the Martian caps have been well described by de Vaucouleurs:

"Let us begin to observe Mars at the end of winter—for example, that of the southern hemisphere in 1939 or 1941—and we see that the polar cap is very extensive, going down as far as latitude 60°. It covers at this time a spherical cap extending about 30° from the center, that is, 10 million square kilometres (4 million square miles).

"In the course of the following months it progressively diminishes in extent, at first slowly, then more and more quickly. Near the middle of spring rifts appear in it, breaking up the main cap and showing up regions of varied brightness. The minor spots, isolated from the main cap, persist for a time and then disappear finally during the Martian summer of the hemisphere concerned. The polar cap itself continues to decrease, and becomes so minute that it seems to be on the point of vanishing completely; but generally it does not do so. Near the end of the summer, when the cap has become very small, some diffuse spots are seen to appear in the polar regions, of a duller whiteness than that of the cap; they extend rapidly and finish by completely covering the polar zone and even a good part of the temperate zone as far as lat. 40° or 50°. These bright moving veils persist thus through the autumn and winter, and do not break up and disappear until the end of the winter. We then see the reappearance of the polar cap; it is rather dull at first, but then becomes white once more, brilliant and very extended, as in the preceding year at the corresponding epoch.

"Then the seasonal cycle of these phenomena recommences, and the process is repeated each year with great regularity—such regularity, in fact, that we can draw up permanent tables, giving the dimensions of the polar cap for any epoch of the Martian year."

However, he notes, "this regularity is not perfect and rigorous; in certain years the polar cap diminishes a little more quickly than usual, in others a little less quickly." *

So obvious is the explanation of the Martian polar caps as a layer of ice that this explanation was given centuries ago and is still held, although at one time, about 1903, it was suggested that they consisted of solid carbon dioxide—dry ice! This theory, however, has been completely refuted. Kuiper, at the McDonald Observatory, photographed the infrared spectrum of the caps and found the spectrum to be very different from the spectrum of dry ice. Instead, it resembled very closely the spectrum of snow and other forms of frozen water, such as hoarfrost formed on chilled metal plates.

A LAYER OF FROST

Dollfuss, at the Pic du Midi in 1951, also made polarimetric observations of the polar caps and found the polarization characteristics duplicated those obtained when moisture was allowed to condense on a metal plate that was cooled by liquid air and placed in a vacuum chamber, which reproduced the low pressure of the Martian atmosphere.

As for the thickness of the deposits, some idea can be obtained from the rate at which they disappear, knowing how much heat they receive from the Sun. Though this method is only approximate, it shows that they may be as thin as 0.1 inch—but no thicker than 10 inches. So they are far different from the ice caps of the Earth.

In 1939, a Russian astronomer named Tikhoff photographed the caps in light of various colors. His study of these pictures showed that the caps have a bluish-green tinge. He then photographed ice and snow in the same way, and found that the former corresponded most closely. He thought that it would be very difficult for snow to fall in the very thin atmosphere that exists on Mars. Therefore, he explained the formation of the polar caps in this way: "With the arrival of the cold season the liquid existing on Mars (most likely water) begins to freeze from the respective pole. Later this ice becomes coated with hoarfrost which, however, remains a very

* By permission from *The Planet Mars,* by G. de Vaucouleurs. Copyright, 1950, Faber & Faber, Ltd., London.

thin layer. With the arrival of spring the hoarfrost is the first to vanish and the cap acquires its bluish-green color."

Thus, compared to the ice caps, many thousands of feet thick, which surround the poles of Earth, those of Mars are very thin, and there is very little water on that planet. If there were any oceans or even good-sized lakes, the surface should act as a mirror, and occasionally we should see a glint of light as it picked up reflections of the Sun. What, then, happens to the polar caps as they melt?

The fact is that they may not melt. It is possible for water to change directly from the solid state (ice) to that of vapor, without passing through the liquid phase of water. Thus it is that even on a very cold day, with the temperature well below freezing, wet clothes, hung out on the line and immediately frozen stiff, will dry, although slowly. This process is called sublimation, and it would be particularly likely to occur with the low atmospheric pressure that probably prevails on Mars. However, some water may be released from the shrinking polar caps. As the caps diminish in size with the approaching spring, astronomers have sometimes noticed a black border as much as several hundred miles wide. Perhaps this is a region where the soil has been dampened by the melting ice.

Some astronomers have used the spectroscope, attached to a telescope, in an effort to detect and measure the intensity of absorption bands in the Martian atmosphere, as water vapor absorbs particular wave lengths. No such bands were found, which shows that there is much less water vapor than in our atmosphere. The amount of vapor in our air layer is such that, if it were completely converted to liquid, it would make about a third of an inch of water all over the Earth. From these measurements, the Martian vapor would be equivalent to a layer over that planet not more than $\frac{1}{57}$ of an inch and perhaps very much less.

Or we may get at it another way. The southern polar cap covers a larger area than the northern—some 4 million square miles at its maximum. If its average thickness in terms of solid ice were 0.4 inches, there would be about 100 billion tons of water. If this were all to be distributed over Mars as vapor, and then fall as rain, it would make a layer about $\frac{1}{75}$ inch in depth. But actually, the polar caps are almost always present, around one pole or the other, so the total would not be available, and a good estimate of the amount of water is perhaps about 1/250 of an inch. This is the value estimated by de Vaucouleurs.

THE MARTIAN ATMOSPHERE

The spectroscopic method is used also to determine other constituents of the atmosphere of Mars. Thus far we do not have, above the Earth, satellite observatories where the planets could be observed from above our own atmosphere. Consequently the light from Mars must pass through Earth's air, which contains some of the same elements that we seek on Mars. How, then, can we disentangle one from the other?

This is done with the aid of the Doppler effect, whereby the lines and bands that appear in the spectrum are shifted toward the red and blue end, depending on whether the distance between the object and the observer is increasing or decreasing. Of course, there is no relative movement between the Earth's atmosphere and the observer (ordinary winds would have no appreciable effect), so the bands due to terrestrial absorption would not be displaced. But if the observations are made when Mars is either rapidly receding from the Earth, or approaching it, any lines caused by components of the Martian atmosphere will be shifted a little, while those from the Earth's atmosphere would "stay put." Even if the two bands are not actually separated, the displacement may cause a lack of symmetry from which the relative intensity may be determined.

The use of these methods, however, has failed to reveal much definite information about the gases in the atmosphere of Mars. Oxygen bands that have been observed have been identified as terrestrial in origin.

Another method is to compare Mars with the Moon, when both bodies are at the same height in the sky and their light has to pass through the same thickness of Earth's atmosphere. Thus, if the intensity of a particular band was greater in the Martian spectrum, it would be good evidence for the existence of the gas responsible for that band. In this way, Kuiper, at the McDonald Observatory in Texas, has found evidence for carbon dioxide over Mars. It was with similar methods that Dunham, at Mount Wilson, found this same compound over Venus.

However, no appreciable oxygen has been found, although we should be able to detect as little as 0.15 per cent of the amount of oxygen that our atmosphere contains. This, then, sets the maximum amount over Mars. The test for water vapor is not as delicate; if there were 1 per cent as much as we have, the spectroscope should reveal it, and none has been found. However, as we already have seen, there is probably some water vapor there.

Scattering of light also gives some clues to the gases present, and it seems that there is some nitrogen. But the atmosphere of Mars is not only very thin, it also lacks the proportions of the gases that are in the Earth's atmosphere. There seems little doubt that a human being could not survive on that planet without wearing some sort of space suit providing a supply of the kind of air that he needs.

CLOUDS OVER MARS

Although there is so little moisture in the atmosphere of Mars that it never rains, there are clouds in the planet's sky. These are not uncommon; indeed, they were first observed more than a century ago. Some are white, some bluish, and some yellow in color. Just what they are is still uncertain, but it seems certain that they are not clouds of small water droplets, like those commonly seen in the Earth's sky.

Possibly the blue and white clouds are the same. They seem to be very high—perhaps 12 miles above the surface. At such an altitude the air is very cold, something like −150° F., and the clouds may be made of ice crystals; possibly like high cirrus clouds above the Earth. Generally there is a bluish haze, of which the clouds may represent a condensation. However, this haze sometimes seems to clear away, for as much as a few days, and reveal details of the planet generally invisible.

The yellow clouds are much lower, 2 to 3 miles high, and they often cover huge areas of the planet. This happened in 1956 when Mars made its closest approach in years and astronomers around the world were observing it. For several weeks at the critical time an entire hemisphere was obscured. About August 20, Japanese observers noticed a small but bright spot which gradually spread until it covered thousands of square miles.

Students of Mars generally assume that these yellow clouds are veils of dust or sand blown aloft from the desert areas, but there are some objections to this idea. From the movements of the clouds themselves, it is possible to determine the wind speeds, and these are quite feeble, not more than 2 to 4 miles per hour. These hardly seem violent enough to throw up sandstorms which cover so much of the planet, and for so long a time, even allowing for the lessened pull of gravity. Others have suggested that the clouds originate in volcanic eruptions. Earthly volcanoes have produced clouds that extended thousands of miles from the eruption and lasted for weeks or months. However, on Earth, volcanoes are always near the sea, and it is somewhat difficult to imagine them on a planet so dry as Mars. Objections have also been advanced that the clouds are not quite the same color as the desert areas. However, with the atmosphere so thin and the winds so weak, it is likely that only the very smallest dust particles would be blown aloft and their small size might well make them somewhat lighter in tint. In any event, despite objections, it seems that dust storms do occur on Mars.

One of the first discoveries to be made with the telescope, which was applied to astronomy in 1610, was of the four larger moons of Jupiter; before the end of the seventeenth century, four moons of Saturn had been discovered. With one moon for Earth, and four for Jupiter, it seemed appropriate that Mars should have two. Jonathan Swift, in his *Voyage to Laputa*, written in 1726, gave it two, and so did Voltaire in his *Micromegas*, written in 1752. In fact, by some very clever reasoning, and analogy with the two innermost moons of Jupiter, Swift arrived at data for these then imaginary satellites which later proved surprisingly accurate.

TWO LITTLE MOONS

In 1877, there was a favorable opposition of Mars. The U.S. Naval Observatory, in Washington, had a new 26-inch telescope, the largest in the world at that time, and astronomer Asaph Hall turned it on Mars. On August 11, he picked up one moon and on August 17, another. But there were some puzzling features, for, as Swift had predicted, the inner moon revolves around Mars in less time than it takes the planet itself to rotate. No natural satellite of any other planet does so. The two moons were named after the two sons of Mars in mythology—Phobos and Deimos, i.e., "fear" and "terror."

The moons are so small that their diameters cannot be measured from the Earth with any precision, but astronomers estimate that of Phobos as about 10 miles and of Deimos 6 miles. Phobos

is innermost; its distance is given as 5,800 miles, which is from
the center of Mars. If we subtract the planet's radius of 4,070
miles, we find that it is only 3,730 miles above the surface. It
goes around Mars in 7 hours, 39 minutes or about three times in
one Martian day. Thus, the planet's day is actually longer than
the month, as measured from this moon at least!

Another curious feature is that even though the planet turns
from west to east as the Earth does, Phobos overtakes it, so
Phobos rises in the west and sets in the east 4½ hours later.
About 6½ hours later it would rise in the west again. Moreover,
as it rushed across the sky, in the opposite direction from other
heavenly bodies, it would go through about half its cycle of
phases. When it rises in the west just after sunset, it appears as
a narrow crescent. A couple of hours later, it is seen in the south,
in first quarter; then, a little before setting, it would be full. And
when it sets it is past the full phase.

Although the distance of Phobos from Mars is about a sixty-
fourth of the distance of our Moon from Earth, Phobos' diameter
is about 1/216 of the Moon's. Thus, to a Martian observer, it
would appear only about a third as big as the Moon does to us.
He could see its phases, but they would not be as conspicuous as
those of our Moon. Moreover, even though the greater distance
of Mars from the Sun would make that orb look smaller than it
does from Earth, the Sun would still be about twice as large as
Phobos. Thus, there could never be a total eclipse of the Sun on
Mars, only an annular eclipse.

Deimos is 14,600 miles from the center of Mars, and goes
around once in 30 hours, 18 minutes, not greatly longer than the
Martian day. As Mars turns, Deimos nearly keeps up with it.
It rises in the east, but not until about 2½ days later does it set
in the west. Its phases would hardly be visible, since its diameter
in the Martian sky is only about a twenty-fourth of the diameter
of our Moon. It would appear like a brilliant planet, changing
considerably in brightness as it goes through its invisible phases.
When full, it is about a two-hundredth as bright as our full Moon.
But this would be some 25 times as bright as Venus appears to us
when most brilliant. And when Deimos passed in front of the
Sun, as it does some 120 times in every Martian year, it would
only be a black spot on the solar disc.

THE CONTROVERSIAL CANALS

So far we have not mentioned the most controversial of all features of Mars: the so-called canals.

When Mars was close in 1877, a leading Italian astronomer, Giovanni Schiaparelli, director of the Milan Observatory, was observing the planet. He saw the familiar polar caps and the light and dark areas. But in addition, he reported, the light regions were crisscrossed by numerous dark, fine lines. He charted them and repeated his observations when Mars approached Earth again, in 1879 and 1881. He called these lines *canali,* an Italian word meaning "channels." However, the word was translated into English as "canals," suggesting an artificial origin, which "channels" does not.

Other observers saw them, particularly Percival Lowell, an American astronomer, privately wealthy. He founded his own observatory primarily for planetary observation at Flagstaff, Arizona, where the skies are beautifully clear. He found that the canals even extended across the dark areas of Mars which showed that these were not bodies of water.

No natural markings, he argued, would follow such straight lines across the planet. Therefore they must be artificial, and a high degree of intelligence would be required to plan and construct them. Their function, Lowell surmised, was to carry water from the melting polar caps all over the planet. He did not suggest that the lines were the actual channels; they would have had to be some 30 miles or more in width to be detected. Instead, he proposed, the lines that were seen were irrigated areas along the "canals."

But while Lowell was able to see and chart these curious lines, and others did, too, some were never able to detect them. Edward Emerson Barnard, one of the most skillful of observers, could not see them, even with telescopes larger than the one Lowell used. At the Meudon Observatory near Paris another expert, E. M. Antoniadi, looked for them in vain. In his book on Mars, published in 1930, he wrote: "No one has ever seen a true canal on Mars. The rectilinear canals of Schiaparelli do not exist."

One explanation is that the human eye, when it sees disconnected spots and streaks that are not quite near enough to be clearly recognized, tends to join them into lines. An English astronomer named Maunder reported an experiment with a drawing of Mars showing, not canals, but some roughly aligned dark patches. Holding it a little beyond the distance of clear vision, he showed it to a group of schoolboys, who were told to copy it. They didn't know what they were supposed to be drawing, but many of them did put in straight lines.

Confirmation for this idea came in 1948 when Audouin Dollfuss, the French astronomer whose studies of the polar caps were mentioned above, was studying Mars. He made use of the 24-inch refracting telescope, which is a good-sized instrument, at the observatory on the Pic du Midi in the Pyrenees. The viewing conditions there, it is claimed, are as fine as anywhere on Earth. Under their usual conditions—probably better than the best at most observatories—he saw many canals. But on a few occasions, he said, seeing was not merely "good"; it was "perfect." The lines then broke up into smaller spots and patches. Then would come a slight tremor of the atmosphere; they would join together again to form canals.

What are they? Why should there be rows of markings? No doubt they have a natural and not an artificial origin. Probably their exact nature will remain a puzzle until astronomers can observe Mars much better than they can at present. Perhaps this will be from a satellite observatory, far above the Earth's atmosphere and all the interference that it causes. Or perhaps it will be from a rocket ship orbiting Mars itself.

9

Beyond Mars

After the Bode-Titius "law" was published in 1772, it provided a very puzzling problem. Its first four numbers gave, quite accurately, the distances of Mercury, Venus, Earth, and Mars from the Sun; so did the sixth and seventh for Jupiter and Saturn. But where was the planet for the fifth number, 2.8 times the Earth's distance? This became even more surprising when Herschel discovered Uranus in 1881, and its distance was close to the eighth Bode number, 19.6.

Thus it seemed more and more evident that there must be a planet somewhere between Mars and Jupiter—one that had not yet been discovered. In 1800, a group of German astronomers set themselves up as a sort of celestial detective bureau, to track down the missing body. Each of the group of six was to take one section of the zodiac and examine it closely.

But they were anticipated before the program could really get into operation. Giuseppe Piazzi, an Italian monk and astronomer, had founded an observatory, at Palermo on the island of Sicily, and was using it to prepare a catalog of the stars. On the very first day of the nineteenth century—January 1, 1801—he picked up a strange object. Although it looked like a star it was not one, since it moved across the sky as he watched it on successive nights. At first Piazzi thought it to be a comet. After a few weeks he was taken ill; by the time he recovered, it had moved close to the Sun's direction and was lost in the glare.

The techniques then used to compute the orbit of a comet, or a planet, were inadequate for the limited observations of Piazzi's object. But the German mathematician, Karl Friedrich Gauss, proceeded to invent, for the purpose of relocating the object, a new method of orbit computation. This requires only three separate observations, and it has been used ever since. With the data so obtained, Piazzi's object was found again, nearly a year after the original discovery, and proved to be a planet. Piazzi, exercising the discoverer's privilege, named it Ceres, in honor of the patron goddess of Sicily. Its mean distance from the Sun, on the Bode scale, was 27.7, close to the predicted 28.

But, though a planet, it was a curious one, hardly to be ranked with Earth and Mars, much less Jupiter, for it is only about 480 miles in diameter.

By this time, the celestial police in Germany had their program in operation, and one of them, Heinrich Olbers, in March, 1802, found a second small planet, very similar to Ceres in its path and size, about 304 miles in diameter. Olbers named it Pallas; he proposed that the two might be fragments of a larger planet which had exploded. The search continued and in 1804 Karl Harding discovered Juno, the third, followed in 1807 by Olbers' second discovery, Vesta. Juno's diameter is about 120 miles and Vesta's 240. But the latter seems to reflect more light, so it becomes brighter than the others, sometimes just reaching naked-eye visibility. These little planets attracted great interest among astronomers and, following the suggestion of Sir William Herschel, the name "asteroid" (meaning "starlike") was applied to them.

ASTEROIDS MULTIPLY

For a number of years after 1807, although the search continued, no more asteroids were found, because the searchers were not looking for faint enough objects. But after 1830 a German amateur astronomer, K. L. Hencke, decided to resume the search on his own. Success came in 1845 when he found Astraea, about 60 miles in diameter and considerably fainter than the first four. In 1847, he found another, Hebe, and in the same year, in England, John Russell Hind found two more, which he named Iris and Flora. Since then not a year has passed without the discovery of at least one. Sometimes several hundred have been found in a single year. By 1870 the total was 109, and in 1890 it had increased to 300.

Then the number began to increase at an unprecedented rate, with the use of a photographic detecting method developed by Max Wolf of the Königstuhl Observatory at Heidelberg. He made photographs of an area of the sky where asteroids were likely to be, using a wide-angle lens and moving the camera to follow the daily movement of the stars. The resultant exposures show the stars as sharp points of light. An asteroid moves among the stars and leaves a streak instead of a dot.

This method was improved by Joel H. Metcalf, a Unitarian minister and amateur astronomer of Portland, Maine. Although the camera is moved by clockwork to follow the stars, the plate-holder itself moves so as to follow the expected motion of the asteroid. Thus the stars appear as trails, while the asteroid—if its movement is correctly anticipated—makes a dot. Because it remains in the same place on the plate, its light has a chance to soak in, which it does not by Wolf's method. Thus much fainter asteroids can be detected.

By such means, so many asteroids have now been found that they have become somewhat of a nuisance—they have been termed "the vermin of the skies." By 1950, about 1,500 had been catalogued and their orbits computed. While perhaps a thousand more had been found, the orbits had not been worked out. Formerly the Astronomische Recheninstitut at Berlin was responsible for keeping records of the asteroids, but since World War II this task has been transferred by the International Astronomical Union to the University of Cincinnati.

Those officially listed represent only a small fraction of the total number. Some years ago, Walter Baade and Edwin P. Hubble, of the Mount Wilson Observatory, counted the number of asteroids that had been found by accident on photographs taken with the 100-inch telescope, and they estimated that there were at least 30,000 which could be photographed with that instrument. With the 200-inch, now the world's largest, and improved photographic techniques, this might be increased to 50,000 or even more. The vast majority of these, of course, are tiny things, perhaps of the order of a mile or so in diameter, and some even smaller. Their total mass is probably from 1/500 to 1/1000 of that of the Earth.

This does not mean, however, that the exploded planet, whose remnants they are (for Olbers' theory now seems quite plausible), was so small. Perhaps only the fragments whose orbits happened to be nearly circular turned into asteroids or, perhaps, swarms of meteors. Others, with orbits stretched out into longer ellipses, may have been pulled by Jupiter and the other large planets and hurled into outer space, far removed from the Solar System. Others may have turned into comets.

CLOSE TO THE EARTH

While most asteroids are of little interest, some have significant features. For example there is Hermes, which Walter Reinmuth discovered from the Heidelberg Observatory in 1937. Only about a mile in diameter, it passed within 485,000 miles of the Earth, about twice the Moon's distance. It could come even closer than the Moon, and this has led to conjectures as to whether it might actually hit us. Probably not. Even at 200,000 miles, it would be 25 Earth diameters away. If you are shooting at a foot-long rabbit and your best shot misses him by 25 feet, bunny isn't in much danger!

Then there are some others that approach the Earth—though not as closely. Adonis, which Delporte, of Brussels, discovered in 1936, comes to a distance of $1\frac{1}{3}$ million miles, while Apollo, a Reinmuth discovery in 1932, makes a 7-million-mile approach. And Amor, which Delporte found in 1932, came to 10 million miles.

Even more significant is Eros, which G. Witt, of Berlin, discovered in 1898. Its closest approach to Earth is 14 million miles, and its orbit has been very accurately calculated. It takes about $1\frac{3}{4}$ years to go around the Sun. Not until 1975 will it make its minimum approach, but in 1931 its distance was only slightly more—about 16 million miles—and 44 observatories in many parts of the world made numerous observations, following a program arranged by the International Astronomical Union. The purpose was to find more accurately the mean distance of the Earth from the Sun—the *astronomical unit.*

The relative distance of planets from each other and from the Sun can be determined with great precision as a result of the various laws of planetary movement. As noted earlier, you can draw a map of the solar system, in which the proportions are very accurate, but this is of little use unless you have a scale of miles. However, if you determine one distance accurately, in miles, then you can make the scale. The 1931 program was designed to find accurately the distance of Eros. The fact that it was so near made this possible. After 10 years of work in analyzing these observations, Sir Harold Spencer Jones, then Astronomer Royal of England, announced that the astronomical unit was equal to 93,003,000 miles, a little longer than astronomers had previously put it.

Another interesting asteroid is Icarus, which Walter Baade, of Mount Wilson, discovered in June, 1949. Then it was about 8 million miles away; it can come within 4 million. But its main feature is its close approach to the Sun—a matter of merely 19 million miles, which is a little more than half the distance of Mercury. It was on this account that Baade named Icarus after the youth who, according to mythology, escaped from Crete with wings that he fastened to his body with wax. On the flight he flew so close to the Sun that the wax melted, the wings dropped off, and he fell to his death in the sea. At aphelion, when the asteroid Icarus is farthest from the Sun, its distance is 183 million miles, farther out than Mars.

And then there is Hidalgo, which takes 14 years to encircle the Sun, the longest period known for an asteroid. At perihelion it is only about twice as far from the Sun as the Earth; at aphelion it is more than ten times as far, out beyond the orbit of Saturn. So stretched out an orbit is more like that of a comet than an asteroid, but observations through the greatest telescopes have failed to detect any fuzziness of its image, so it is classed with the tiny planets. At one point its orbit comes within 26 million miles of Jupiter's orbit, so it might come that near to Jupiter itself. It might have done so at some time past, and the gravitational pull of that giant threw it into its present extraordinary path.

Another asteroid that is far out from the Sun is Achilles, about 150 miles in diameter, which moves practically in the same orbit as Jupiter and encircles the Sun in a similar period. However, it keeps well ahead of Jupiter, about a sixth of the way around. They have been compared to two spots of paint on the rim of a turning wheel.

Soon after Wolf had discovered Achilles in 1908, another asteroid was found to be moving in Jupiter's orbit, but behind rather than ahead of the big planet. This was named Patroclus. Twelve of these are now known, seven ahead and five behind. They have been named after Homeric heroes, so as a group they are called the Trojan asteroids. However, no attempt has been made to keep separate the two heroes of the opposing sides, so Trojans and Greeks are mixed up, with Hector and Achilles actually close neighbors.

The significance of the Trojan group is found in connection with a problem of celestial mechanics—that of three bodies. If there are two bodies in space, say a star and an encircling planet, it is relatively simple to figure out how one moves with relation to the other. But with three bodies it is far more complicated. Indeed, mathematicians for more than 200 years sought in vain a general solution to the problem. Then a Finnish mathematician, Sundman, finally succeeded, but his solution is far too complex to be used in practical computation.

A century and a half ago, however, the French astronomer Lagrange obtained a solution for a special case—when three bodies are located equal distances from each other. The Trojan asteroids exemplify this, for each group forms an equilateral triangle with Jupiter and the Sun. That is, they are just as far ahead of, or behind, Jupiter, as they, and that planet, are from the Sun.

JUPITER

Now, on our trip outwards from the Sun, we come to the greatest of the planets: Jupiter. Its mean distance from the Sun is 5.2 times that of Earth, or 483,900,000 miles. Thus it can approach our planet, when in opposition, to about 390,000,000 miles. Or, if this should happen when Jupiter is at its least distance from the Sun, which distance varies by about 47,000,000 miles, it can approach us as closely as 367,000,000 miles. On the other hand, it may recede to as much as 600,000,000 miles.

When nearest, Jupiter is more than 2.5 times as bright as when it is most distant, and is a brilliant object in the sky, shining through the night. It is then about 25 times as bright as a typical star of the first magnitude. Only Venus ordinarily exceeds this among the planets; it may get about 4 times as bright, when it is prominent in the evening or morning sky. On rare occasions, when it makes one of its very close approaches, Mars may get a little brighter than Jupiter. Whenever you see a bright planet in the sky late at night and far from the Sun's direction, it is most probable that you are looking at Jupiter, particularly if it does not show a red color, as Mars does.

Jupiter takes 11.86 years to make one trip around the Sun, and one opposition follows another after an interval of about a year and a month (actually 399 days). If you watch Jupiter through the year, its general motion against its background of distant stars is toward the east, for that is the way it is revolving around the Sun. But about two months before opposition it halts this movement and backs up. Then, approximately two months after the opposition, it is stationary again and starts moving toward the east once more. Such a backward, or retrograde, motion is also displayed by Mars (as well as Saturn, Uranus, Neptune, and Pluto) when near opposition, but with Jupiter it is most easily observed.

It was to explain this effect that the ancient Ptolemaic theory of the solar system made use of epicycles (as described on page 151), but no such mechanism is needed with the modern concept, whereby the Earth and other planets all revolve in the same direction around the Sun, more rapidly the nearer the planet is to that body. Perhaps you have had the experience of riding on an express train and passing a freight train, moving more slowly on the next track. As the express rushes past, it often seems that the freight is going backwards, although you know that it is going the same way that you are. At the time of opposition the Earth, rushing along at its orbital speed of 18.5 miles per second, overtakes Jupiter, whose speed is only 8.1 miles per second. Then, like the freight train seen from the express, it seems to go backwards for a time.

Seen through even a moderate-sized telescope, Jupiter is an interesting object, for a magnification of as little as 60 diameters makes it look, even when farthest from the Earth, as large as the Moon does to the naked eye. One can see that it is not round, but elliptical. Its diameter at the equator is 88,770 miles, but that from pole to pole is about 6 per cent less: 83,010 miles.

The reason for this polar flattening is easily understood when you watch details on its surface and from them measure the time it takes to spin on its axis; that is, the length of its day. This is only 9 hours, 55 minutes; with its great size, the speed of rotation at its equator is 28,000 miles per hour. Thus the centrifugal force at the equator is so great that this part of its surface is forced nearly 3,000 miles farther from the planet's center than at the poles. The similar equatorial bulge of the Earth is only a little more than 13 miles because of our far smaller size and slower rotational speed (about a quarter mile per second at the Equator).

GREEN AND RED CLOUDS

Looking at Jupiter through a telescope, one is impressed with the amount of detail visible on the face of the planet. For it is crossed by light and dark bands approximately parallel to the equator. These display a variety of color: orange, red, brown, and occasionally even green. Since the features may change greatly, sometimes very rapidly, it is apparent that these features are not a solid surface. Instead, as with Venus, they are the tops of clouds.

But where the clouds of Venus are merely parts of a relatively thin layer of atmosphere that surrounds it, those of Jupiter make up, in fact, most of the planet's volume. If you could land on Jupiter's visible equator, and then descend down to its center, you would go about 8,000 miles before you reached the bottom of the atmosphere, according to a generally accepted concept.

Then, it is believed, you would come to a layer of ice, but probably there would be no sharp boundary; rather a slushy region becoming more and more solid as you moved farther down. Some 17,300 miles more, at a total depth of over 28,000 miles, you would reach the bottom of the ice and the top of the central core, which probably is made of rock and metal and is more than 38,000 miles in diameter.

Thus, the solid part of Jupiter is only a small proportion of its total volume, actually, about 8 per cent. This has an estimated density of about 6 times as much as water. The ocean of ice which surrounds it has a density of about 1.5, in terms of water, while that of the surrounding clouds is less than a third of water's. Thus, the average density of the whole planet is about 1.3, about a quarter that of Earth and even less than the Sun's. In its enormous volume, about 1,312 times that of Earth, is contained about 318 times as much matter as that which makes up our planet; see Fig. 33. At the visible surface, the pull of gravity is 2.64 times that on the Earth. A 200-pound man (assuming that he could stand on top of the clouds) would weigh 528 pounds!

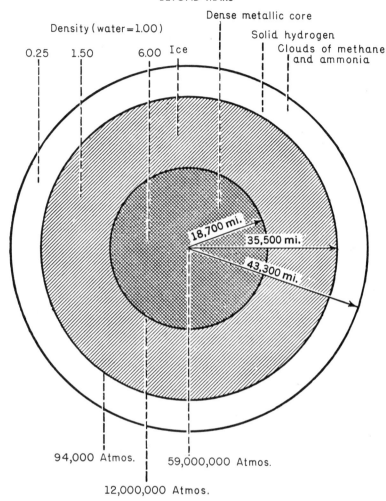

Fig. 33. Internal structure of Jupiter, according to Rupert Wildt. (By permission from *Astronomy*, by W. T. Skilling and R. S. Richardson. Copyright, 1947, Henry Holt & Co., Inc., New York.)

Not only are the clouds covering Jupiter far deeper than those above Venus; they are very different in their constitution. The spectrum of Jupiter shows some striking dark bands that puzzled astronomers for a long time, until they found that the bands could be produced in laboratories by passing light through methane and ammonia. Methane is commonly known as marsh gas; it is produced by decaying vegetation, and is, incidentally, one of the constituents of the natural gas which is piped into many of our homes.

Also it is "fire-damp" which sometimes, mixed with air, causes mine explosions. And ammonia is familiar, with its pungent odor, in the form of the so-called ammonia which housewives use for cleaning purposes, really a solution of the gas in water. In order to produce, in the laboratory, bands as intense as those observed in the spectrum of Jupiter, light has to be passed through some thirty feet of ammonia, at atmospheric pressure, and about half a mile of methane.

Astronomers have long suspected that the atmosphere of Jupiter also contains hydrogen, which is the most abundant element in the universe. Unfortunately, however, it is much more difficult to detect molecules of hydrogen in a planet's atmosphere than to find ammonia and methane. But in 1960 the National Bureau of Standards, in Washington, disclosed the results of a three-year study which showed not only that hydrogen is present, but also that there are enormous amounts of it. Apparently it extends several miles above the visible cloud layers.

The surface temperature of Jupiter is about −150° F., and, since ammonia freezes at −144° F., most of the ammonia would be solid, with only a small proportion in the vapor form needed to produce the spectral bands. Methane has to be cooled to about −195° F. before it will condense to a liquid, and to −238° F. to freeze, so probably most of it is in the gaseous state. Of course, any water vapor that might be present would be frozen also. The freezing point of hydrogen is much lower. It must be cooled to −436° F. before it becomes solid.

Methane is a compound of carbon and hydrogen, ammonia of nitrogen and hydrogen; so any available carbon and nitrogen has entered into combination with hydrogen, some of which is left over. Mixed with these gases are doubtless some vapors of metals from which the clouds get their reddish and yellowish colors.

One of the belts of Jupiter extends around the south equatorial zone of the planet, and just south of this astronomers noticed, in 1831, what seemed to be a hollow. In 1878, this became very prominent as a great red spot, 30,000 miles from east to west and 7,000 from north to south. After a few years, the color disappeared for a time, but the hollow remained visible. Since then it has reappeared on several occasions, notably in 1936.

The nature of this Great Red Spot, as it is generally called, is still a mystery. It doesn't stay fixed but drifts about 20,000 miles east or west of its mean position. According to one theory, it is some sort of solid body, floating in the atmosphere, which sometimes rises to the top and becomes visible, only to disappear later as it sinks to lower levels. Or it may represent the result of some kind of "volcanic" eruption that takes place below, although volcanoes such as we have on Earth could hardly move around as much as the spot does. It has been suggested that the Jovian equivalent of an earthly volcano might be more like an enormous bubble rising from the semifluid interior, bursting and erupting metallic vapors into the clouds above. Radio waves have also been picked up from Jupiter. These may be static from violent electrical storms in its thick atmosphere.

THE MOONS OF JUPITER

Of all the planets, Jupiter is best equipped with moons. Four are quite large, three bigger than our Moon, and two even larger than Mercury. They are famous, in astronomical history, as the first discoveries made with the telescope.

After this useful instrument was invented in 1608, by Jan Lippershey, a spectacle-maker of Middlebourg, Holland, specimens were distributed to various parts of Europe. One reached a German astronomer named Simon Marius. In the fall of 1609, he used it to look at the stars and also at Jupiter. Near this planet he saw what seemed to be three fainter stars.

The telescope was a little slower in reaching Italy, but, in 1609, Galileo Galilei, the great Italian astronomer, heard reports of it and what it would do. Although he had no details, he made his own experiments and finally made a telescope himself. In January, 1610, he turned this on Jupiter, and also saw what seemed to be three stars nearby. Two were to the east and one to the west. The next night he looked again, and all three were now to the west of the planet. Clouds then interfered, and he missed one night, but two days later he looked again. Now there were only two, both to the east. Before a week had passed, he saw four nearby stars, one to the east and three to the west. By this time he recognized what they were: not stars, but satellites revolving around Jupiter. He announced his discovery and suggested calling them "Medicean Stars," in honor of his patron, Cosimo II, Grand Duke of Tuscany and a member of the Medici family.

After Galileo announced his discovery, Marius apparently realized that he had seen the satellites even earlier and published a book claiming the discovery for himself. History now gives him credit for the prior observation, but awards the main honors to the Italian, whose keen insight immediately recognized the significance of what he saw. This was particularly important, because of the great controversy then current over the rival Ptolemaic and Copernican theories of the universe. Jupiter, as Galileo showed, was a small model of the Solar System, with Jupiter representing the Sun and the satellites, the planets.

Galileo's name, however, did not survive. Instead, we call them by the names given by Marius: Io, Europa, Ganymede, and Callisto, mythological characters who were involved in Jupiter's love affairs.

Io is the innermost of the satellites. With a diameter of 2,310 miles, it revolves around Jupiter in 1 day, 18 hours, 28 minutes, at a distance of 262,000 miles. Then comes Europa, at a distance of 417,000 miles, 1,950 miles in diameter. One revolution around Jupiter takes 3 days, 13 hours, 14 minutes. Ganymede is next, 666,000 miles away; its diameter is 3,200 miles, and its period of revolution 7 days, 3 hours, 48 minutes. Still larger is Callisto, with a diameter of 3,220 miles, and 1,170,000 miles from the planet, which it encircles every 16 days, 16 hours, 32 minutes.

Except for Callisto, each of these satellites is brighter than the sixth magnitude, on the astronomer's brightness scale, which is considered the limit of naked eye visibility. Thus they could be seen without a telescope if they were not lost in the glare of Jupiter itself. You can see them through a good pair of field glasses or binoculars; indeed such an instrument is much better than the little telescope with which Galileo discovered them.

However, as you watch them, you will sometimes see all four, sometimes three, two, one, or even none at all. This is due to the fact that a satellite may disappear behind Jupiter, or even without doing that, it may be eclipsed as it passes into Jupiter's shadow. Or it may move in front of the planet, in a transit, when it would again disappear, except possibly with quite a large telescope. Sometimes, also, the shadow of a moon may be seen on the surface of Jupiter. It was such disappearances of the satellites that so puzzled Galileo when he saw first three, then two, and later four, of the moons. Their motions are accurately known, by the way, and the *American Ephemeris*, published annually by the U.S. Naval Observatory, gives predictions of their positions.

From their movements, astronomers have been able to calculate the masses of the satellites, and, knowing their size, they could also find their densities, which are somewhat curious. Io and Europa are 2.9 times as dense as water, not greatly different from the density of our Moon, which is 3.3. Probably these are made of rock. But Callisto is far lighter; its density is only 0.6, and it is believed to be a chunk of ice. Ganymede's density is 2.2, so it may be of rock covered with ice.

MORE MOONS

For many years, only these four satellites of Jupiter were known, but in 1892 Edward E. Barnard, an astronomer at the Lick Observatory in California, using what was then the world's largest refracting telescope, found a fifth. This is a tiny body, probably not more than 150 miles in diameter, going around the planet every 11 hours, 57 minutes. Its distance is 113,000 miles, closer to Jupiter than Io. Sometimes it is called Amalthea, although this name has not been widely accepted. Generally it is known simply as the "fifth satellite," or Jupiter V.

In 1904 and 1905, another Lick Observatory astronomer, Charles D. Perrine, discovered VI and VII, which are probably even smaller; their estimated diameters are 120 and 50 miles. These are farther out than Callisto, at distances of 7,120,000 and 7,290,000 miles, and they take 251 and 260 days to go around. In 1908 came the only modern discovery of a Jovian moon not made at a California observatory, when P. J. Melotte, at the Royal Observatory, Greenwich, England, found Jupiter VIII. Perhaps 35 miles in diameter, it goes around in 739 days, at a distance of 14,600,000 miles.

In 1914, again at the Lick Observatory, Seth B. Nicholson picked up Jupiter IX, probably 17 miles in diameter, at a distance of 14,-700,000 miles and with a period of 758 days. Later, in 1938, Nicholson, who was then at the Mount Wilson Observatory, found two more, X and XI, and then scored again in 1951 with XII. Perhaps there are some others not yet discovered.

All these outer satellites are tiny bodies, with a hundred-mile diameter for VI and less than 40 miles for the others. Satellites VI, VII, and X, all a little more than 7 million miles from the planet and with periods of 250-260 days, form one of two groups, while

VIII, IX, XI, and XII form the other. These are 13 to 15 million miles from Jupiter, and they take from 625 to 758 days to make their circuit. Moreover, their motion is retrograde; they go around from east to west instead of from west to east, the usual direction for a satellite. Perhaps these are not truly moons of Jupiter, but asteroids that once ventured too close, and were captured by that planet's great gravitational pull.

SATURN

To observatory visitors, the most interesting of all the planets to view through the telescope is Saturn with its strange system of rings. It is 886,100,000 miles from the Sun and takes 29.5 years to go around, so its position in the sky changes little from one year to the next. The diameter of the ball is 75,100 miles, so it has 763 times the volume of the Earth—but only 95 times its mass. Thus its density is extremely small, about 0.7 that of water. It could float on water, the only planet of which this can be said (although it is also true of Callisto). It revolves on its axis in 10 hours, 14 minutes. Like Jupiter, the centrifugal force at the equator is terrific; there is a great equatorial bulge, with the diameter from pole to pole only 67,000 miles, about 8,000 less than at the equator. The pull of gravity at the surface is only 1.2 times Earth's; a 200-pound man there would weigh 240 pounds.

Because of its low density, astronomers think Saturn is constructed much like Jupiter—only more so. Probably the rocky core (28,000 miles diameter) accounts for only 35 per cent of the volume, the 8,000-mile deep layer of ice around it 20 per cent, and the cloudy atmosphere, with a thickness of 16,000 miles, 45 per cent. The spectrum indicates that this atmosphere also is made of methane and ammonia, although the bands of the latter are weaker than on Jupiter. At the low temperature prevailing on Saturn an even larger proportion of the ammonia would be frozen. Much of the atmosphere is probably hydrogen. University of Michigan astronomers have detected radio waves from Saturn, which indicate that its atmospheric temperature is about $-283°$ F. This is about the temperature expected on the basis of optical studies. These waves, generated naturally, seem to be emitted at various depths in the planet's atmosphere.

There are belts on Saturn, like those on Jupiter, but much less prominent and with less conspicuous colors. Also there seems to be some sort of activity on the planet because spots sometimes appear in the cloudy surface, but these are not as striking as Jupiter's red spot. A prominent white spot was discovered near Saturn's equator in 1933. It disappeared after a few months.

Saturn has nine known satellites, one of which, called Titan, is the largest and most massive in the Solar System. Its diameter is 3,500 miles, and it has twice the mass of our Moon. Moreover, it is the only moon in the system on which an atmosphere has been detected. Its spectrum shows bands similar to those on Saturn itself. It is 759,000 miles out, and goes around in 15 days, 23 hours.

Nearer Saturn, at distances ranging from 115,000 to 327,000 miles, are five other moons: Mimas, Enceladus, Tethys, Dione, and Rhea. The diameters range from about 1,100 miles for Rhea down to perhaps 300 for Mimas. They probably consist largely of ice, not only frozen water, but perhaps also frozen ammonia.

Farther out than Titan are three more: Hyperion and Phoebe, with diameters of a few hundred miles, and Iapetus, possibly as much as 2,000 miles across. As our Moon does to Earth, Iapetus always keeps the same face toward Saturn. When seen to the west of Saturn, it is nearly as bright as Titan, but after 5 weeks, when it has shifted to the east of the planet, it has dropped to about a fifth of its former brilliance. It may be irregular in shape, or perhaps one part of its surface, which faces us when it is brightest, reflects light better than other areas.

Phoebe, the last to be discovered (by W. H. Pickering, of Harvard, in 1898) is at a distance from Saturn of more than 8 million miles, more than 3.5 times as far as the next (Iapetus). Like Jupiter's four outer satellites, its motion is retrograde, so perhaps it, too, is a captured asteroid.

SATURN'S RINGS

But the really unique feature of Saturn, which makes it so beautiful when seen through a medium-sized telescope, is the system of rings. With his crude instrument, in 1610, Galileo saw that there was something peculiar about Saturn, but not until 1655 did Huygens realize that there is a ring, surrounding the planet and nowhere touching it. Later observers saw gaps in the ring, and we know now that it is not a solid structure. In fact, no solid ring could hold together under the strains that would be involved.

Instead, the ring system is really a swarm of tiny moons, some perhaps as large as golf balls, others no larger than grains of sand or particles of dust. These are so close together that from the distance of the Earth, which ranges from 746 to 1,028 million miles, they look continuous. The outside diameter of the ring system is 171,000 miles. With a total width of 41,500 miles, there is a space of some 7,000 miles between the inside and the planet, almost enough to let the Earth squeeze through.

But despite its huge size the system is not more than 10 miles thick. So thin is the ring that once every 15 years, when Saturn comes to certain positions in its orbit, the ring is presented edgewise to Earth for a few days and cannot be seen even through powerful telescopes. Halfway between these positions, it is opened up to its full extent, and that is the best time to see the planet.

We have referred to the ring as a system, because there are three main parts. Ring A, the outermost, is more than 10,000 miles in width. Then comes a gap, about 3,000 miles wide, known as Cassini's division, after the astronomer who discovered it (as well as Titan). Next is Ring B, which is a little less than 16,000 miles wide. It is brighter than Ring A and less transparent to the light from stars or satellites which can sometimes be seen behind it. Innermost is the crepe ring, much less prominent and sufficiently transparent to allow the edge of Saturn to be seen through it. Its width is about 11,500 miles. The shadow of the ball can often be seen on the rings. (See Plate 8b.)

Besides Cassini's division, there are other gaps in the system, although they are much less conspicuous. These gaps are apparently caused by gravitational effects from the inner satellites, particularly Mimas, for these satellites will "sweep clean" a region at a distance where the period is a simple fraction (such as ½ or ⅓) of their period around the planet. Cassini's division corresponds to half the period of Mimas, a third that of Enceladus and a quarter that of Tethys. The other gaps correspond to other fractions of these periods of the satellites. There are also gaps in the orbits of the asteroids, corresponding to similar fractions of the period of Jupiter around the Sun.

Originally, it is thought, Saturn had no rings, but perhaps it possessed another satellite, even closer than Mimas. At such a distance, the satellite would have a strong tidal effect on the planet which, in turn, would produce tides in the satellite itself. Being so close, the difference in tidal pull between the part of the moon nearest Saturn and the opposite part would be so great that it would literally be pulled apart. If the satellite were liquid, and of the same density as the planet, this "danger zone" would come at 2.44 times the planet's radius; this is known as Roche's limit. This would be different for a solid moon, but the entire ring system is well within it, while Mimas, at 3.11 times the radius of Saturn, is safely outside, so the theory seems plausible. However, it is perhaps more likely that there was material for an inner satellite, which never coalesced to form one, because of the tidal instability. Some astronomers believe that, in the far distant future, our own Moon will move in closer to Earth than Roche's limit. After that we also may have rings around our planet.

URANUS

Until 1781, the solar system, so far as men knew, ended with Saturn. But in that year Sir William Herschel, a German musician who had, as a youth, emigrated to England and become the greatest astronomer of his day, was observing the constellation of Gemini, the twins. He saw a strange object, greenish in color, which he first took to be a comet, and he announced it as such. As he watched it further he realized that it was a planet. At first he wanted to name it "Georgium Sidus" (George's star), after his patron, King George III, while other astronomers sought to name it Herschel. However, neither name was adopted; instead, astronomers followed Bode's suggestion of Uranus, the god of the heavens, which was in keeping with the names of the other planets, also taken from Graeco-Roman mythology.

With its path calculated, they figured its positions in previous years and found that it had been observed a number of times before Herschel's discovery, as early as 1690. On each occasion, however, it had been taken for a star. Actually, it is not hard to observe; sometimes it is barely bright enough to be seen with the naked eye —if you know just where to look.

The mean distance of Uranus from the Sun is 1,783,000,000 miles, or 19.3 times as far as the Earth. Thus, it agrees closely with Bode's law, which put it at 19.6 astronomical units. It takes 84 years to make one revolution. The diameter, at the equator, is 32,000 miles, and its period of rotation is 10 hours, 45 minutes.

In its structure, Uranus seems to resemble Jupiter and Saturn, with a rocky core of perhaps 14,000 miles diameter at the center; around the core a 6,000-mile deep layer of ice is overlaid with an "atmosphere" for some 3,000 miles. On account of its great distance, it cannot be observed as clearly as its two inner neighbors, but it, too, shows belts, and its spectrum shows much of methane, with even less ammonia than on Saturn. This is not surprising because it is still colder, around −310° F., probably, and practically all the ammonia would be frozen out. There seems to be some evidence for disturbances on Uranus, not as great as those on Jupiter, but perhaps more than on Saturn.

Herschel thought he had observed six satellites of Uranus, but four proved to be stars that happened to be in the same direction. Two were real. These were named Titania and Oberon. However, another English astronomer discovered two more in 1851. These were named Ariel and Umbriel. Nearly a century later, in 1948, Gerard P. Kuiper, at the McDonald Observatory in Texas, found a fifth, which he named Miranda.

Miranda is the innermost satellite, 81,000 miles from Uranus, around which it revolves in a little less than a day and ten hours. Then, in order, come Ariel, Umbriel, Titania, and Oberon, the last at 364,000 miles, and with a period of 13 days, 11 hours. Their sizes are uncertain, but studies made in 1948 by W. H. Steavenson, of Cambridge University in England, indicate that they may be larger than formerly supposed. Ariel, Titania, and Oberon may thus be of the order of 1,500 miles in diameter and Umbriel around 800, while Miranda is not likely to be more than about 200.

As astronomers tried to calculate the exact orbit of Uranus, they ran into difficulties. First of all, they could not make the earlier, pre-discovery observations fit those they were then making. So the old ones were discarded, as probably inaccurate, and a new orbit computed on the basis only of those made after 1781. In working out these predictions, allowance was made for the gravitational pulls, or perturbations, of all the other planets.

But still Uranus didn't behave, and by 1845 it was about two minutes of arc out of place. While this is only about a fifteenth of the Moon's diameter and hardly perceptible to the naked eye, it was astronomically intolerable. One explanation of the discrepancy was that there might be another planet out beyond Uranus, whose pull had not been considered.

Knowing of a planet, calculating its perturbations is not a very difficult piece of astronomical computation. Working backwards, to find the planet from its perturbations, is far more of a problem. But two astronomers, an Englishman named John Couch Adams and a Frenchman, Urbain Joseph Leverrier (who later was to accept Lescarbault's "discovery" of Vulcan), decided to attempt it.

THE DISCOVERY OF NEPTUNE

Working independently and without knowledge that the other was also doing it, they figured where the more distant planet would be. Adams finished first and sent his data to George Airy, the Astronomer Royal. But Airy, partly due to a misunderstanding and partly, perhaps, because of lack of confidence, did nothing about it.

Then Leverrier finished his task and wrote to Johann Gottfried Galle, at Berlin, telling him to direct his telescope to a certain position, in the constellation of Aquarius, where he would find the new planet. Galle looked; sure enough, there was a strange object within 1 degree of the place that Leverrier had given! It was the new planet. After that, English astronomers also located it, close to where Adams had predicted, so now history shares the honors between Adams and Leverrier.

With a diameter of about 26,800 miles, Neptune, as the new planet was named, is a little smaller than Uranus. It is somewhat heavier, however, for its density is about 2.5, instead of 1.56, that of Uranus. From the Sun, its mean distance is 2,791,000,000 miles, about 30 times that of Earth. Thus, Bode's law fell down badly, apparently, for the next number is 38.8. Neptune takes nearly 165 years to go around the Sun.

Once again, it seems, we have the customary construction for one of the large planets, with the rocky core—this time 12,000 miles in diameter—surrounded by an ice layer (6,000 miles deep) and a gaseous blanket of 2,000 miles' thickness. These clouds contain methane, and apparently hydrogen also, but no ammonia. This is hardly surprising, for the surface temperature of −360° F. would freeze it out of the atmosphere.

There seems to be some sort of belted marks on Neptune, but details are very hard to observe, on account of the planet's great distance. When nearest Earth, it reaches a magnitude of 7.6, so that it can never be seen except with a telescope.

After the discovery of Neptune and the determination of some data about it, the orbit of Uranus was revised, this time allowing for the perturbations of the new planet. Now the early observations fitted very closely, and afterwards Uranus moved just about the way that was predicted. It turned out that, in 1822, Uranus and Neptune were in line with the Sun. Prior to that Neptune was ahead, so it tended to pull Uranus forward, while after that its pull caused that planet to hang behind a little. Thus the effects of the then unknown planet were at their greatest. A century earlier or later, with Neptune on the opposite side of the Sun, the effect would have been much less, and a longer time might have been required before the perturbations became obvious.

Lassell, discoverer of Ariel and Umbriel, found a satellite of Neptune soon after the planet was discovered. He named it Triton. It is one of the largest satellites, about 3,000 miles in diameter, although this is hard to determine accurately. Kuiper, in 1944, found what seemed to be evidence of methane in its spectrum, so perhaps, like Titan, it has some atmosphere. Triton is 220,000 miles from Neptune; it goes around once in 5 days, 21 hours.

It was Kuiper, in 1949, who found the second satellite, to which he gave the name of Nereid. This is much smaller, perhaps 200 miles in diameter, and at a distance of nearly 3.5 million miles. Its period is about 359 days.

THE SEARCH FOR PLANET X

Although, at first, the discovery of Neptune seemed to remove the discrepancy between the predicted and actual motion of Uranus, there remained a slight difference, which became apparent around 1900. Percival Lowell, founder of the Lowell Observatory and a very able mathematician, decided that there must still be another object—Planet X, he called it—out beyond Neptune and that this was responsible for the remaining errors.

Neptune itself should also be affected by Planet X, but it had only moved about a third of a revolution in its orbit since discovery, and the difference might not be so evident. About 1905, Lowell set out to locate the unknown object; first on paper, then in the sky. In 1915, less than a year before he died, he published his conclusions: that Planet X was nearly 4 billion miles from the Sun, that it went around once in 282 years, and that it was about six times as massive as the Earth. However, his careful search of the sky failed to reveal it.

A little later, William H. Pickering, of the Harvard College Observatory, also worked on the problem, utilizing the motions of Neptune, and he came to conclusions quite similar to those of Lowell. In 1919, Milton Humason, at the Mount Wilson Observatory, made photographs of the suspected region. His method was much simpler than that, used by Galle, of comparing the actual sky with star maps. The planet moves against the background of stars. Thus, with two photographs taken a day or more apart, the stars will all be in the same position, but the planet will have shifted. By an ingenious device called the *blink microscope*, it is possible to compare the plates. As the view shifts from one to the other, the object that has moved shows up against the fixed stars by jumping rapidly back and forth. But Humason was unable to find any new planet.

After Lowell died, his successors continued the search and began to use a new telescope, especially designed for the purpose. Clyde Tombaugh, a former amateur astronomer who had joined the staff, was assigned to make a survey along the path of the sky where the planet might be, comparing plates taken on different nights by use of the blink microscope. In January, 1930, he found a strange object. Further observations were necessary to confirm its planetary character, but finally the announcement that a planet beyond Neptune had been discovered was made on March 13, 1930. The date had a double significance. It was the anniversary of Herschel's discovery of Uranus; and also Lowell's birthday!

It was named Pluto, after the god of the underworld—very appropriate for a body so far out in space, away from the light of the Sun. It was much fainter than expected, which was why Lowell had not found it. Actually, when the orbit was calculated and they looked back on earlier plates, the Lowell astronomers found an image of it on one taken before Lowell's death—one which he had actually handled.

And also it was found on two of the 1919 plates taken by Humason in his search. Only a piece of bad luck had prevented its discovery at that time, because one image happened to fall on a flaw in the plate; the other happened to be close to a star which partly hid it.

PLUTO

The mean distance of Pluto from the Sun is 3,666,000,000 miles or 39.5 astronomical units. Thus its distance is close to Bode's ninth number (38.8). Its period is 248 years. The orbit is very eccentric, i.e., it is pulled out far from a circle, more than any other planet. When nearest the Sun, its distance is only 2,761,000,000 miles, or about 35 million miles closer than the mean distance of Neptune. However, it is inclined about 17 degrees to the plane of Neptune's orbit, and the two cannot, now, come closer than about 240,000,000 miles.

The size of Pluto is still uncertain, although measurements made at Mount Palomar in 1950 with the 200-inch Hale telescope gave an estimate of 3,600 miles—smaller than any planet except Mercury. And in 1955 two Lowell Observatory astronomers found its rotation period to be 6.39 days. Since it is only with the greatest of telescopes that Pluto shows as barely more than a point of light, they could not observe the movement of details across the face of the planet. What they did observe was a slight but regular change in brightness. Apparently one part is darker than the other, and, as it turns, it dims slightly on each revolution.

With such a small diameter, it seems impossible that Pluto should have a mass as great as Lowell assumed or that it could have produced the effects on the movements of Uranus and Neptune that Lowell and Pickering utilized in their predictions. And if this is so, it was only a very remarkable coincidence that Pluto was found so close to the place where they said it would be.

On the other hand, it may be larger. One hypothesis is that Pluto is covered with a polished or shiny surface, perhaps ice or liquid methane (which could exist there, even at the surface temperature of around −400° F.). If so, what astronomers see is the reflected image of the Sun, while the rest of the planet reflects only the darkness of space. You can see this effect if you look at a ball bearing held against a dark background, with a brilliant light behind you. It is hard to see the whole ball; all that is visible is the brilliant reflected spot. However there is no confirmation that such an effect is responsible for the small apparent size of Pluto.

Pluto now is unquestionably a planet, by definition, for it is a body revolving around the Sun. However, it seems likely that it has not always had this status; it may well be a former satellite (of

Neptune) that broke away to set itself up in the planetary business. Compared with its neighbors, its smaller size and slower rotation period, the orbit's high tilt and great eccentricity, make it probable that its origin was different from that of Neptune, for example. But if it had been formed as a satellite of that planet, which left its parent, these features are readily explained.

A LOST MOON OF NEPTUNE?

Raymond A. Lyttleton, of Cambridge University, has made the ingenious suggestion that it became independent when it came too close to Neptune's present satellite, Triton. This is the way he explains it:

"If Pluto had once been a satellite of Neptune, its period of motion round the planet would very likely be measured in days, since that is the kind of rotation period it would have if it always faced its primary. The present satellite, Triton, actually has an orbital period of just under six days. Now it will be recalled that our own Moon always presents the same face to the Earth, and therefore has a rotation period equal to its orbital period, namely 27⅓ days, and that this has been brought about by the back action of the tides on the Moon. The same thing is likely to have happened on other planets, and a pretty clear reconstruction can be arrived at of what may have occurred for Neptune.

"Originally both Triton and Pluto may have been ordinary satellites circling the planet in the same forward direction; their tidal attractions would by their secondary effects gradually push the satellites further out, but the inner one would recede the faster. Sooner or later the satellites would be brought sufficiently close together that they would so affect each other's motion that one would be reversed in direction—that would be Triton—and the other speeded up to such an extent that it escaped from the planet altogether; and that would be Pluto." * (See Fig. 34.)

Here, all at once, we have an explanation why Pluto rotates so slowly, why its orbit crosses that of Neptune, and why Triton's revolution around it is retrograde. However, Lyttleton points out, "all this partakes of the nature of circumstantial evidence, as must almost all theories of past events, and strong as it is does not yet rise to the level of unquestionable proof."

* By permission from *The Modern Universe*, by R. A. Lyttleton. Copyright, 1956, Harper & Bros., New York.

"But," he adds, "it is not necessary to make any final decisions; science does not proceed that way. What rather is done is to say: Here is a certain possible explanation; these facts seem to bear it out; are there others in favor, are there any against, and are they fatal objections? The problem always remains open against new evidence, and until we feel that an adequate amount of evidence

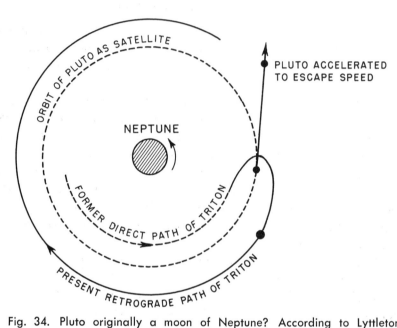

Fig. 34. Pluto originally a moon of Neptune? According to Lyttleton's theory, Pluto was once a satellite of Neptune, along with Triton which traveled in an inner orbit. They happened to approach so closely that the gravitational attraction pulled Pluto away completely, to give it independent planetary status. Triton was pulled completely around, into its present retrograde path, outside the old orbit of Pluto. (By permission from *The Modern Universe*, by R. A. Lyttleton. Copyright, 1956, Harper & Bros., New York.)

has been obtained we hope for more, and refrain, or at least try to do so, from making up our minds that a particular explanation is necessarily the correct one."

If Pluto did originate this way, it is rather a curious coincidence that it happened to take up an orbit in which the mean distance from the Sun is 39.5 astronomical units, so close to the ninth number of Bode's Law: 38.8. On this basis, it might be considered that Neptune itself is the interloper, rather than Pluto!

Are there any more planets, out beyond Pluto? William H. Pickering, whose calculations led to the ill-fated observations of Pluto in 1919, thought there is one, at least. He based this conclusion on a study of comets, bodies which will be more fully discussed in the next chapter. We can anticipate a bit here to say that these visitors come in close to the Sun, then move to the outer reaches of the Solar System. Some fifty, at their greatest distance from the Sun, just about reach the orbit of Jupiter. For Saturn, Uranus, and Neptune, there are a few that come out to their distances. Some may even be associated with Pluto, despite that planet's small size.

Pickering pointed out that for 16 comets the aphelion is about 7 billion miles from the Sun. This figure, by the way, corresponds to about 75 astronomical units, which is close to the next Bode number, 77. So, he concluded, there must be a planet at that distance, perhaps larger than Uranus or Neptune. At such a distance, from Kepler's third law, it would take about 650 years to go around the Sun. But Planet P, if it really exists, must be so far away that only the largest telescopes would reveal it. And, moving so slowly, it will probably be a long time before its perturbations of Pluto (or Neptune or Uranus) would be noticeable. So it will probably be a long time—if ever—before it is actually found!

LIFE ON OTHER PLANETS?

It wasn't long after men began to realize that the Earth was only one of a number of planets revolving around the Sun that they began to wonder whether the others were inhabited, like Earth. Sir William Herschel even thought that the Sun might be inhabited. He conceived that there was a luminous atmosphere around a solid core on which people might live. Sunspots, he supposed, were openings in the luminous covering, through which the dark surface below was visible.

But, when the temperature of the Sun was appreciated, men realized that nothing solid could exist there, so it has been eliminated as a possible abode of life. So have the other stars. But the planets were left. Mars, especially, seemed a possibility, and Percival Lowell concluded that the "canals" were actually evidence of intelligent beings there. Then, too, the green areas that develop on Mars as spring comes seemed to be the result of some sort of vegetation.

In considering the possibilities of life elsewhere in the universe, we must, almost necessarily, think of life as we know it, which is based on the element carbon and requires water and oxygen to support it. It has been suggested that an alternative form of life might be based on silicon, which resembles carbon in many ways. In recent years, chemists have produced silicon-containing compounds, called *silicones,* which are quite analogous to more familiar compounds of carbon. There is, for example, a silicone rubber, which retains its rubbery qualities at temperatures considerably higher than the ordinary kind, which is basically carbon. Thus, a living form made of silicon might possibly live on a planet that would be much too hot for carbon organisms, like ourselves.

However, with no evidence for the existence of such organisms, it is of little profit to speculate about them, or about other forms, made perhaps of still different elements.

Life, as we know it, requires an environment that is not too hot nor too cold. Very few forms of life can exist at temperatures as high as the boiling point of water, so that is a practical upper limit. Most forms also cannot survive cold much below the freezing point of water. In those that can, life becomes dormant; under such conditions it could hardly evolve into higher forms.

Animals need oxygen, which combines with carbon to form carbon dioxide and so provide energy. On the other hand, plants, using carbon dioxide, are stimulated by the Sun's rays to build up carbohydrates, and these are basic foods for animals. Both require water, as a liquid or in the form of vapor. Thus it seems that a planet on which plants or animals are to reach a high stage of development will need: a moderate temperature, oxygen, carbon dioxide, and water (or water vapor). As far as we can determine, no planet in the Solar System—except the Earth—is so provided.

Mercury, of course, is too hot, and seems to have no appreciable atmosphere. Pluto is too cold, and probably it doesn't have an atmosphere, either. The large planets, Jupiter, Saturn, Uranus, and Neptune, have atmospheres, as we have seen. But these seem not to contain any oxygen or water vapor; they are made of gases that are poisonous to life as we know it.

Venus has an atmosphere in which carbon dioxide has been detected. But not oxygen or water vapor. Its temperature is higher than ours, because it is nearer the Sun. Also, it is likely that there is a pronounced *greenhouse effect.* A layer of carbon dioxide acts much like the glass in a greenhouse, i.e., it lets in heat rays from the Sun but stops the longer waves that the planet's surface may radiate out into space again. It thus seems very likely that on the surface of Venus, below the clouds, the temperature is considerably higher than that needed to boil water.

This leaves Mars as our only hope. But, as we have seen, no oxygen can be detected in its thin atmosphere. There is carbon dioxide but no detectable water vapor. However, if the polar caps really are made of ice or even frost, they must let a little water vapor into the Martian atmosphere as they evaporate.

Plants on Earth are green in color because of the presence of chlorophyll. This reflects green light and absorbs other wave lengths, which is why it gives the color sensation that it does. In addition, chlorophyll reflects strongly some of the invisible infrared rays. Photographs have been made of Mars, through color filters passing different regions of the spectrum, both visible and invisible. These show that the green areas are not due to chlorophyll.

MARTIAN VEGETATION

However, they still might be some form of plant life, as we have plants on Earth that show a different spectrum of reflected light from those most familiar to us. These are the lichens, which can exist under some of the most extreme conditions.

A lichen is not a single plant but two separate ones living together and, even, reproducing the combination. One part is an alga, which builds up organic materials by the use of light, in the process of photosynthesis. Thus, it supplies food. The other part, a fungus, supplies inorganic material, and so protects the alga, and keeps it from drying out. The lichen is a sort of a complete world in itself; even in surroundings with very little oxygen, it could supply its own oxygen and, from oxygen, carbon dioxide.

On Earth, lichens exist under conditions where no other plants can survive. They are found in the Himalayas, as high as 15,000 feet. They will survive immersion in liquid air at a temperature lower than −300° F. Some live always in shadow, on the ceilings of caves; others in the hot Sahara desert, where it never rains. Thus it seems very likely that terrestrial lichens could exist on Mars, and so the vegetation there may be similar. It seems quite unlikely that exactly similar forms would have developed there.

One rather good argument for the presence of vegetation on Mars has to do with the yellow clouds that occur there. If these are dust storms, it would seem that a layer of dust would cover the entire surface of the planet. But, as Ernst Öpik, an Estonian astronomer now in Ireland, has pointed out, vegetation would be able to push up through this dust, while most inorganic and non-living material would remain covered. Thus it is hard to imagine any process, except for the growth of vegetation, which would cause the regular appearance of the green areas.

Another question is where life came from in the first place. A Swedish scientist, Svante Arrhenius, once suggested that living spores exist all through space, ready to fall on any planet and to develop if conditions are right. But that would not explain where the living spores came from, so the question is merely pushed back one step.

Experiments performed in recent years by Stanley Miller, at the University of Chicago, show that, with a mixture of water vapor, hydrogen, methane, and ammonia, bombarded for days with electrical discharges, the organic compounds called amino acids are formed spontaneously. And these are the building blocks of proteins, one of the main constituents of animal tissue.

As now on Jupiter, it is likely that in Earth's early days there was ammonia, methane, and hydrogen in the atmosphere, along with water vapor. No doubt there were frequent and, perhaps, continuous lightning storms to produce electrical discharges, so a similar process may have occurred, finally leading to actual living organisms. As a famous American astronomer, Harlow Shapley, says:

"Biochemistry and microbiology, with the assistance of geophysics, astronomy and other sciences, have gone so far in bridging the gap between the inanimate and the living that we can no longer doubt but that whenever the physics, chemistry and climate are right on a planet's surface, life will emerge, persist and evolve. The mystery of life is vanishing. Objective science is replacing the subjective miraculous. The many researches of the past few years in the field of macromolecules and microorganisms have now made it quite unnecessary to postulate miracles and the supernatural for the origin of life." *

* By permission from *Of Stars and Men*, by Harlow Shapley. Copyright, 1958, Beacon Press, Boston.

10

Between the Planets

Look at the sky on a dark, clear night. Shining overhead are the stars, arranged in the familiar constellation figures that they occupy week after week, year after year. You may also see one or more of the naked-eye planets. These move around among the stars and are not in the places where you saw them a year ago.

If you keep on looking you will see, perhaps five to ten times each hour, a moving point of light—a "shooting star." Some will just barely be visible; one rarely may rival the brightest stars or planets. An occasional bright one may even leave a luminous trail that persists for minutes, and may be bright enough to cast shadows on the ground. In fact, it may even explode! On the other hand, many such objects are too faint to be seen at all with the naked eye. Occasionally, as an astronomer is observing some other object through his telescope, one of these may flash unexpectedly across the part of the sky he is watching.

Actually, these are not stars, but *meteors*. Originally this term was applied to anything in the atmosphere—a flash of lightning, for example—and thus came the name of meteorology for the study of the weather. But now the term *meteor* is applied to bits of solid matter that approach the Earth from outer space with speeds of perhaps 40 miles per second. At a height of some 60 miles, the atmosphere, though highly rarefied, is dense enough to make considerable friction. This heats the meteor to incandescence and it is turned into luminous vapor, which is what we see moving across the sky.

A very bright one, that may leave a persistent trail, is called a fireball, while one that explodes—perhaps audibly—is called a *bolide.* And very rarely one arrives that is large enough to survive its fiery passage through the atmosphere and land on the ground. This is called a *meteorite.*

The entire surface of Earth—both land and water—covers a little less than 200 million square miles. From any one position we can see the sky over an area of about 2,000 square miles, about 1/100,000 of that above the entire Earth. Thus, five meteors per hour from one place would mean 500,000 per hour over the whole Earth of naked-eye brightness. Actually the number is probably even larger, since more come after midnight than before.

This is because of the way the Earth turns in relation to its movement around the Sun. Between sunset and midnight, we are on the rear, while from midnight to sunrise, we are on the front of our planetary vehicle. Meteors come from all directions but, in the evening hours, only those moving fast enough to catch up to us can be seen. In the early morning, however, we meet them head-on. It's like walking along a busy street; you usually meet many more people going the other way than are going the same direction that you are.

Moreover, we also meet many meteors after the Sun rises, until noon, but only very rarely is one bright enough to be seen in broad daylight. Radio astronomy reveals these, however. The gases in the meteor's path are ionized and reflect radio waves, so they may be observed by radar.

MILLIONS OF METEORS

Then also there are many more faint meteors than ones bright enough to be seen with the unaided eye. One authority, Fletcher G. Watson, of Harvard University, estimates the Earth's daily catch as 75,000,000 bright enough to be visible on a dark clear night directly overhead (i.e., about the fifth magnitude). If we include meteors down to the tenth magnitude, a hundredth of the brightness needed to be seen without a telescope, the total number, he estimates, is about 4.5×10^8. The faintest of these would be extremely small objects; well over a million would be needed to make an ounce.

Still smaller are the micrometeorites, about a ten-thousandth of an inch in diameter, so small that a microscope is needed to see them. They are so minute that they filter down without meeting enough air atoms to cause the friction that would vaporize them. Such particles may be found in rain water. Many are attracted by a magnet, indicating that they are rich in iron, as meteorites are known to be. Particles much smaller than this—a twenty-five thousandth of an inch or less—would probably not reach Earth at all. The actual pressure of the light from the Sun would blow them out of the Solar System.

It is quite impossible to tell the height, or distance, of a meteor observed from one location. Bright fireballs, especially, are often thought to be much nearer than they really are. Several years ago, for example, one passed over Philadelphia late at night. A taxidriver, returning home after work, thought he saw it land in a nearby field. So confident was he of its closeness that the next day he phoned a local museum and offered to get it for them, when he had time off the following weekend.

However, a number of people, in widely scattered places, saw it go overhead, and these data were collected by an astronomer, who determined the real path. It had passed over Philadelphia, in a northeasterly direction, over New Jersey, Long Island, Cape Cod and, finally, fell into the Atlantic Ocean about 300 miles east of Boston!

Astronomers who study meteors often set up two observing stations, perhaps 20 miles apart, each equipped with cameras aimed to photograph the same region some 50 miles high. Time exposures are made, and, if a meteor happens along, it leaves a trail on the film in each camera. The stars out in the distance also are recorded, but each meteor trail has a different background. The astronomers measure the displacement of the trail on each negative, and from it they determine the height of the meteor. The beginning of the path may be 60 to 70 miles above the ground, and the end at a height of perhaps 35 miles.

Usually a circular shutter, or "chopper," revolves in front of the lens of each camera, several times per second, and this puts a series of gaps in the trails as photographed. With the speed of rotation of the shutter known, astronomers can determine exactly how long the meteor took in flight. Finally, having determined the length of the trail, as well as the height, they can find the velocity.

Meteors vary in speed, but the average is about 45 miles per second. To this is added, or subtracted, the Earth's own speed in its orbit around the Sun—about 18.5 miles per second. Thus, a meteor that hits Earth head-on, which would be seen after midnight, may have an apparent speed of 60 to 65 miles per second. But if you observe one in the evening hours, one that has caught up to us, it may seem to be moving as slowly as 25 miles per second. Even this is about fifty times the speed of a bullet as it leaves the muzzle of a high-powered rifle.

The faster a meteor moves the more friction it generates as it hits the molecules of the atmosphere; this makes it hotter and bluer, in color, as well as brighter. Thus, a meteor weighing only a thousandth of an ounce, and coming in at high speed, might equal a first-magnitude star in brightness. Coming in more slowly, the same meteor might be of fifth magnitude, barely visible to the naked eye.

Watson estimates the total number of meteors hitting the Earth every day to be of the order of several billion, of which by far the greater number are well below naked-eye visibility. Their total mass is hard to determine precisely, but it seems to be at least a thousand—and perhaps as much as 10,000—tons, which might add 5 to 10 pounds daily to each square mile of the Earth's surface. This may add a million tons or more to the Earth's mass each year, an amount which seems large, but is trivial compared to our planet's total "weight" of more than six sextillion tons.

METEORITES

The average weight of meteorites that land on Earth each day (including those that plunge into the seas) is probably less than a ton, although one weighing many tons will sometimes fall. The largest "in captivity" is on display in New York City, at the Hayden Planetarium of the American Museum of Natural History. Known as the Ahnighito meteorite, it was found in Greenland by Admiral Peary, discoverer of the North Pole, and brought to the United States after great difficulty. It is mounted on a scale which shows that it weighs 34 tons.

Even larger is the Hoba West meteorite, at Grootfontein in South Africa, estimated to weigh about 60 tons. It has never been moved from this location, where it fell.

For a long time even intelligent people refused to believe that there were such things as meteorites. Of course, they had been found, and were recognized as being peculiar, differing in many respects from ordinary stones. Some scientists said they were rocks that had been hit by lightning and so altered in character. Then, on April 26, 1803, such stones actually fell at L'Aigle, in France. J. B. Biot and other French scientists made a thorough investigation and reported to the Academy their conviction that the stones had indeed come down from the sky.

But still there were skeptics. Thomas Jefferson was an excellent scientist as well as a statesman. On December 18, 1807, while he was president, a meteorite fell in Connecticut and was investigated by two Yale professors who, like Biot, became convinced of its meteoritic character. When he heard about it, Jefferson said that he "could more easily believe that two Yankee professors would lie than that stones would fall from heaven."

A meteorite is the only object that we can touch and handle and that we know originated elsewhere than on Earth, and for this reason they have been extensively studied in the laboratory. Hoba West and Anighito are examples of iron meteorites. These, typically, consist of about 90 per cent iron and 8 per cent nickel, along with small amounts of cobalt, phosphorus, carbon, chromium, and copper. Others are stone, but even they contain about 25 per cent of iron, along with 1 per cent or so of nickel. In fact, the presence of nickel is one of the first tests made of a suspected meteorite; if none is present, it probably isn't meteoritic.

Very often, when a person finds any unusual kind of stone, he assumes it to be a meteorite. Few of these are genuine; sometimes it is a mass of slag or cinders, with cavities and pores, which are never present in meteorites. However, this does not mean that real meteorites cannot be found.

Lincoln LaPaz, director of the Institute of Meteoritics at the University of New Mexico, says that "anyone who systematically watches, either in the field, or in rock, rock-garden, and mineral collections, for exceptionally heavy (generally of density greater than 3) 'stones,' fragmental or otherwise, with rounded corners and edges, will sooner or later find a meteorite.

"In case the discovered masses are coated, at least partially, with a dark- to reddish-brown crust, exhibit 'thumb-marks' . . . or, in particular, can be shown by grinding to consist even in small part of a shining, malleable, silvery metal resembling stainless steel (which indeed is an article of commerce patterned after the natural nickel-iron alloys first found in meteorites), then the discoveries are quite likely to be meteorites."

However, to make a real identification, it takes an expert, so if you find what seems to be a meteorite, and want to be sure, send it to one of the large museums which have outstanding collections, such as the U.S. National Museum in Washington, D.C.; the American Museum of Natural History, in New York City; or the Chicago Museum of Natural History.

While many—if not a majority—of the meteors we see flashing across the sky are small bits of iron and stone like the meteorites that are completely burned up in their flight, research with high-altitude rockets has given evidence that some may be of an entirely different composition. These rockets have been equipped with microphones, and the sounds they picked up have been radioed back to the ground. In many cases, such sounds have indicated that the rockets were hitting some unidentified objects at high elevations, yet, when they were recovered after their descent, they bore no marks of such collisions. Surely ordinary stone and iron meteorites would have left scratches or dents or some other trace of the collision.

Possibly there is another kind of meteoric body, consisting of frozen gases, which is very fragile and incapable of leaving any marks on the rocket casing. As we shall find presently, there is a definite association between some meteors, which come in swarms, and comets. And comets, according to one plausible theory, have nuclei consisting of masses of frozen gases, which do not melt in the low temperature of outer space. Thus meteors may originate in two quite different ways. The stones and irons may be related to the asteroids, and may well have resulted from the breaking up of some primitive planet. The solidified gases may be the debris of comets of past ages.

THE PUZZLING TEKTITES

Still another type of meteorite—if they really are meteoritic in origin—is the mysterious tektite. These strange objects are of glass, very different, however, from any artificial glass or any of the kinds that occur in nature, such as obsidian, a volcanic glass. They have been found in many parts of the world, particularly

Australia and the land areas around the South China Sea. Others have been found in Czechoslovakia, near the Moldau River (where they were first identified), in South America and Texas, along the Ivory Coast of Africa, and in the Philippine Islands. Geologically, these regions differ greatly, possessing little in common to explain a terrestrial origin for tektites.

Many attempts have been made to explain their origin on Earth: as products of volcanoes, as the result of fusion of atmospheric dust by lightning, or a similar fusion of materials in the ground, as well as in many other ways. However, no such explanation has been without serious objections. Thus, obeying Sherlock Holmes' famous dictum that when you have eliminated the impossible, what remains, however improbable, must be the truth, it is now quite generally accepted that tektites are meteoritic. This has come about despite the fact that they are entirely different in practically all respects from any meteorite that has actually been seen to fall, of which there are many, comprising several thousand specimens, of some 80 different types.

One theory was that they were produced when meteorites hit the Earth, but this too has been rejected. However, they may be chips off the Moon, blasted loose as large meteorites hit at high speed, according to H. H. Nininger, founder and director of the American Meteorite Museum at Sedona, Arizona.

The shape of most tektites suggests that they were formed from blobs of molten stuff spinning in space, while many also bear signs of a second melting on their surfaces. This may have occurred when they hit the Earth's atmosphere and encountered the friction which heats other meteorites as well. But since they only came from the Moon's distance, of less than a quarter of a million miles, they might well be moving more slowly than the others arriving from distant space.

With no atmosphere on the Moon, even small meteorites would hit it with full speed. Larger ones, as we have seen, would have so much energy when they hit that they would make a terrific explosion, with their own material, as well as much of the surrounding lunar surface, turned into gas. Such an explosion would hurl into space pieces of the Moon's own rocky material, at the same time melting much of it into a glassy liquid. But these blobs of liquid would soon cool into rounded pebbles of glass—the tektites. Of course, most of this shower of debris would fall back on the Moon.

But, with the weak lunar gravitational field—only a sixth that of Earth's—some pieces would be moving rapidly enough to escape into space. And some of these might be pulled in toward the Earth, suffering their second melting by the friction of our atmosphere.

While this hypothesis would be hard to prove, it does seem quite plausible. It makes the tektites most intriguing. Perhaps, here on the Earth, in many museums as well as in private collections, we already have real pieces of the Moon, even before astronauts have travelled there to make personal studies and bring back specimens.

TERRESTRIAL METEOR CRATERS

We have already mentioned the idea that lunar craters are scars of explosions made by huge meteorites. In a number of places on Earth, there are craters that resemble lunar craters, although they are not as large as most of those which astronomers can observe through their telescopes.

The crater that has been most extensively studied is located near Winslow, Arizona. It is about ⅘ of a mile in diameter and about 600 feet deep, while the rim rises more than 100 feet above the plain. The strata of rock under the crater are powdered, as shown by borings, while around the rim they are tilted upwards. Evidently some violent explosion has occurred there.

Few people visited this rather inaccessible crater in the early days of settlement of the West, while the Indians had abandoned the region some centuries earlier because it was so barren. But in March, 1891, a prospector did reach it and found quantities of iron, in lumps of varied sizes, scattered over the ground. He thought he had found a new vein of iron, which might be mined, and sent a sample to a mining firm in New Mexico. Part of this soon reached A. E. Foote, a mineralogist in Philadelphia, who recognized it as meteoritic. Since he dealt in minerals, he visited the crater in June and brought away more than a hundred specimens, all of them definitely meteorites. As a result of his study, he was convinced that the crater had been caused by the impact of a huge meteorite, of which his samples were fragments.

So radical did this idea seem, however, that it met considerable opposition. One prominent geologist of the period was G. K. Gilbert, of the U.S. Geological Survey. A man of wide interests, he had studied the Moon, and, in 1893, he read a paper supporting the idea that the craters there had resulted from the impact of meteorites. At first, he accepted the theory that the Arizona crater had a similar origin, but finally he rejected it. In a paper published in 1896, he adopted the alternative idea that it had resulted from a steam explosion that occurred when volcanic heat below the crater had vaporized a large body of water. It was a mere coincidence, he felt, that a large number of meteorites—if indeed that was what they were—had fallen in the same region. Gilbert's authority was such that, for some years, it was the orthodox theory.

It was largely the enthusiasm—and missionary spirit—of a Philadelphia mining engineer, Daniel Moreau Barringer, that revived the impact theory. Today, there seems to be no doubt that the crater had such an origin. Barrington and his associates were convinced that the main mass of the meteorite, perhaps millions of tons, was still buried in the ground, but they were never able to reach it. Now it is generally supposed that the bulk of the missile was vaporized in the explosion that occurred as the meteorite was halted in its flight and the energy of its motion converted into heat.

By comparison with terrestrial explosives, Charles Clayton Wylie, of the University of Iowa, has made an estimate of the size of the mass that entered the Earth's atmosphere on that memorable day, perhaps 50,000 years ago, when the crater was formed. It seems to have come from the northeast, and, according to Wylie, its velocity was probably between 10 and 20 miles per second; its diameter was probably between 35 and 50 feet; and its mass between 5,000 and 15,000 tons. The several tons of meteorites that have been found around the crater were doubtless on the edge of the main cluster and thereby escaped the destruction by vaporization in the explosion.

A number of other meteor craters have been found, in Kansas, Texas, Estonia, Siberia, Australia, and Canada. With the exception of one in northern Quebec, none of these are as large as the Barringer Crater.

The Quebec crater is located in the Ungava Peninsula, and is named after F. W. Chubb, a prospector, who was studying aerial photographs of the region in 1950 and noticed a lake, among the glacial finger lakes, that was perfectly round. V. B. Meen, a Canadian geologist, led an expedition to study it. The party flew in a plane that had pontoons and landed on the lake itself. The crater is more than 2 miles in diameter, while the lake is over 800 feet deep. The rim, upturned like that of the Barringer Crater, is nearly 500 feet high. It is in a sheet of granite, with no evidence of volcanic activity in the neighborhood.

Granite boulders are scattered thickly all around the crater, and the search for meteorites was unsuccessful. However, it seems most probable that Chubb Crater also had a meteoritic origin.

SIBERIA BOMBARDED

These craters all go back far into geological history, but, twice in the twentieth century, masses of meteorites have landed in Siberia and produced craters. On June 30, 1908, such an agglomeration, moving northward, landed in an isolated region near the Stony Tunguska River. The explosion was so great that windows 50 miles away were broken and the air wave sent out was recorded 5 hours later on a sensitive barograph in England, 3,400 miles away.

A scientific expedition under L. A. Kulik reached the site in 1927. Even though this was nearly 20 years later, they found tremendous devastation. As far as 18 miles away from the point of impact trees had been blown over and lay pointing away from the center. In the middle they found at least ten craters from 30 to 160 feet in diameter.

The region where this occurred is about the same latitude as Leningrad, then called St. Petersburg. If the meteorite had landed 4 hours, 47 minutes later, the rotation of the Earth would have brought that city into its path, and there might have been a disaster comparable to the effects of an atomic bomb.

Siberia was visited again by a great meteorite on February 12, 1947, when one came in from a northerly direction and hit ground a couple of hundred miles north of Vladivostok, far to the west of the Tunguska region. A huge column of brown dust rose some 20 miles into the air.

Soviet scientists soon reached the scene, which again showed many trees felled radially while others had been hurled high into the air. They identified 106 craters, the largest nearly 100 feet across and 30 feet deep. Moreover, 5 tons of meteorites were collected, each of the largest ones weighing more than a quarter of a ton.

So it seems that meteorites of huge size do occasionally land on Earth and produce terrestrial craters. But the effects of wind and rain eventually erase their scars. Otherwise, the Earth might be as pitted as the Moon.

METEOR SHOWERS

On most nights, as you watch the sky for meteors, you find that they may come from any direction. But on certain nights they seem to show a preference, and the majority may originate in one part of the sky, even in one constellation. Thus, about August 11 and 12 , you will find that they seem to come from the direction of Perseus, and about November 17, from Leo. These are called meteor showers and are named after the point from which they radiate—the radiant. Thus, those of August are known as Perseids, and those of November the Leonids.

Normally, about August 11, instead of seeing 5 to 10 meteors per hour you may see as many as 50 or more. As for the Leonids, on one famous occasion, in 1833, they came down at something like 50 per second—they looked like a heavy snowfall. Again in 1866 there was a remarkable display. After another interval of 33 years, in 1899, another was expected but didn't appear. Nor did it come again in 1932. However, a few were observed in these years, as they are annually.

There are a number of other showers, such as the Quandrantids, which come out of the northern sky about January 3 (they are named after an old constellation—no longer recognized—the quadrant); the delta Aquarids, seen about July 29, one of two showers with their radiant in Aquarius; the Lyrids, which emerge from Lyra about April 21; the Orionids, from Orion, about October 22; the eta Aquarids, the other shower from Aquarius, about May 4; etc.

Actually the meteors of each of these showers are moving through space in parallel paths, and their luminous trails in the atmosphere are parallel. These seem to converge in the distance, like the parallel tracks of a railroad, so the radiant effect is merely one of perspective. We encounter some of them every year because their path crosses the Earth's orbit, and when our planet gets to the intersection, we meet them.

The orbits of meteor showers are generally long ellipses. That of the Perseids extends out to a distance of some 4 billion miles, but perihelion—the point at which it is nearest the Sun—is only slightly less than the Earth's distance. The Leonids go out a little beyond Uranus, to a distance of 1,767 million miles from the Sun.

For the Perseids, like many of the swarms, the meteors are rather uniformly scattered around the orbit, and every year we meet roughly the same number. However, even they may vary. In 1921, there was a notable display, with some 250 per hour. Yet only 10 years before—in 1911 and 1912—there had been only a few per hour. Some meteor observers feared that the shower had disappeared. Evidently the distribution of Perseids is not uniform, but the concentration is greater in some parts of the orbit and less in others; which part we encounter determines the number that we see. They take about 108 years to make a round trip in their orbit.

The Leonids, on the other hand, are concentrated at one point and are very sparse along the rest of the ellipse. They take 33 years to go around, so the Earth met the main swarm in 1799 (when there was also a good shower, though not as extensively observed as the next two, 1833 and 1866). But in 1870, the dense swarm passed near Saturn and in 1898, near Jupiter. The gravitational attraction of these planets pulled the swarm aside, changing both the period in which they went around the Sun and the shape of the orbit. On the date of the expected return in 1899, the Earth was more than a million miles away, and we met only a few that were far off course. Further encounters with the giant planets could pull them back again, so that we would again have brilliant displays, but that seems unlikely.

Both visual and photographic observations of meteors, of course, depend on a dark sky, so such studies must be made at night. This meant, until recent years, that those arriving during daylight hours were missed completely. Now, radio astronomy has filled this gap and has also been of value at night, because such observations may be made through thick clouds. In the early thirties, radio was first used to find the height of the ionized layers of the atmosphere, by sending up a short pulse of radio waves and measuring the time required for the echo to return.

On some occasions, as this work was carried out, sudden abnormal effects were observed. Often these seemed to be the result of a meteor which had penetrated the ionosphere and changed the ionization. Also, at times, radio experimenters noted peculiar signals, apparently due to the meteors themselves. These would leave in their wake a trail of ionized atoms which would reflect the waves being sent up by a radio transmitter. With the development of radar, to detect airplanes, echoes were also recorded which seemed to be caused in the same manner. Sometimes these came just as a bright meteor flashed overhead, so the possibility of detecting meteors by radio was recognized. A new technique for meteor research had its birth.

Astronomers not only were able to follow well-known streams of meteors into daylight hours, but, even more important, they found at least four streams which never appear in darkness, yet are as strong as any of those that appear regularly each year at night. These move in orbits that extend somewhat farther out from the Sun than the Earth's orbit, and approach the Sun to a third or even less of our distance. Moving in toward the Sun, they miss the Earth by wide margins but cross our orbit on their way out. Thus, coming from the Sun's direction, they hit Earth only during daylight hours; only radio observations reveal their presence.

METEORS AND COMETS

The stretched-out ellipses which form the orbits of these meteor streams are very different from the nearly circular orbits of most of the planets. Even asteroids do not travel over as wide a range of distances from the Sun. But comets do.

In the second year of the Civil War, a comet that appeared in the northern sky was visible to the naked eye but was not conspicuous. Following the usual system, it is recorded as 1862 III, meaning that it was the third comet to pass near the Sun that year. After it had faded from view, astronomers correlated the various observations and computed its path. It approached the Sun a little closer than the Earth does, then receded to a distance greater than Neptune.

About this same time an Italian astronomer, G. V. Schiaparelli (discoverer of the canals of Mars), was studying meteor streams, and he noticed that this cometary orbit was practically identical with that of the Perseids. This was, of course, a strong indication that meteors and comets were somehow connected; it was most unlikely that the similarity was merely a coincidence. Then another faint comet came in 1866. Astronomers computed its orbit, which brought it to about the same distance from the Sun as the Earth and took it out a little beyond Saturn. Schiaparelli (and, independently, two other astronomers) discovered that its path was about the same as that of the Leonids.

This immediately led astronomers to make a systematic search among cometary orbits to find whether any others could be associated with meteor streams. Very quickly they found that comet 1861 I had followed the path of the Lyrids, which reach a maximum every year about April 21, radiating from the constellation of Lyra. Now at least eight well-known streams of meteors have thus been connected with comets. Probably they all have similar connections, but in some cases the comet has not been identified.

Best known of all comets is Halley's, and that also has its meteor stream—two of them, in fact, as befits so distinguished an object. This is because its orbit happens to pass near that of Earth both on the way in to the Sun and on the way out. First are the eta Aquarids, which radiate from a point close to a star in Aquarius. These are seen at their height May 4. In October, for a similar period, we can see the same shower again, this time coming from Orion and therefore called the Orionids. At this time of year the Earth is more than 9 million miles from the orbit of the comet, showing how widely the meteors must be scattered for so many to reach us. And the fact that each shower lasts about a week is additional evidence as to how widely the meteors are spread out.

Originally, it seems, the meteors of such a stream remain close to the comet from which they were formed. In the course of successive revolutions, they may pass close to planets, which *perturb* them, pulling them off path a little; not enough to change their orbit greatly, but enough to alter their period of revolution. Now they may run ahead of, or behind, their parent comet, and thus spread out all around the orbit, like those of the Perseids, which come in similar numbers each year. But the Leonids are still fairly well concentrated a little behind comet 1866 I.

S. E. Hamid, of Harvard College Observatory, has studied the past history of the Perseid shower. Originally its orbit, and that of its parent comet, 1862 III, were more nearly in the plane of the Earth's orbit than now. But about 40,000 years ago—343 revolutions earlier—it approached closely to Jupiter, and the pull of that planet shifted it into the orbit it now follows. Since then the meteors have been gradually dispersed all the way around the path.

In addition to perturbations by planets, another mechanism affects the particles in a meteor stream. This sorts them out by size, so that only those of similar dimensions will move together. It is known as the Poynting-Robertson effect, after the scientists (an Englishman, J. H. Poynting, and an American, H. P. Robertson) who developed it.

This effect occurs as the meteoric particles absorb energy from the Sun's radiation, then reradiate heat out into space in all directions. In a rather complex manner (of which the full explanation involves the theory of relativity), this causes a braking action. The smaller particles are affected the most, so they slow down more rapidly than the larger ones. With change in speed, there is a change in orbit, so it takes only a few thousand years before the little particles are travelling in paths quite different from their larger companions.

Eventually the smaller particles will spiral toward the Sun and finally fall into it. It takes only 60,000,000 years for a particle $\frac{1}{25}$ inch in diameter to reach the Sun from the distance of the asteroids, between Mars and Jupiter. For one as large as 4 inches it would take 4 billion years, which is the approximate age of the Earth. Since we still find, scattered among the planets, particles only a fraction of an inch in diameter, it is evident that they must have been formed in much more recent times, from an asteroid or perhaps a comet.

COMETS

But what about the comets themselves? Some are very conspicuous, visible even in full daylight. And at night the bigger ones, which may have extended from horizon to zenith, must have been awesome objects to early men. Anything so far out of the ordinary would seem a portent of doom, and comets had a bad reputation. In particular they were believed to herald the death of some prominent person. Thus Shakespeare has Caesar's wife say:

> When beggars die, there are no comets seen;
> The heavens themselves blaze forth the death of princes.

In earlier times it was thought that comets were some peculiar kind of cloud in the atmosphere. But, in 1577, Tycho Brahe observed one from his observatory on the island of Hven. Reports from other astronomers showed that, as far away as Prague, the comet appeared against the same background of stars, so it must be at least as far as the Moon. Tycho thought that comets moved in circles around the Sun, but Johann Kepler, his associate and successor, believed they moved through space in straight lines.

In 1682, Sir Isaac Newton published his great book, the *Principia Mathematica,* in which he explained his theory of gravitation. Using these principles, another English astronomer, Edmond Halley, calculated the orbits for 14 bright comets that had been recorded in past times. He noticed that those of 1456, 1531, 1607, and 1682 were very similar and were separated by about the same period of 75 or 76 years.

So, when Halley published these orbits, in 1705, he called attention to this and suggested that the comets of 1456, 1531, 1607, and 1682 were successive reappearances of the same object. Moreover, he predicted that after another interval of about 75 years—in 1758 or 1759—it would appear once more.

Although Halley died at the age of eighty-six in 1742, his prediction was not forgotten. It was brilliantly confirmed on Christmas night of 1758, when a faint comet was picked up by astronomers through their telescopes. During the ensuing months it became brighter and brighter, until it was again conspicuous in the night sky. Computations of its orbit soon proved that it was, indeed, the same comet, and so it was named after Halley. It came again in 1835 and 1910.

When it reached perihelion (its position closest the Sun) in 1910, it was at about half the distance of Mercury. Then it drew away, and in 1948 was at aphelion (farthest from the Sun), out beyond the orbit of Neptune. Now it is coming in again, gaining speed as it approaches the Sun. Perhaps in 1984 or earlier—possibly from some electronic super telescope in an observatory on the Moon—astronomers will pick it up as it nears the orbit of Jupiter, 400 to 500 million miles away. As it passes the Sun in 1985, it will again be easily seen from Earth; see Fig. 35.

Past visits of Halley's comet have been traced in old records, such as ancient Chinese and Japanese annals. The earliest recorded appearance was in 240 B.C. No records have been found of the next, in 163 B.C., but of the one after that, in 87 B.C., there is a definite record, as there is for every return thereafter. Now it seems to be coming back slightly more frequently than it did at earlier times. The average period, over the years for which records exist, is 77 years, with a variation either way of about 2.5 years.

One famous return occurred in 1066 A.D., the year of the Norman Conquest, and it is pictured on the Bayeux Tapestry. It also appeared in 1453, the year that Constantinople fell to the Turks. Of course, it would be most surprising if some of its numerous appearances had not happened to coincide with important historical events!

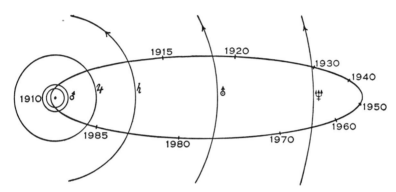

Fig. 35. Path of Halley's comet. After it approached the Sun and Earth in 1910, it moved out beyond the orbit of Neptune. Since 1948 it has been moving in once more and will come into view about 1985. The innermost circle represents the orbit of the Earth. The outer circles, identified by the symbols for the respective planets, are the orbits of Mars, Jupiter, Saturn, Uranus, and Neptune. (By permission from *Astronomy*, by J. C. Duncan. Copyright, 1936, Harper & Bros., New York.)

COMET OR ASTEROID?

There is one comet, discovered by two German astronomers, Schwassmann and Wachmann, in 1927, which moves in an orbit completely between those of Jupiter and Saturn. In fact, it moves like an asteroid and would be so listed if it didn't possess many of the characteristics of a comet. However, the typical comet orbit is a much more eccentric (stretched-out) ellipse.

An ellipse is one of three types of curve that are formed if you slice a cone; hence they are called conic sections. A circle is really a special form of ellipse, which can be stretched out more and more until it is no longer a closed curve, but one that extends out to infinity, a parabola or a hyperbola. The parabola is the special case that marks the transition between ellipse and hyperbola; see Fig. 36.

No matter which of these possible curves a comet follows, the part near the Sun, while it is being observed from the Earth, is very similar. Consequently, when a comet is discovered (three separate observations are needed to calculate an orbit and the method used is basically similar to that which Gauss developed to keep track of the first asteroid), it is assumed that its motion is parabolic. This

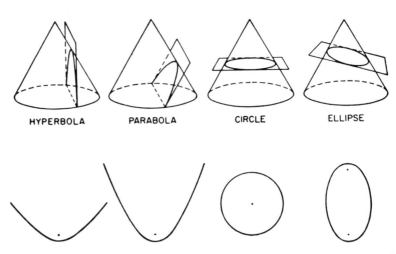

Fig. 36. Conic sections. The hyperbola, the parabola, the circle, and the ellipse are all conic sections; that is, they are formed when a plane cuts through a cone. For the parabola, the plane is parallel to the edge of the cone; its arms continually diverge toward the base of the cone, so it is an open curve. If the plane is more nearly parallel to the axis of the cone than to the edge, it forms an hyperbola, also an open curve. But if the plane is more inclined to the cone's axis than to one of the edges, it cuts the cone in an ellipse, which is a closed curve. With the plane perpendicular to the axis, the intersection is a circle, a special case of the ellipse. (By permission from *Introduction to Astronomy*, by Cecilia Payne-Gaposchkin. Copyright, 1954, Prentice-Hall, Inc., Englewood Cliffs, N.J.)

simplifies the problem, and the astronomers can keep track of its movement. Later, after the comet has departed and three observations, as far apart as possible, are available, a definitive orbit is computed. This almost always comes out as an ellipse, perhaps a very long one. Thus it seems that comets are part of our Solar System, for they are moving in closed curves. If the orbit was a hyperbola, it would mean that the object came in from outer space for a visit, then retreated, never to return.

Generally six or seven comets may be discovered in a year, none of which is likely to be visible to the naked eye. However, 1947 and 1948 set new records with 14 each. About a third of those discovered annually are periodic comets returning, the rest are new. Perhaps they, too, are periodic but with periods so long that there is no record of their last visit.

The International Astronomical Union maintains an International Bureau of Astronomical Telegrams at the Copenhagen Observatory in Denmark. Using a special code, the discovery of a new comet, as well as other objects, is reported by telegraph, cable, or radio. From Copenhagen, by the same media, astronomers all over the world are notified, so a discovery made one night in Sweden will be known the next night in Australia, and astronomers there may be making additional observations. In the United States, the Harvard Observatory at Cambridge, Massachusetts, acts as a clearing house, and relays the announcements from Denmark to American observatories.

Some years ago, there was a famous case when a telegram announcing a new comet reached the Lick Observatory in California. That night the astronomers looked at the part of the sky indicated and saw a comet, so they reported their confirmation of the discovery. But then a correction came; it seemed that there had been an error in transmission. A different position was given, and when they looked at that place they saw the original comet! It happened, by a remarkable coincidence, that there had been a comet at the erroneous position as well. It was never settled who deserved credit for the second discovery!

JUPITER'S COMET FAMILY

Records show a group of about 70 comets, with periods around 5 to 10 years and which go out about as far as Jupiter, thus forming a distinct family. Probably they originally moved in longer orbits, but happened, some time in the past, to approach close enough to Jupiter to be pulled by its gravitational attraction into smaller orbits. The Brooks comet showed this effect. Formerly it receded to a position well beyond the orbit of Saturn. Its period of revolution around the Sun was 31 years, and it came in within the orbit of Jupiter. Then, in 1886, it passed within a hundred thousand miles of Jupiter, whose pull produced a radical change in its orbit. It returned, in about 7 years, along an orbit entirely within that of Jupiter and coming almost as close to the Sun as Mars. And there was Lexell's comet which came, in 1767, within 2 million miles of Jupiter. Its period was changed from 11.4 years to 5.6 years. But in 1779, it again passed close to the giant planet—within about 400,000 miles—and the period was lengthened, to 16.2 years.

In contrast are the long-period comets, of which about 40 are known, with periods up to a thousand years or even more. Halley's is one of these. They take so long for a round trip that they rarely pass close to a planet, so their orbits are more stable.

The popular picture of a comet includes a tail, but many never show such a feature. However, most of those that become conspicuous to the naked eye do so. Usually, when a comet is first detected, it is merely a hazy spot of light. As it approaches the Sun, a tail may develop, but, unlike tails of animals, it is as likely to appear on the front as on the rear. This is, at least in part, due to the fact that light actually exerts a pressure, which can be shown in the laboratory with delicate instruments. The light from the Sun pushes like a wind on the very tenuous material in the tail and forces it away from the head. In addition, small particles shot out from the Sun may push on the material in the tail. Thus, as it approaches the Sun the tail is behind; as it recedes the tail goes first, like the traditional idea of a commoner, backing away from an audience with royalty!

Although a comet may be millions of miles long, it is really an "airy nothing." Lexell's comet, on its 1770 visit, came so close to Earth that our attraction changed its period by several days, but the Earth itself was totally unaffected. This indicates that the mass of the comet was less than 1/13,000 of the Earth's. This could mean a total of a quintillion tons, but it was probably far less. Even this is spread over an enormous volume, so it is very sparsely distributed. There is, for example, no more material in a cubic inch of air than in 2,000 cubic miles of a comet's tail. In 1910, the Earth passed through the tail of Halley's comet—and nothing happened.

The head of a comet is more condensed, but still not very solid. The head of Halley's comet went in front of the Sun in 1910, yet astronomers watching the Sun could see nothing. On other occasions, a comet has passed in front of a star without appreciably dimming the star's light.

As it approaches the Sun, a comet brightens, as it would be expected to do, because the illumination is more intense. But it brightens considerably more than this; it seems that there is some effect of fluorescence, whereby invisible solar radiations excite parts of the comet to shine. Analysis, with the spectroscope, shows the light to come from a number of simple chemical compounds and radicals (which are combinations of atoms that cannot ordinarily exist by themselves on Earth). There is carbon; simple hydrocarbons (combinations of carbon and hydrogen); cyanogen (carbon and nitrogen); nitrogen by itself; nitrogen atoms combined with either one or two hydrogen atoms; hydroxyl (hydrogen and oxygen); and a few others.

ICY COMETS

While out in distant space, according to the theory of Fred L. Whipple, of Harvard, a comet seems to be a swarm of small particles of stone or metal, embedded in small lumps of ice. It is mainly ice of frozen gases, for the temperature is down near absolute zero, 459 degrees below zero on the Fahrenheit scale, at which an object would have no heat at all. This swarm of particles is the nucleus and it may be as much as a few hundred miles in diameter.

Nearing the Sun, it undergoes a change, as the ices begin to turn to gas. A cloud—the *coma*—forms around the nucleus. Particles a hundred thousandth of an inch or less in diameter will be pushed away by radiation pressure and may cause the formation of a tail.

According to Whipple, the nucleus may be rather porous, something like a "very yeasty raisin bread," and a poor heat conductor. Thus, the inside parts would be warmed up very slowly. But evaporation of the outer layers would continue, and lumps of solid material would become exposed. These, being darker than the ice, would absorb more of the Sun's rays; the region nearby would be heated. This would increase the evaporation of the frozen gases and cause explosive jets to shoot out. These have actually been observed in some comets. Moreover, as the nucleus rotates, and they are known to do so, cleaner and dirtier parts would be exposed to the Sun. Thus the rate of evaporation—and the formation of parts of the tail—would be irregular.

Every time it approaches the Sun, a comet suffers considerable damage and much of its material is lost; so comets must be slowly disintegrating. In fact, astronomers believe, a short-period comet with a close approach to the Sun cannot be expected to last more than a few hundred such passages. The lifetime, at most, would be a few thousand years. In fact, comets have been known to vanish completely. This happened with Biela's comet, originally discovered in 1772. It returned every 6.6 years and was observed fairly regularly. In 1846 it was seen double! It had split into two parts, apparently the result of a close approach to Jupiter. The twin comets returned in 1852, but have never been seen since. However, in 1877 and 1885, as the Earth crossed the comet's orbit, and after an approximately exact number of periods had passed, tremendous showers of meteors were seen emanating from Andromeda and moving in the same path. In 1892 and 1899, fairly strong showers were seen, but since then all traces of Biela and its meteors have vanished.

Other comets also have broken into two. This happened with the great comet of 1882, which was visible in daylight. After it had passed the Sun, it was in four pieces, moving in slightly different orbits. They will not return together, but about a century apart, between 2500 and 2900. And the 1882 comet itself moved in an orbit very similar to those of other brilliant comets seen earlier. Perhaps the original comet, which must have been a most extraordinary object, had suffered previous breakups by the tidal forces of the Sun.

WHERE DO THEY COME FROM?

But where do comets come from? Certainly, for those of short period, there must be a source of supply, and even many of long period must have originated, in their present condition, well after the formation of the solar system, some 4 or 5 billion years ago.

One interesting hypothesis, originally suggested by the Estonian astronomer, Ernst Öpik, and developed by Jan Oort, of the Netherlands, puts a vast cloud, of perhaps a hundred billion comets, around the solar system. Their total mass might be as much as a tenth of the Earth's. They may extend out to about 14 quadrillion miles, 150 times Earth's distance from the Sun; so far that the Sun would have only a weak gravitational hold upon them.

In fact, at such a distance, they would be more than halfway as far as alpha Centauri, the nearest star, which is about twice as massive as the Sun. Thus it, and other nearby stars, might perturb the comets as much as the Sun itself. These comets would be moving in more or less circular orbits normally, but occasionally the combined attractions of these stars might pull back on a particular comet, slowing it up so that it would move in toward the Sun in an extremely long ellipse—one that we would be unable to distinguish from a parabola.

Without any further perturbations, it would eventually return to the suburbs of the solar system where it originated. On the other hand, it may be pulled by one of the large planets into a smaller orbit. Once this happened, it seems likely that Jupiter would finally capture it, converting it to a short-period comet, and then it would have only a few hundred revolutions left. Also, by this time, much of the icy material from which cometary tails are formed would be depleted, and this would explain why short-period comets do not have conspicuous tails.

An alternative hypothesis of cometary origin was proposed, in 1953, by Raymond A. Lyttleton. According to him, they were formed when the Sun, in its motion through space, passed through one of the huge dust clouds which exist in our Galaxy between the stars. As the Sun passed into such a cloud, the particles were drawn toward it. Some, of course, hit the Sun, but much of the dust farther out from its path was drawn into paths that brought the dust together in a trailing line behind the Sun. With particles coming to this line from all directions, the density there was considerably increased, and they collided with each other, giving up their energy of movement to generate heat. This slowed down their motion, and they were pulled toward the Sun.

Aggregations of such particles would form by their own gravitational attractions as they were pulled together. In this way, by a hypothetical process which Lyttleton developed rather fully, the nucleus of a comet might be formed. Few such masses would be so accurately aimed as to hit the Sun directly, but they would sweep past it and around it in the typical cometary orbit, perhaps developing a tail. And of course comets so formed might suffer perturbations by Jupiter and other planets, as mentioned above.

In all, then, comets are still puzzling objects. Ancient man watched them as they appeared above—and wondered what doom impended. Modern astronomers watch them with just as much wonder—but their wonder is what they are, and where they came from. Some day we will have the answer.

11

Travel in Space

Astronomy—oldest of the sciences—began thousands of years ago, and there have been several occasions since then when it was revolutionized by some radical technical advance. One was the introduction of the telescope in the seventeenth century; another, the application of spectrum analysis more than two centuries later. The birth of radio astronomy in the past few years began a revolution which will doubtless be equally far-reaching.

But even greater than any of these is one that now seems to be rapidly approaching: the change from a purely observational science to one of experiment and exploration. The Moon, the planets, perhaps even the stars, are losing their traditional inaccessibility. No longer will astronomers be limited to studying them, with telescopes, spectroscopes, and other instruments, from the bottom of an atmosphere that interferes greatly with much of their work. Instead they will be able to observe from above that atmosphere, to approach closely to the objects of their study and even land on some for direct examination.

Men have long dreamed about travel into space. At first these dreams were closely associated with thoughts of aerial flight. If man could fly at all, it seemed reasonable to suppose he could fly to the Moon. The invention of the balloon in the eighteenth century provided man with his first means of flight. He soon found that the atmosphere does not extend indefinitely; it thins out with altitude and comes to an end far short even of the Moon.

No form of flight which depends on properties of the air—the balloon which utilizes buoyancy; or bird flight and the airplane, which take advantage of motion through the air—could raise man very far from the Earth's surface. If he wanted to get into space, man finally realized, he must use a mode of travel that would work without air.

Since it is the force of gravity that holds men, and other things, to this globe, some means of neutralizing gravity might allow escape from Earth. Fiction writers (such as H. G. Wells in his story, *First Men in the Moon*) have used this idea. Unfortunately, there seem to be excellent theoretical reasons why this will not be possible. Despite this, however, there are groups that are studying gravity with the idea that some approach may turn up that would make some sort of anti-gravity device possible.

Then there was the idea of shooting men out into space in a projectile fired from a huge cannon, but this also seems quite impracticable. To attain the necessary speed, extremely high acceleration would be required—enough to squash the space traveler to a pulp. Other serious objections are concerned with the resistance of the air, both inside the gun barrel and outside. Jules Verne used this idea in his *From the Earth to the Moon,* which is a good story but scientifically impossible.

THE ROCKET

Long before balloons or airplanes or guns, men had used another method of sending things through the air. This was the rocket, which was employed by the Chinese at least as early as 1232 A.D., perhaps even before that.

The rocket doesn't "push against the air," as the uninformed sometimes think. It operates by the reaction principle, of which the "kick" of a gun is a familiar example. Expanding gases, from the explosion in the cartridge, push the bullet down the barrel and send it on the way to its target. But the same gases also push back on the gun itself, forcing it against the gunner's shoulder and thus causing the kick or recoil. Even with a blank cartridge, there is some such reaction, which would be greater if the muzzle were constricted to form a jet through which the escaping gases had to emerge at extra high speed. In a rocket, fuel is burned to provide such a continuous recoil and send it on its way; see Fig. 37.

The Chinese used rockets as weapons; so did other nations in more modern times. The British used them in the bombardment of Fort McHenry, leading Francis Scott Key to write the words we sing so often, of the "rocket's red glare." By the end of the nineteenth century, guns had replaced rockets in warfare, but World War II revived them, on a small scale, to be used by the individual soldier, as in the "bazooka," and in the V-2's developed by Germany to bombard England. The large and ever-growing family of missiles that is now so important a part of our defense is a family of rockets of many types and sizes.

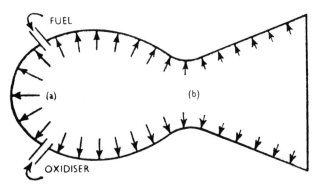

Fig. 37. A rocket combustion chamber. Here the fuel and oxidizer are mixed, so that they will burn. The heated gases that are formed, expand and push against the walls of the chamber. No pressure is exerted at the open end; thus the pressure in the opposite direction (at *a*) forces the rocket to move in that direction. (By permission from *The Exploration of Space*, by Arthur C. Clarke. Copyright, 1951, Harper & Bros., New York.)

Not only Verne but many other authors also wrote fictional accounts of space travel; some even suggested use of rockets. But the first truly scientific paper on the subject appears to be one that Konstantin Eduardovitch Ziolkovsky, of Kaluga, Russia, wrote in 1898. It wasn't published until 1903, and even then it attracted little attention, although it did give him a justifiable claim for priority.

The great pioneer experimenter with rockets for exploring great altitudes and even, perhaps, escaping from the Earth's attraction completely, was an American physicist, Robert H. Goddard, of Clark University at Worcester, Massachusetts. His studies, around the time of World War I, were supported by the Smithsonian Institution and, later, by the Guggenheim Foundation. In 1919, the Institution published his now classical paper, *A Method of Reach-*

ing Extreme Altitudes. Primarily this dealt with the use of rockets to explore the upper atmosphere, above the 20 miles or so that could then be reached by sounding balloons. However, he did suggest the possibility of using similar methods to escape completely from the Earth's gravity, and presented estimates of the quantities of photographic flash powder that would need to be ignited on the Moon to produce a flash visible from Earth.

In 1926, Goddard first successfully used liquid fuel, instead of the solid charges that earlier rockets had mainly employed for propulsion. He continued his studies during the 1930's, with experiments at Roswell, New Mexico, where, in 1935, he sent a rocket up to a height of about a mile and a half. But then his funds were exhausted and serious work in the United States came to a temporary end. Germany then became the center of rocket research, which culminated in the V–2 rockets used to bombard England and gave such an impetus to rocket and missile development in the years since World War II. Goddard lived to see how far his ideas had developed, unfortunately for destructive purposes. After his death in August, 1945, the American Rocket Society referred to him as "the creator of the modern science of rocketry."

With the end of the war, many German experts came to the United States while others went to Russia, and each group contributed much to rocket developments in these nations. While the work in each country has been primarily in weapon development, peaceful applications, for investigation of the upper atmosphere and the planets, was another important factor. As plans for the International Geophysical Year were made, both the U.S. and the U.S.S.R. announced that they would put artificial satellites into orbit.

SPUTNIK I

What happened is well known: how the Russians launched Sputnik I on October 4, 1957, much to the surprise of many Americans, who had mistakenly believed that Soviet scientists and engineers were incapable of such a development! Actually, papers in Russian journals had given full warning of what they were going to do.

For the first time, man had hurled something into space with enough speed that it did not fall back to the ground. He had overcome gravity! The spherical satellite itself, 22.8 inches in diameter, with scientific instrumentation of 184 pounds, circled the Earth once in 96 minutes. It went out as far as 588 miles, while its closest approach brought it to an altitude of 142 miles. And along with the satellite travelled parts of the rocket that had brought it to its full height. According to an estimate by the National Aeronautics and Space Administration, a total weight of about 4 tons was placed in orbit.

But even at these altitudes there is some atmosphere, and the rocket, with its irregular shape, was slowed up by air resistance more than the sputnik itself and finally fell to Earth. The satellite, too, was slowed, and ended its career on January 4, 1958. Sputnik II was launched November 3, and moved in an orbit from a minimum altitude of 140 miles to a maximum of 1,038 miles. Its period was about 104 minutes. Again the total payload, as estimated by the NASA, was about 4 tons, and this time the scientific equipment weighed 1,120 pounds. It carried a dog as a test animal, to ascertain the effects on a living creature. As with its predecessor, data obtained on pressure, temperature, etc., as well as on the animal, were automatically radioed back to Earth. Since the transmitters were powered by chemical batteries, their life was limited. Sputnik I stopped transmitting after 23 days; its successor after a week. Sputnik II finally fell to Earth on April 14, 1958.

The first successful U.S. attempt was from Cape Canaveral, Florida, on January 31, 1958, when Explorer I was launched. This satellite is a cylinder, 80 inches long, 6 inches in diameter, weighing 30.8 pounds, and with a scientific payload of 18.13 pounds. Its two radio transmitters were supplied with power from mercury batteries. One stopped after about 11 days, but then somehow came on again two weeks later, for about 4 days. The other stayed on the air for nearly 4 months, its transmission stopping on May 23.

Explorer I has a period of 115 minutes, taking it from as low as 224 miles to a maximum height of 1,573 miles. This altitude put it well above most of the atmosphere, so the air makes very slight resistance to its movement. Thus, early in 1960, it was still aloft with every prospect that it would be there for several years more.

This satellite is credited with one of the most important discoveries made during the International Geophysical Year, that of the Van Allen radiation belt, as described earlier.

Still higher went Vanguard I, launched March 17, 1958, a sphere 6.4 inches in diameter weighing 3.25 pounds. This went into an orbit ranging from 409 miles to 2,453 miles above the ground, and it is expected to remain there for centuries. Its radio transmitter, powered by solar batteries, should keep on sending indefinitely, as it has a continual supply of energy from the Sun's rays. Observations of this satellite, by radio, from islands in the Pacific Ocean, were used by the Army Map Service to determine their positions with greater accuracy than was previously possible. In addition it was also used for very accurate measurements of the Earth's shape.

There is no need to list all the satellites that have been sent into orbit by the United States and the U.S.S.R. However, the Pioneers are of special interest (because of their use as probes) although they did not go into satellite orbits.

Pioneer I was launched October 11, 1958, and it fell the next day, having reached an altitude of 70,700 miles. It was 29 inches in diameter, 30 inches long, weighing 84.4 pounds, including scientific instrumentation of 39 pounds. This provided a determination of the height to which the radiation band extended.

After Pioneer II was unsuccessful, reaching an altitude of only 963 miles, Pioneer III was sent up December 6, 1958. This was a conical "space probe," weighing just under 13 pounds, and was 23 inches long and 10 inches in maximum diameter. It took about 38 hours to rise to 63,580 miles and return. With Pioneer III the second and outer of the Van Allen radiation belts was discovered.

ARTIFICIAL PLANETS

Complete escape from Earth's attraction was achieved January 2, 1959, when the Russians sent up their space probe, Mechta, with a total weight of 3,245 pounds. It assumed an orbit around the Sun, with a period of about 15 months, so it is an artificial planet rather than a satellite.

This was followed, on March 3, by the U.S. Pioneer IV, similar in size, shape, and weight to Pioneer III. The day after launching it passed within 37,300 miles of the Moon, which was not close enough to permit the lunar observations that had been planned. After that it, too, assumed an orbit around the Sun, thus becoming the second artificial planet.

On September 12, the Russians fired their Lunik II into space, and 36 hours later it landed on the lunar surface—the first time that an object from Earth had been placed on the Moon.

Lunik III was launched on October 3, and about three days later it crossed the Moon's orbit, passing that body at a distance of less than 5,000 miles. When it was about 4,000 miles from the Moon, radio signals from Earth operated its two cameras, so that they took photographs of the hemisphere, opposite Earth, which is never visible to us. As Lunik III returned to the vicinity of Earth these photographs, which had been developed automatically, were radioed back. Crude though they were, they gave Earth-dwellers their first look at this "far side" of the Moon.

Although the launching vehicles for these satellites, probes, and planets have been quite different in many respects, they have all been step rockets. That is, the satellite vehicle is the *payload* of a small rocket; which, in turn, is the payload of one larger; and that of one still larger. With the first Explorer there were four such stages. To understand why several steps are desirable, consider what must be done to escape from Earth's attraction.

If a body at a very great distance from Earth were to be released, and fall toward Earth, the speed (if we neglected atmospheric resistance) would gradually increase as it neared our planet, finally reaching 7 miles per second, or 25,000 miles per hour, as it touched ground. And, if an object at the surface were hurled upward with this speed, it would just be able to get away from the Earth. This is our *escape velocity*. At any speed less than this, the object would fall back and, if there were no atmosphere to cause resistance, it would land with exactly the speed of take-off.

For any single-stage rocket, there is an upper speed limit set by the dead weight remaining when the fuel has been entirely burned. In a typical case the weight may be distributed something like this: structure, 20 per cent; propellant, 75 per cent; payload, 5 per cent. Here the total weight at take-off is four times that remaining after the fuel supply is exhausted, which gives a "mass ratio" of 4. With no payload, and adding more propellant to a total of 80 per cent, the mass ratio would be 5.

A formula, used in rocketry, which relates the mass ratio and the velocity of the exhaust gases with the final speed, shows that a rocket with a ratio of approximately 3 will finally be traveling as fast as the exhaust gases. To get a speed of twice that of the gases, the ratio would have to be 7, with the weight of the structure and payload only a seventh that of the fuel. It seems unlikely that a figure much better than this can be reached with present techniques.

Details of the performance of newer rocket fuels, developed in government laboratories, have not been made public, but we may guess that they cannot give exhaust velocities of more than 10,000 miles per hour. Even this, with the very favorable mass ratio of 7, would still lead to a speed of 20,000 miles per hour, well below the required escape velocity.

The step rocket, however, gets rid of dead weight when it is no longer needed. The first stage pushes the assemblage to a height, perhaps, of 50 miles and a speed of 4,000 miles per hour. Now it drops off and the second stage begins operation with a fresh start. It is already above the bulk of the atmosphere, so it is far more efficient than the first stage was down at sea level. It gains another 5,000 miles per hour, or more, as well as altitude, so the total speed is now at least 10,000 miles per hour. And so on, until all stages are utilized, and the final payload is in orbit. No doubt future improvements in rocket propulsion will make it possible to get a single rocket up to escape velocity or more, and then the complications of a step rocket, with the special devices to make each stage drop off and the next one ignite, will no longer be needed. But at present the step rocket seems to be the only way to get into an orbit or away from the Earth completely.

To ride in an orbit around the Earth, a speed of 18,000 miles per hour is needed. Once you are in such an orbit, a gain in speed of only 7,000 miles per hour will be enough to take you off to other parts of the solar system.

STATIONS IN SPACE

Such considerations have led to the suggestion that future space trips start from a space station—a manned satellite. Perhaps it will be assembled in space, the components being carried aloft in small pieces by ferry rockets. There will then be no need for streamlining the vehicle; it is already above the atmosphere and does not need to go through it. From such a location, the ship may start very slowly, taking a long time to reach the speed required for the interplanetary journey.

Some rockets use solid fuels; these are essentially similar to the powder that drives a simple skyrocket. Others employ liquid fuels;

the V-2, for example, burned alcohol with liquid oxygen. Many more exotic chemical fuels have been developed by later research. With every one of them, one element unites with another, forming highly heated gases which are forced out of the rear of the rocket. Their reaction drives the rocket on its way.

With nuclear energy being applied as a source of power for airplanes and ships, it is hardly surprising that engineers have looked at it longingly as a means of propulsion for rockets as well. However, there is a complication. The rocket moves forward because of the reaction against the material thrown backwards. This material has mass—it must have in order to provide the thrust to push the rocket ahead. But a nuclear reactor is primarily a source of energy, usually in the form of heat, although future developments may make it possible to get electricity directly without going through the intermediate stages of steam, turbine, and generator.

Thus, to drive a rocket, something (the propellant) must be thrown backwards, and the gaseous combustion products of chemical fuels provide it. Not so the nuclear reactor; its energy alone cannot be tossed backward. This means that, in a nuclear rocket, it will be necessary to provide the propellant separately, instead of having it already present along with the fuel. Water might be carried, and the reactor heat employed to make high-temperature steam. Then a steam jet might provide the propelling force. But if you must carry along a supply of water, you lose one of the great advantages of nuclear fuel—its compactness. And if you are going to carry this propellant separately, perhaps you might as well take chemical fuels, which have it there already.

As with all types of nuclear power plants, whether used on land, sea, in the air, or in outer space, there is the problem of shielding. A nuclear reactor emits copious quantities of particles and radiations like those from radium. For this reason a reactor used in an Earth-bound power plant must be surrounded by thick shields of concrete, through which these rays cannot pass. Moreover, materials inserted into the reactor also become radioactive, which means that the steam or other propellant emitted to drive the rocket might be lethal. If the rocket took off from the ground, this might contaminate the surrounding area.

Thus it may be necessary to provide a chemical fuel to take the rocket aloft. Then, when high above the Earth, the atomic rockets could be started, and the radioactive propellant would be dispersed through space and soon be spread so thin that it would no longer be dangerous. Or else the flight might begin from a space station.

Take-off from a satellite would also make possible another kind of drive, with very low thrust. The station is already moving at the speed needed to keep it in orbit, and so is the rocket ship docked beside it. With the need for take-off from Earth thus eliminated, a very small push or thrust will gradually move it at increasing speed, until it reaches the velocity needed to escape entirely.

PUSHED BY PARTICLES

The particles that are given off in the radioactive processes in the reactor are themselves moving at high speeds, some 6,000 miles per second for the heavier ones and even higher for the electrons that form the beta rays. Moreover they have mass—small for each particle, but large in the aggregate. Perhaps they could be used to generate the necessary thrust. While any such thrust would be small, it would be enough to permit escape from the space station.

The principal trouble seems to be that the particles come off from the reactor in many random directions. It might be possible to line them up and shoot them all toward the rear, with electromagnets, but large amounts of power would be needed for operation. This would require heavy generating equipment.

The push, or *thrust,* on a rocket depends both on the mass and speed of the material ejected backward. Projecting the material at very high speed, approaching that of light perhaps, much less propellant would be needed, and this would reduce the weight that had to be carried aloft. Chemical rockets, compared to some other possible types, do not have large amounts of energy, and this sets a limit to the temperatures that can be given the propellants and hence to their speed of ejection.

Nuclear rockets are not limited to this extent in the amount of energy that can be provided. However, the temperatures that can be used are limited by what the rocket materials will stand.

There is a possibility of electric propulsion. Wolfgang E. Moeckel, chief of the Advanced Propulsion Division of the National Aeronautics and Space Administration's (NASA) Lewis Research Center at Cleveland, where active work is being done in this field, described the advantages when he spoke before a Congressional committee.

"We can put in all the energy we want, and we are not limited by material temperature; the reason is this: If we heat the gas or the propellants by electric means, we find that we can use electric fields and magnetic fields to keep the hot gases away from the wall, thereby avoiding the heat transfer problem or the high temperature problem.

"If we do have electric power, though, we do not really have to heat the gas very hot, because high temperature is only one way in which we can get very high jet velocities and, therefore, low propellant consumption. If we can ionize the propellants as they come out, that is, strip off an electron and make charged particles of them, then we can accelerate them to almost any speed we want to by putting sufficient voltage on them. Charged particles can be accelerated very easily with sufficiently high voltage. So this seems to solve the problem of getting very high jet velocities."

Moeckel cited actual figures, when he told the committee that the chemical rocket yields jet velocities of about 10,000 miles per hour, and the nuclear rocket 25,000 miles per hour. But with an electric rocket, using a nuclear reactor to supply power to a turbo-electric generator (a type which "seems to be the most promising from the standpoint of light weight for very large power output") jet velocities around 200,000 miles per hour can be obtained.

"So," he continued, "we can save a large amount of propellant, and it turns out that the weight estimate we have made of the rest of the propulsion system indicates that overall this will weigh much less than the chemical rocket and moderately less than the nuclear rocket for the same mission.

"Due to the high weight, though, of the electric propulsion system; that is, the power plant required to generate the electric power, we find that we cannot develop much thrust. We get a low thrust, which is much lower than the weight of all the equipment. That means the electric propulsion system will never be used to launch anything off the ground, because it cannot lift its own weight. It ... has to be launched into orbit; from there it can undertake space missions to the other planets."

THE ELECTRIC DRIVE

A possible electric drive for a rocket is shown in Fig. 38. The propellant, which might be liquid cesium metal, is pumped into the first chamber, where it is heated, and the liquid metal converted into vapor. Then it flows through a plate with many small holes which distributes it evenly to the next stage. This distributor plate is connected to the positively charged side of an electrical circuit operating at 40,000 volts. Then the vapor passes through a grid made of tungsten and is heated electrically. Cesium atoms have only a weak hold on some of their outer electrons, while hot tungsten has a strong attraction for them. The result is that the cesium

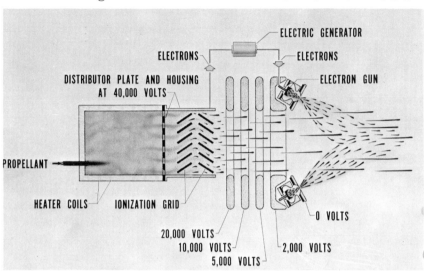

Fig. 38. Simplified diagram of ion rocket. The propellant is heated and ionized (i.e., electrons are removed from its atoms). The ions are then accelerated by electrical fields and forced toward the rear of the rocket, to provide propulsion. To keep the electrons from accumulating and giving the rocket an enormous electrical charge, they are also shot rearward by electron guns. (Courtesy National Aeronautics and Space Administration.)

atoms lose some of their electrons; that is, they become ionized, and assume a positive electrical charge. Therefore they are repelled by the positive charge on the distributor plate and are pushed toward the rear. On the way, the ions enter regions where the voltage is progressively lower—20,000, 10,000, 5,000, 2,000, and finally zero. In each, they are accelerated further, and the ions finally emerge from the back with the high velocity needed to provide the necessary thrust.

The electrons that are detached from the cesium atoms are likewise shot rearward from electron guns. They have very little mass, and do not add appreciably to the thrust, but they must be ejected.

If these negative electrons were not removed, the entire rocket would build up a tremendous negative charge. The positive charges on the cloud of ions behind the rocket would exert an attraction, on the electrons, which would reduce the vehicle's speed. So it must be kept neutral electrically, by getting rid of the positive and negative charges equally.

Such an ion rocket represents one of the two possible types of electric propulsion. The other is the plasma rocket. Another NASA scientist from the Lewis Research Center, J. Howard Childs, chief of the Center's Electric Propulsion Branch, explained it this way before a Congressional committee:

"The plasma rocket differs from the ion rocket in that here we do not separate the ions and the electrons and eject them in two separate beams. Rather we leave the ions and electrons intermingled and accelerate them together in a common beam.

"By definition, plasma is simply a mixture of positive ions and negative electrons. The way you produce a plasma is to take any body of gas . . . and heat it up until the temperature is so high that the molecules of the gas dissociate—separate into positive ions and negative electrons. You will have the same number of positively charged particles as you have negatively charged particles . . . so the whole mass of gas is still electrically neutral."

PLASMA JETS

There are various ways of using electric—and magnetic—forces to accelerate plasma into a jet. In one method, plasma is allowed to pass between two copper bars connected to a source of high-voltage electricity. The plasma is conductive, so a current flows across from one bar to the other. The bars and the stream of plasma are in the field of a powerful magnet. When a current flows at right angles to a magnetic field, there is a force which tends to move the material, carrying the current, in a direction at right angles both to current and field. This basic principle is responsible for the operation of any electric motor. By a similar mechanism the current-carrying plasma is forced backwards to form the jet.

Another type makes use of exactly the same kind of force that a farmer uses in milking a cow by hand. A laboratory arrangement, used at the Lewis Research Center, is shown diagrammatically in Fig. 39. Around one end of the tube is a coil of wire connected to a high-frequency electrical current like that used in a radio transmitter. The propellant vapor enters, and the electrical oscillations agitate it so violently that it is heated and converted to a plasma. The heat also causes it to expand, so it starts moving down the tube.

Then it comes to a place where there is an accelerator coil around the tube. A sudden burst of current, sent through this coil, creates a magnetic field which squeezes the plasma. The pressure of the expanding gas behind prevents it from going back, so it is forced

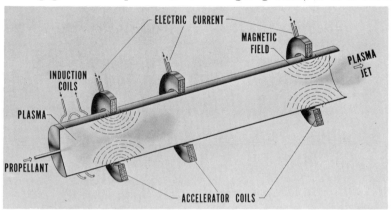

Fig. 39. Plasma accelerator for rocket propulsion. The propellant enters from the left and is converted to plasma by electrical energy supplied by the induction coils. As pulses of current enter the accelerator coils, these create magnetic fields which squeeze the plasma and push it along the tube, until it emerges in a jet. (Courtesy National Aeronautics and Space Administration.)

down the tube at higher speed. Then it encounters a second accelerating coil, a third, and so on. Each time the plasma is speeded more, and finally it emerges from the other end as a jet.

But what is to supply the electric current for either the ion or plasma rocket? With a solar battery the energy of sunlight might be collected and converted to electricity. Perhaps more practicable at first, however, would be a nuclear power plant. In this way nuclear energy may be used more efficiently than by simply utilizing its heat to expand a propellant and ejecting it as if from a chemical rocket.

Scientists of the NASA have actually made studies of a nuclear-powered, electric space vehicle to take an eight-man expedition to Mars, which is illustrated in Fig. 40. The entire weight would be 350,000 pounds and the length 600 feet. By putting the reactor at the front and the crew's cabin at the rear, there would be enough distance to protect them from the reactor's radiations, without need of heavy shielding. The propellant, perhaps cesium, would be stored just behind the reactor. Some of the heat from the reactor might be used to keep the cesium liquid, but this would not be difficult, since this element melts at 83° F.

About a quarter of the way back, connected by a slender pipe, is the turbogenerator, where steam from the reactor would drive the turbines and produce electricity. Cables would carry it back to the electric rocket at the rear, to which the cesium would also be supplied, through tubes.

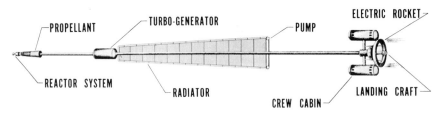

Fig. 40. Proposed electric space vehicle for an 8-man expedition to Mars. With a total length of 600 feet, the crew quarters are safely removed from the nuclear reactor at the front. The whole vehicle, weighing 175 tons, would be launched from a station in space. (Courtesy National Aeronautics and Space Administration.)

In an electric power station it is necessary to condense the steam, and this would be essential in the rocket, for the same water would have to be used over and over again. Terrestrial plants usually employ water from a river or lake to cool the steam and so condense it. This could not be done in space, so there is a large radiator, where the heat would be radiated away, thus converting the steam back to water, which would then be pumped back to the turbogenerator.

Although this entire space vehicle would weigh 350,000 pounds, only 76,000 pounds would be taken up with propellant, giving a far better mass ratio than chemical rockets in which the propellant, combined with the fuel, takes up a majority of the total weight at take-off. The nuclear-electric power plant weighs 70,000 pounds, so even when this is added to the propellant weight, the ratio is still very favorable.

The power contemplated for this electric vehicle is 12,600 kilowatts, which would give a thrust of only 58 pounds. Thus it would have to be placed into a satellite orbit around the Earth with some type of propulsion that would give the high thrust needed to get it off the ground, and this probably means that chemical rockets would be used at the beginning. Or perhaps such a vehicle might be assembled in space at a satellite station. If so, high-thrust rockets would again be needed to take the materials aloft.

For a trip to the Moon, a low-thrust electric rocket would not be very promising. Even assuming that such a rocket is in orbit around the Earth and that it has a thrust of, let us say, 2 pounds for each 5 tons of weight, it would have to spiral around the Earth many times as it built up speed, and might take some 50 days to reach the Moon. A high-thrust rocket could get there, directly from Earth, in about 2 days.

So, as Moeckel pointed out, the electric rocket does not seem particularly attractive for an Earth-to-Moon expedition, although it might still be very useful for transferring large payloads from Earth satellites to Moon satellites, if you are not interested in fast times but you are interested in economy of operation.

TRIPS TO THE PLANETS

If the electric rocket keeps on accelerating beyond the Moon, it can finally reach a velocity sufficient to leave Earth entirely, and go on to Venus or Mars. In that case, the time differences between high and low thrust are not nearly so great. Moeckel explained it this way:

"The reason is that for both cases, when we leave the Earth, we have to follow a fairly long coast path out to the orbit of Mars, and the coast time from the Earth to Mars' orbit is about the same for the two systems. . . . Also, once we arrive at Mars we have to wait quite long periods of time before Mars and the Earth are in the right position so that we could come back and reach the Earth's orbit when the Earth is at the right place, and again the waiting times are about the same for the two systems. So the overall time for the whole roundtrip mission is not too much different, 973 days for the high-thrust and about 1,060 days for the low-thrust vehicle.

"These times are for the most economical paths. They are the ones that permit us to accomplish the mission with the least total weight. Obviously we would like to reduce these times as much as possible. Our preliminary estimates indicate that we should be able to reduce 1,000 days to about 600 days, with rather moderate increases in the initial weight for the mission."

The push of light itself may also be used to propel space vehicles. In the last chapter we saw how pressure of light from the Sun forces comet tails to point away from that orb. Richard L. Garwin, of Columbia University, has proposed a solar sail for space ships. If a circular sail 230 feet in diameter were attached to a 21-pound Vanguard satellite, the solar light pressure would give it an acceleration of about 0.0016 per cent of that of a body falling to the ground by gravity. If the light were reflected, acceleration would be increased.

A far larger sail, perhaps made of some very thin plastic and coated with aluminum to reflect the radiation, might be attached to a space vehicle which was already in orbit around the Earth. The acceleration would slightly increase its speed. But when it had gone half way around the Earth, it would now be approaching the Sun and light pressure would slow it down. Therefore it would be necessary to furl the sail, or perhaps turn it sidewise so it was no longer pushed by the radiation, while it was moving toward the Sun. As it completed the first revolution, the sail would be opened up again, and would receive an additional acceleration. Repeating this process, it would go faster and faster on each revolution, and eventually reach a speed fast enough to take it away from the Earth. This might seem to be a slow process, but would have the great advantage that it could be done with no expenditure of fuel except to furl and unfurl the sails.

PHOTON ROCKETS

Another possibility of using light for propulsion is in the *photon rocket*. Not only does light exert pressure on things it shines upon, but it produces a "kick" as it leaves a luminous body. When you turn on the headlights of your automobile at night, they produce a recoil tending to reduce your speed. Fortunately, it is so minute an effect that it is quite inappreciable!

If a brilliant enough light, sent backward from a rocket, were formed into a tight beam by ultra-accurate mirrors of high reflectivity, it could produce a slight acceleration. After all, the photons (parcels of light energy) that constitute the propellant would be leaving at the highest possible speed, that of light! But the mass would be so small that high accelerations could hardly be reached. The accelerations possible would be in the *milligee* range, that is, a thousandth of g, the normal acceleration of gravity.

With such values, a British physicist, L. R. Shepherd, has calculated the time for a journey to the nearest star, alpha Centauri, which is 4.2 light-years distant. If for the first half of the trip, the ship had an acceleration of about a thousandth of that of gravity on the Earth, and decelerated equally over the second half, the trip would take 130 years. The maximum speed reached would be only about 12,000 miles per second, or about 6 per cent of the velocity of light. So such methods seem impossible, with our present technology, but who knows what future and now totally unforeseen developments might come to make them practicable?

SPACE TRAVEL AND THE ASTRONOMER

The value of space exploration to astronomy is obvious. Personal investigation would quickly settle such problems as: What is on the other side of the Moon? What are the canals of Mars? Are the clouds of Venus water, or something else? What is the nature of the surface below them? What is the red spot of Jupiter? Are some of its satellites made of ice? It might even be possible for astronomers to take a close look at Halley's comet when it returns, even to go into it, and find just what comets are made of.

But even without such extensive exploration as this, the first steps into space promise us valuable data; they have already yielded many important facts. Studies of the first artificial satellites, for example, gave new information about the shape of the Earth and the density of the atmosphere high overhead. They revealed that the Earth is surrounded by the Van Allen radiation belts. Observations of weather, made from the ground, would gain immensely if they were supplemented from above, with such data as the distribution of clouds all over the Earth. From such a vantage point, storm areas should be easily visible, and their movement accurately traced.

With a manned satellite, information could be sent to the ground by radio from the satellite observers. And even if they were unmanned, television cameras could look over the Earth and report automatically what they saw, as was shown in 1960 by the first Tiros satellite and later by Tiros II.

But most of all, astronomers are looking forward to a satellite observatory. Even a rather small telescope above the atmosphere, which so hampers present work, would do tasks that cannot now be accomplished with the world's largest instruments. Eventually, no doubt, there will be a manned satellite, and astronomical observations will constitute one of the major parts of its program. But before this is accomplished, astronomers will probably be observing from an unmanned observatory, in orbit around the Earth at a height of some hundreds of miles.

Plans for such a space telescope have been made by several groups of scientists. One is in Cambridge, Massachusetts, at the Smithsonian Astrophysical Observatory, under its director, Fred L. Whipple. The frontispiece shows the telescope in orbit above the United States, with two control stations, one on the east coast, one on the west. The telescope will be of the reflecting type, with an 8-inch concave mirror reflecting the light to form an image on a television camera tube. The picture formed will be transmitted by radio to one of the ground control stations, where it can be displayed on a TV picture tube, and photographs taken for a permanent record.

An elaborate control system will be needed in order to point the telescope to the part of the sky that the astronomers want to observe. The instrument will be moved by means of three gas jets on the side, supplemented by three motor-driven flywheels. As a signal from the ground sets a flywheel spinning in one direction, the entire satellite will slowly turn in the opposite sense, as a result of the reaction to the flywheel's motion. And when the flywheel stops, the telescope will remain pointed in that direction.

The short radio waves that will be used cannot travel around the Earth, so ground operators can only make use of the satellite when it is in the part of the sky visible from their location. If the satellite were at an altitude of 500 miles, which would take it around the Earth in about 1 hour, 40 minutes, and a signal could be obtained at a ground station whenever it was within 80 degrees of the zenith (i.e., at least 10 degrees above the horizon), it could only be used for about 10 minutes from a single station. Then it would be necessary to wait for an hour and a half, until it came around again, and then make more observations.

If placed in a larger orbit, so that it would be at a greater altitude, it would take longer to go across and could be used for a longer period. Increasing the number of stations also would extend its availability, for as it went out of reach of one, it could be reached from the next. A continuous chain of stations around the Earth would permit it to be used all the time.

Preliminary plans called for a satellite with a total weight of somewhat less than 300 pounds, including about 150 pounds of batteries to supply the power needed for the TV transmitter and other electrical equipment. This was to be placed in an orbit, inclined about 40 degrees to the equator, that would keep a continuous altitude of about 1,000 miles (unless the radiation in the Van Allen belts interfered at this altitude). In such an orbit the satellite would take about 2 hours to go around. With two stations within the U.S., and if it were usable within 80 degrees of the zenith, the astronomers would have about 32 minutes of observing time on each revolution.

INVISIBLE COLORS

The first task planned for such a satellite observatory is to map the entire sky in four different "colors" in the invisible ultraviolet, using wave lengths which never reach ground observatories because they are screened by the ozone in our atmosphere. The importance of this was summarized by Whipple and his associates in an article.

"Today astrophysicists investigating the physical nature of celestial objects are rather like the three blind men who variously described an elephant as a rope, a tree and a snake, having touched the animal's leg, tail and trunk. Our atmosphere is a blindfold to students of the universe.

"The Sun, for example, emits a wealth of 'coded' data in the form of electromagnetic radiation from its surface and surrounding gaseous envelope. We on the ground must limit our spectroscopic studies of this radiation to that small fraction of the emitted spectrum that the Earth's atmosphere allows to pass."

As mentioned in Chapter 2, violet light waves are about 1/70,000 of an inch long. Still shorter are the waves of invisible ultraviolet radiation. But our atmosphere is impervious to those shorter than about 1/94,000 of an inch.

However, as Whipple points out, both theory and the meager data from high-altitude rocket flights indicate that these shorter ultraviolet waves, inaccessible to us from Earth, hold the key to many important and basic problems. He continues: "Since the fundamental spectral lines of most abundant elements (hydrogen, helium, carbon, nitrogen, and oxygen) fall in the far ultraviolet, we must have precise data on the spectrum of this region if we are to obtain reliable information on its chemical composition. But even more important, the transfers of stellar energy reach a balance in this region, which, in terms of our simile, thus represents the body of the elephant.

"Recognition that the far ultraviolet holds valuable information is not a recent development in astrophysics. Only recently, however, has there been any realistic hope of obtaining it. As an example, the interstellar gas is energized by electromagnetic and corpuscular radiation from hot stars. But the extent and relative efficiency of these processes can only be estimated from ground-based observations.

"An example much closer to home is the solar corona, whose spectrum lies primarily in the ultraviolet. According to recent ideas of S. Chapman, the corona embraces the entire solar system, enveloping and heating the Earth's upper atmosphere.

"There is no limit to the speculations or the possible discoveries to be made through studies of the ultraviolet spectrum—if we could bring it within reach of our laboratories. Our best hope, at present, is to launch a telescope into space." *

So, the first step will be to map the entire sky in four wave lengths of this region. This will be an over-all survey, without much detail. The detail will come later, as astronomers develop improved satellite telescopes to pinpoint an individual star—or other object—and record the spectrum.

ESCAPING FROM EARTH

Despite any success that may be achieved in observing from satellites, either manned or unmanned, men will still want to get out into the Solar System themselves to inspect the planets at close range, even to land upon them. Finally they will want to leave the Solar System, to visit other stars and the planets that probably revolve around many of them.

* By permission from F. L. Whipple, *Astronautical Sciences Review*, Vol. 1, Jan.-Mar., 1959.

This is a matter of speed. Earlier we referred to the Earth's *escape velocity* of about 7 miles per second—the speed reached by an object freely falling to the Earth from an infinite distance. We noted that one fired upward at this speed would be just able to overcome the gravitational attraction of the Earth, and escape from it.

To become a satellite, a considerably slower speed is required. Imagine a baseball pitcher throwing a ball. The faster he hurls it, i.e., the more energy he puts into it, the farther it will go. A bullet goes still faster—and travels farther. We can imagine a gun powerful enough that the bullet will go all the way around the Earth (if we neglect the effect of resistance of the air) and hit the gunner in the back. This speed is 4.9 miles per second; it is called the Earth's circular velocity, for it is the speed that will maintain a body in a circular orbit so it never falls to the ground (Fig. 41). At a slower speed, even though it might go nearly all the way around, it would fall.

With higher speeds, the circular path of our body stretches out and becomes more and more elliptical. It extends farther and farther away from the Earth. With speeds approaching that of escape velocity, the ellipse reaches far, far out into space. Then, with that velocity (theoretically 6.96 miles per second, neglecting the effects of air resistance), the ellipse opens out into a parabola. Now our moving body ceases to be a satellite; it goes on out, and never returns to Earth, but now circles the Sun. This is what happened with Mechta and Pioneer III, both of which left Earth to become miniature planets, or asteroids.

Moving in such an orbit, our vehicle might pass close to another planet, and that, indeed, is the way they would have to reach other bodies in the Solar System. With all terrestrial means of transportation we must continually apply power. If our automobile runs out of gas, it comes to a halt, unless we happen to be able to coast down a hill. But once in an orbit, a space ship is a little planet itself. Since there is nothing to stop its movement, it continues on its path, without any expenditure of energy, guided by the same forces and laws that guide the Earth and the other planets, comets, asteroids, and the like.

Thus, in an interplanetary voyage, the rockets, whether chemical, ion, photon, or whatever else they may be, will be used at the start to place the vehicle in an orbit that will take the ship to the destination. Since the term *orbit* implies a continual movement around a body, perhaps we should not use it in referring to a path between two planets. Instead *trajectory* is now frequently used to describe a path that has a definite beginning and end, reserving *orbit* to designate one that is indefinitely extended, or is repetitive in character.

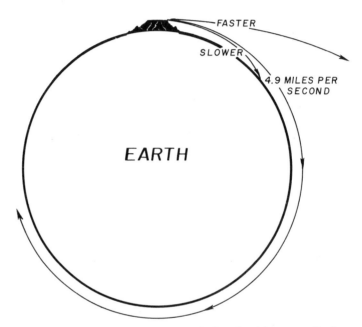

Fig. 41. Earth's circular velocity. If a shell is fired horizontally from a gun on a high mountain, it will fall to the ground, unless it is moving with a speed of 4.9 miles per second. Then it will be moving just fast enough, the circular velocity, to overcome the attraction of the Earth. At a higher speed, it will leave the Earth and travel out into space.

REACHING MARS

The easiest trajectory to use is one which forms part of an ellipse (around the Sun) that is tangent to the orbit of the planet it is leaving and also to that to which it is going. Fig. 42 shows such a path from Earth to Mars.

Having escaped from the surface of the Earth and perhaps being in a satellite orbit around our globe, the vehicle is travelling along through space at a speed of 18.5 miles per second, which is the Earth's own orbital velocity. With extra velocity of 1.8 miles per

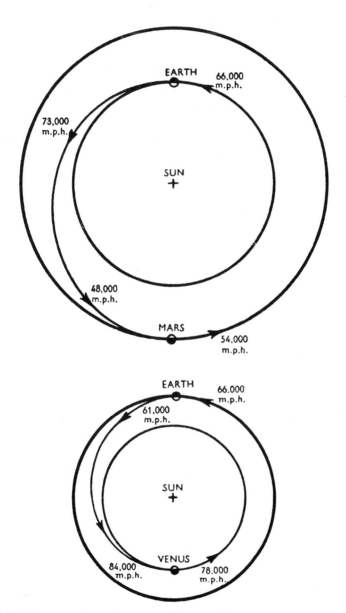

Fig. 42. Routes and speeds required for a rocket journey from Earth to Mars and to Venus. (By permission from *The Exploration of Space*, by Arthur C. Clarke. Copyright, 1951, Harper & Bros., New York.)

second (in the direction of the Earth's motion), it would pull ahead of the Earth into an orbit which would take it to the orbit of Mars. When it got there, it would be moving more slowly, at 13.4 miles per second, or a little more slowly than Mars itself, with an orbital velocity of 15.0 miles per second. Thus it would not remain there, but would begin to drop back to the orbit of Earth.

If, before this happened, the rockets were started again to give the vehicle an extra 1.6 miles per second to bring it to the Martian velocity, it would remain in that planet's orbit, keeping in pace with the planet itself. It might become a satellite of Mars, or perhaps a landing could be accomplished. To keep the rocket from falling freely and crashing on the surface, the rockets would have to be used in reverse. This would mean operating at the equivalent of 3.1 miles per second, the escape velocity of Mars and the speed at which a freely falling object from space would hit the surface.

If this were all done in the same space vehicle, it would mean a speed of 7 miles per second to get off the Earth, 1.8 to transfer to the elliptical trajectory for the voyage, 1.6 to transfer from that to the Mars orbit, and 3.1 to land on Mars. Thus the total "speed budget," measured from the beginning of the trip, would be 13.5 miles per second. This would be the minimum. With losses at various stages of the trip, possible corrections to the course, etc., it would have to be larger—perhaps 15 miles per second. Figuring on a similar basis, a trip to the Moon would require about 10 miles per second. Thus the energy to give the additional 5 miles per second is all that is needed, beyond that needed for a trip to the Moon, to make one to Mars, even though the trip is a thousand or more times as long. The whole journey would take 259 days.

Of course, we should note that the time of leaving the Earth must be chosen so that Mars will be there when the ship reaches its orbit. And because the orbit of Mars is so eccentric, there would be considerable variation from the figures given, which are for Mars at mean distance. If the trip could be arranged to reach Mars when it is nearest the Sun, the time would be shortened to 237 days.

Moreover, the trip described is one-way, and our explorers would doubtless like to return to Earth, in order to give a full report of their expedition, if for no other reason. This would require the same total speed, using rockets to land on Earth, and would mean a total for the round trip of some 30 miles per second. If the ship were able to sprout some sort of wings when it returned to Earth, and glide down through the air without having to use the rockets, the total requirements might be reduced to about 24 miles per second. We can figure, in a similar way, the requirements for a trip to Venus. This time, in order to fall toward the Sun after the ship has escaped from Earth, the speed must be reduced by about 1.5 miles per second. Reaching Venus' orbit, the vehicle would be going too fast, and it would have to slow down by about 1.7 miles per second to move along with Venus. Then a braking velocity of 6.5 miles per second would be needed to land. The total, then, is 16.7 miles per second for the minimum, or perhaps 20 miles per second for an actual journey. This is higher than the figure for the Mars trip, but the Venus trajectory would be covered in less time, 146 days.

A trip to Jupiter would require a total speed of about 16.0 miles per second, without any landing there. We would hardly want to make a landing, when we recall the nature of that planet's atmosphere: hydrogen, methane, and ammonia. It might, however, be interesting to visit Jupiter's moons. Once in the Jovian orbit, it would be simple to land on these bodies, with escape velocities of one or two miles per second. Such a trip, along the minimum energy trajectory, would take 2 years, 9 months.

HAZARDS OF SPACE

Every time man has crossed a new frontier of exploration, he has encountered new hazards. The exploration of space will certainly present a full complement. Some hazards, no one can anticipate; others can be foreseen and their possible effects evaluated. Some will concern man himself: problems of nutrition in a closed environment, isolation from society, the emotional manifestations such conditions may impose, handling himself in a weightless condition when he is free of Earth's gravity, for example.

Other hazards are of an astronomical nature. Perhaps the one that has been most widely considered is that of meteorites. As stated in the preceding chapter, billions of these little objects, bright enough to be visible, at least through a moderate-sized telescope, i.e., of the tenth magnitude or brighter, strike the Earth every day. While the space ship would present a far smaller area than the Earth, the danger from meteors is far from negligible. Whipple has estimated that a sphere of 3 meters (about 10 feet) diameter, and an aluminum skin an eighth of an inch thick, would be penetrated by a meteor of the 13th magnitude. This would be about 1/250 inch in diameter, and its speed might be about 14 miles per second. Nearly 40 billion of this size strike the Earth daily, and, once in about three weeks, on the average, we might expect the three-meter sphere to be struck—and punctured. Probably our space vehicle would be considerably larger, and so the chances of a hit would be that much greater, though it might not be on a vital part of the structure. Even if it were, some self-sealing composition, like that used in gasoline tanks of fighter planes as a protection from damage by antiaircraft fire, might be the solution. If the skin were made thicker, it would take a larger meteorite to penetrate, and they are much rarer. However, to save weight, the skin will have to be kept as thin as possible.

Whipple has proposed the use of a "meteor bumper." This would be a layer of material, similar to that used for the main skin and about a tenth as thick, placed, outside the ship, at a distance of several times the thickness of the skin. Then, when a meteor struck, it might go through the bumper, but would probably be converted to vapor, which would spray the skin harmlessly over a large area. He estimates that such a bumper would reduce the number of punctures between ten and a hundred times.

Another anticipated hazard is from cosmic rays. These are mainly protons, with about a sixth as many alpha particles, and some nuclei of heavier elements, even iron. They hit the gas atoms in the upper atmosphere and produce the secondary particles called *mesons* which are continually bombarding the surface of the Earth. In a space ship, of course, the primary rays would be encountered. These have the power to ionize atoms, and, when they do this to the atoms that make up living cells, they may cause considerable damage and even destruction. Some of the most serious damage is done to the chromosomes, the parts of the cell that control reproduction.

It is not only the primary particles themselves that may cause such damage; the secondary radiations, perhaps produced inside the body when the primaries strike, will also cause ionization effects. And these secondary particles, which may spread over a region considerably larger than that reached by one of the primaries, may be the more dangerous. Thus, the relatively rare heavy particles—nuclei of such elements as iron, sodium, calcium, magnesium, etc.

—may be more significant as a source of biological damage than the far more numerous protons and alpha particles, because they produce many more pairs of ions and thus spread their effects more widely. The effect is a cumulative one; an exposure of weeks or months would be more harmful than one of a few days. In addition, at distances well away from the Earth and from its magnetic field, the intensity of cosmic radiation probably increases, and a trip out to another planet might be more hazardous than one to the Moon or one in a satellite that remained close to Earth.

RADIATION DANGERS

In addition, there is the possible hazard of the Van Allen radiation belts, described in Chapter 6. Perhaps a vehicle bound for a distant part of space could get through them so rapidly that their effect would not be very great. Or it might leave by way of the polar regions, as the belts do not extend that far. For a satellite, the orbit might be chosen so that the satellite would travel in the region between the two belts, where the intensity is relatively low.

Not exactly a hazard, but a problem in traveling to distant planets, or, as may some day be possible, to the region of other stars, is the great length of time required. The nearest star is so far that its light, traveling 186,000 miles each second, takes more than 4 years to reach us. So far there seems little prospect of moving at anything like the speed of light, though perhaps this may come eventually. It seems that no one will ever travel faster than light; that is impossible, according to the theory of relativity.

Even at near light speed, a journey to any but the closest stars might take centuries—many lifetimes, which would mean several generations of space travelers on the trip. However, at speeds nearly that of light, a curious effect—time dilatation—may take place. According to the special theory of relativity, which Einstein enunciated in 1905, time actually passes more slowly in a moving system than in a stationary one. At velocities which we have now attained, even those of satellites and rockets, this effect is still inappreciable. But at nearly the speed of light it would become important. Light travels at 186,300 miles per second. If a space vehicle were travelling at about 90 per cent of this velocity—167,700 miles per second—only 10 years would pass while people remaining back on Earth had counted 25 years.

Of course, the crew and passengers of the spaceship would be quite unaware of this slowing down of time, since it would affect all processes. Not only would clocks run more slowly, so would the cellular changes, the heartbeat, and happenings in their bodies. The vibrations of electrically driven crystals of quartz, used as frequency standards in radio, would be equally affected; so would the very vibrations of atoms themselves. To the people in the vehicle, it would seem that time went on normally, but when they returned, 10 years older according to their count, they would find that their friends who stayed at home had recorded the passage of 25 years.

At 99 per cent of the speed of light—184,000 miles per second—a trip that took a hundred years as measured on Earth would take only 5 years by the count of the travelers. And if their velocity were 186,200 miles per second, or 99.99 per cent that of light, a journey taking 1,000 Earth-years would seem to pass in 14 ship-years. At the speed of light itself, time would seem to stand still.

There has been considerable discussion about this, notably in the pages of the British scientific journal *Nature,* and some well-known scientists have argued against it. However, the consensus seems to be in its favor, and there is indeed some experimental evidence to support it.

One bit of favorable evidence has to do with the *mu*-mesons, which are heavy nuclear particles formed high overhead by the action of the primary cosmic rays on nuclei of oxygen and nitrogen atoms. They have enormous energy, which gives them a speed of 99.95 per cent that of light. In the 2.1×10^{-6} seconds of their mean lifetime, one could travel only about 2,000 feet. Since they are formed at an average height of 20 to 25 miles, we would hardly expect very much to reach the ground.

Yet a large proportion of them do reach the Earth's surface! At their average speed, time would be slowed to a thirtieth of normal. They would last thirty times as long, easily allowing them to reach ground.

And now it seems that satellites themselves may allow us to do an actual experiment on the time-dilatation effect. One of the announced items in the program of the National Aeronautics and Space Administration is to place in a satellite a very accurate clock —probably not one with gears and springs, but one using the more precise oscillations of atoms as a time-measuring standard—and, by radio signals, find how fast time passes while in orbit. If a slight variation were detected between the satellite clock and a similar one on the ground, it would indicate that the effect does occur. By providing a clear confirmation of the Einstein theory, it would greatly improve our understanding of the Earth's gravitational field, since the current explanation of the nature of gravitation involves the theory of relativity.

12

The Stars

Look at the sky on a dark, clear night. If it's winter time, you may see brilliant Sirius, the Dog Star, in the star group, or constellation, called Canis Major, the great dog. No other star that you can see at night is as bright. Glancing around in other parts of the sky, you will see many fainter stars, some just barely visible, about one four-hundredth as bright as Sirius.

With a pair of opera glasses you will see still fainter stars, while a telescope will reveal others even less brilliant. With the largest telescopes, astronomers can photograph stars nearly one two-billionth as luminous as the Dog Star.

But Sirius isn't the brightest star. That place of honor is held by the Sun, and Sirius would have to be increased in brightness more than ten billion times to equal it.

The difference is one of distance. The Sun, you will recall, is about 93 million miles away; Sirius about 53 trillion miles. Small wonder that Sirius looks so much fainter! Among the stars that dot the night-time sky, there is a wide range in distance, which accounts for much of the variation in brightness.

But not all. Stars do vary greatly in actual brightness, or candle power. This is shown by the stars in a cluster, such as the Pleiades —the seven sisters—seen on winter evenings in the constellation of Taurus, the bull. The brightest star, Alcyone, is easily visible to the unaided eye, while large telescopes reveal others, mostly red in color, about a millionth as bright. Yet they are all in the same cluster, which is about 60 times as far as Sirius. The differences in brightness, nearly a million to one, must be due to actual differences in the amount of light put out by each star.

Actually, the Sun is not particularly bright; if it were removed to the distance of many of those that are prominent at night, we could hardly see it. Nor is it very faint—it is about average. Some stars are a hundred thousand times as bright as the Sun; others a hundred thousandth as luminous, so the range of stellar candle-power is about 10^{10}, or ten billion.

As you look up at the stars, they seem to be countless, but they aren't. Actually, some 6,000 are bright enough to be seen without telescopic aid. Half of the complete sky is always hidden below the horizon, which cuts down the visible number to 3,000. But, when a star is low in the sky, its light has to pass through a greater depth of atmosphere than when it is high above; so not more than about 2,000 stars can be seen with the naked eye at one time.

THE CONSTELLATIONS

Men have observed the stars for untold ages. Thousands of years before Christ, perhaps in ancient Babylon, they fancied that certain groups of stars resembled familiar creatures and things, so they named them after these. With some modifications, the ancient names have come down to us and are still used. One group that is conspicuous in winter we call the bull, or Taurus, using the Latin name. Another, prominent in the southern evening sky in summer, is Scorpio, the scorpion. Toward the north we see another, called Ursa Major, the great bear, although it is hard to fit the outline of a bear around the stars. In this constellation is a smaller group, of seven stars, which we know as the great dipper, and it does bear a considerable resemblance to a dipper.

In ancient times, the astronomers (mostly astrologers, who had the mistaken notion that they could foretell the future from the movements of the heavenly bodies) used the constellation figures to designate a particular star. Thus they might refer to the star in the shoulder of the bear or in the northern claw of the scorpion. In more modern times, they followed the system introduced, by a German named Johann Bayer, in a star atlas which was published in 1603.

His method was to assign Greek letters to the stars in a constellation, usually in order of brightness, and follow this by the genitive case of the Latin name of the group. Thus, the brightest star in Orion is called alpha Orionis; the third brightest in Draco,

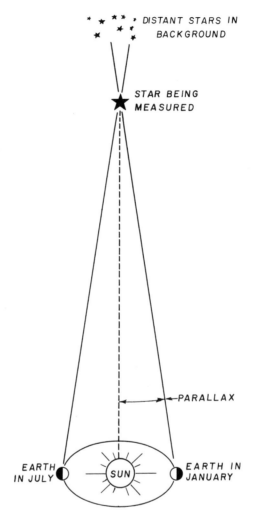

Fig. 43. Parallax. A star that is relatively close appears against a different background of distant stars at various times of year. This gives the parallax of the nearby star, which is a measure of its distance. The nearer the star the larger is the parallax.

the dragon, is gamma Draconis. But the brightest stars also have proper names. Alpha Orionis is named Betelgeuse, derived from an Arabic phrase, *Ibt al Jauzah*, meaning "the armpit of the central one." This star is in Orion's shoulder, as the ancients pictured him.

But modern astronomers no longer bother about these old figures. To them the constellations are merely areas. Just as the United States is divided into a number of areas called states, so the entire sky is divided into 88 areas called constellations, which bear the same names that were applied to these regions in earlier times.

One of the first things we want to know about stars is their distances. You can easily perform an experiment that illustrates the basic means whereby these are measured. Hold your index finger in front of you at arm's length. Close one eye, then the other, alternately, and notice how the finger seems to shift back and forth against the distant background. Now bring the finger to within a foot or so of your eyes and repeat the experiment. This time the finger shifts considerably more against the background.

With the Earth 93 million miles from the Sun, the diameter of our orbit is 186 million miles. That is, 6 months from now, when we are half way around, we will be that far from where we are now. This is enough to produce a very slight shift of the nearer stars against the background of distant ones. At observatories where such distance-measuring is a specialty, astronomers take photographs of stars, through their telescopes, at 6-month intervals. In this way they determine the star's parallax, which is actually half the annual shift. It is the difference in direction of a star as seen from the center of our orbit, and the extreme position, as shown in Fig. 43.

STAR DISTANCES

The nearest star, except the Sun, is alpha Centauri, in the centaur, a constellation that is not visible from most of the United States but is prominent from the Southern Hemisphere. Its parallax is about 0.756 of a second of arc. The smallness of this angle can be understood when you realize that if someone holds up a penny at a distance of 2.448 miles the lines from opposite edges of the coin to your eye have an angle of one second between them. And three-fourths of this is the parallax of the nearest star! Other stellar parallaxes are measured in hundredths or even thousandths of a second, so very delicate measurements are required to determine them.

Basically, this is the same method that a surveyor uses to find the distance of a mountain peak. He lays out a base line of known length, and from each end of this line he measures the angle between the peak and the other end. This gives a triangle, of which he knows the length of the base, and the adjacent angles. By trigonometry, he can find the lengths of the other sides or the distance of the peak. Similarly the astronomer: his baseline is the astronomical unit, the distance of the Earth from the Sun; from the parallax he can find the angles, then determine the height of the triangle, or the distance of the star. The smaller the parallax, the farther away is the star.

Such calculations would show that a parallax of 0.756 second corresponds to a distance of somewhat more than 25 trillion miles, which is the distance of alpha Centauri. But this is a large figure, inconvenient to use, just as it would be inconvenient to give the distance between New York and Chicago in inches. We use miles, instead, and then don't have to manipulate such huge figures.

Similarly with star distances. We often use as a unit the distance that a beam of light, which goes 186,300 miles every second, would travel in a year. This is nearly 6 trillion miles and we call it the light-year. Alpha Centauri is 4.28 light-years away, which means that its light takes 4.28 years to reach us.

Another unit is the *parsec,* the distance of a star with a parallax of one second. (Hence the name, from *par*allax and *sec*ond.) It is equal to 3.26 light-years. The distance of alpha Centauri is 1.3 parsecs. For very large distances, astronomers also use the *kiloparsec,* a thousand parsecs or 3,260 light-years, and the *megaparsec,* a million parsecs, 3,260,000 light-years. A star at a distance of 326 light years would have a parallax of 0.01 second, which is about the smallest that can be determined.

The parallaxes of some 5,000 stars have been measured by these means, and many of these are quite faint—well below naked-eye visibility. There are, for example, 33 stars within 4 parsecs of the solar system (i.e., with parallax greater than 0.25 second), and of these only eight are bright enough to be seen without optical aid. Fortunately, beyond the distances for which such trigonometric parallaxes may be determined, there are other ways to measure distances.

These depend on determination of the actual brightness of the star, and there are various ways of doing this, e.g., by the intensity of certain lines in the spectrum. If you know how bright the star really is, and how bright it looks, you can calculate the distance, since the apparent brightness diminishes with the square of the distance.

FAINT AND BRIGHT STARS

Not only are some nearby stars quite faint; others that look very bright are at considerable distances. The star called Deneb, in the constellation of Cygnus, the swan, is one of the 20 brightest stars we see in the sky, yet its distance is about 1,500 light-years. On the other hand, the closest star that is in the sky at night, in the United States, is in the constellation of the serpent. It is known as Barnard's star, after the astronomer who found it. The distance is only 6 light-years. But it isn't visible without a telescope; it would have to be about 15 times as bright to be just visible to the naked eye. In actual luminosity, or candle power, it is about 1/2,500 as bright as the Sun, while Deneb exceeds the Sun's brightness some 10,000 times.

Astronomers classify stars in brightness using a system introduced about 120 B.C. by a Greek astronomer named Hipparchus. He made the first known star catalog, in which he listed 1,080 stars. All, of course, were visible to the naked eye, since the telescope was not to be invented for many centuries. He gave the brightness according to six grades, 1 for the brightest and 6 for the faintest. These he called magnitudes, and this basic system is still used.

As more accurate measures of star brightnesses were made, scientists found that a star of one magnitude is about 2.5 times as bright as one of the next higher. In modern times, the system has been established on a more scientific basis, and a difference of 5 magnitudes corresponds to one of a hundred times in brightness. A first-magnitude star is actually 2.512 times as bright as one of the second, and so on.

This system accords with a general law of psychology, enunciated first by a German named Fechner. It says that equal differences of sensation are produced by equal ratios of stimuli. If you have a light of, say, 10 candle power, one of 20 candle power will look twice as bright, and one of 40 candle power twice as bright as that. In the first step, it only took 10 candle power additional to double the intensity, but in the next it takes 20, in the next 40, and so on. Fechner's law also applies to sound, and indeed to all sensations.

The original magnitude scale, from 1 to 6, has been extended both upwards and downwards. Sirius, for example, is about 10

TABLE 3

THE NEAREST STARS

(Within 15 light years of Sun)

Name	Constellation	Distance (Light-years)	Magnitude	Luminosity (Sun = 1)
Sun			−26.9	1.0
*Alpha Centauri	Centaurus	4.3	0.3	1.0
Barnard's star	Ophiuchus	6.0	9.5	0.0004
Wolf 359	Leo	7.7	13.5	0.00002
*Luyten 726-8	Cetus	7.9	12.5	0.00004
GC 15183	Ursa Major	8.2	7.5	0.0048
*Sirius	Canis Major	8.7	−1.4	21.
Ross 154	Sagittarius	9.3	10.6	0.00036
248	Andromeda	10.3	12.2	0.0001
Epsilon Eridani	Eridanus	10.8	3.7	0.27
Ross 128	Virgo	10.9	11.1	0.00031
*61 Cygni	Cygnus	11.1	5.2	0.073
GC 14217	Aquarius	11.2	12.2	0.00012
*Procyon	Canis Minor	11.3	0.4	6.6
Epsilon Indi	Indus	11.4	4.7	0.12
*GC 25648	Draco	11.6	8.9	0.0027
*BD + 43° 44	Andromeda	11.7	8.0	0.0062
Tau Ceti	Cetus	11.8	3.5	0.4
GC 32159	Piscis Austrinus	11.9	7.4	0.011
BD + 5° 1668	Canis Minor	12.4	10.1	0.001
GC 29761	Microscopium	12.8	6.8	0.022
GC 6369	Pictor	13.0	9.2	0.0025
*Kruger 60	Lacerta	13.1	9.9	0.0013
*Ross 614	Orion	13.1	10.9	0.00054
BD −12° 4523	Libra	13.4	10.0	0.0013
van Maanen's star	Pisces	13.8	12.3	0.00016
*Wolf 424	Virgo	14.6	12.6	0.00014
GC 13987	Leo Minor	14.7	6.6	0.035
GC 49	Sculptor	14.9	8.6	0.0058

* Double star.

Stars with names in *italics* are visible to the naked eye.

SOURCE: Above data (except magnitudes) from G. H. Herbig and C. E. Worley, *Some Basic Astronomical Data,* Astronomical Society of the Pacific, Leaflet No. 326.

times as bright as the average first-magnitude star, so it is given a negative magnitude, of −1.4. The Sun, on this same scale, has a magnitude of −26.9; about 25 billion times brighter than first magnitude. Going in the other direction, as telescopes revealed fainter and fainter stars, the scale has been extended upwards as well. Even a small telescope shows stars to magnitude 10, while the largest in the world—the 200-inch Hale telescope at Mount Palomar—will photograph to about magnitude 23.

TABLE 4

THE BRIGHTEST STARS

(First Magnitude or Brighter)

Name	Constellation	Magnitude	Distance (Light-years)	Luminosity (Sun = 1)	Color Index
*Sirius	Canis Major	−1.4	8.7	21	0.0
Canopus	Carina	−0.7	100	1500	0.1
*Alpha Centauri	Centaurus	−0.3	4.3	1.3	0.7
Arcturus	Boötes	−0.1	36	100	1.2
Vega	Lyra	0.0	26.5	50	0.0
*Capella	Auriga	0.1	47	130	0.8
Rigel	Orion	0.1	900	50000	0.0
*Procyon	Canis Minor	0.4	11.3	6.6	0.4
Achernar	Eridanus	0.5	150	800	−0.2
Beta Centauri	Centaurus	0.7	500	8000	−0.2
Betelgeuse	Orion	0.7	700	16000	1.9
Altair	Aquila	0.8	16.5	10	0.2
*Aldebaran	Taurus	0.8	68	300	1.5
*Acrux	Crux	0.9	350	4100	−0.2
*Antares	Scorpius	1.0	400	5000	1.8
Spica	Virgo	1.0	230	1400	−0.2
*Fomalhaut	Piscis Austrinus	1.2	23	13	0.1
Pollux	Gemini	1.2	35	30	1.0
Deneb	Cygnus	1.3	1500	50000	0.1
Beta Crucis	Crux	1.3	500	5000	−0.2
*Regulus	Leo	1.4	84	150	−0.1
Adhara	Canis Major	1.5	700	8000	−0.2

* Double star.

SOURCE: Magnitudes from H. L. Johnson, *Sky and Telescope* 16 (August, 1957): 470; other data from G. H. Herbig and C. E. Worley, *Some Basic Astronomical Data,* Astronomical Society of the Pacific, Leaflet No. 325, 1956.

What we have been discussing, of course, are *apparent* magnitudes—the brightness that a star seems to have. There is also *absolute* magnitude, that of a star at the standard distance of 10 parsecs. Our Sun's absolute magnitude is 5, while Deneb is −5. Barnard's star, moved out to 10 parsecs, would be even fainter than it is, of 13th magnitude.

STARS MOVE

While the planets change their position in the sky, sometimes noticeably from one night to the next, the stars seem to keep the same arrangement year after year. The constellation figures look to us just as they did to our grandfathers; even as they did to their grandparents. But the stars are moving, and thousands of years from now the constellations will have changed; see Fig. 44.

Such alterations are produced by movement across the line of sight to the star. If it is coming directly toward us, or moving directly away, its position in the sky does not change. Actually,

THE GREAT DIPPER

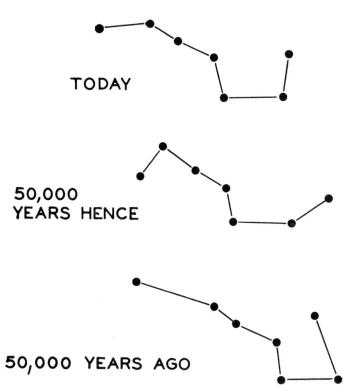

Fig. 44. Changes in the Great Dipper over 100,000 years, due to star movements.

stars are moving in all directions; and, to determine their real motion, we must find how they move both in the line of sight and across it.

The former is done by comparing photographs taken years apart. Even though the movement is not enough to change the star groups appreciably, it can often be detected when such pairs of photographs are carefully measured. The nearer a star, the more rapidly it is likely to move. If you are standing alongside a road, and an automobile drives past at 50 miles per hour, you have to turn your head rapidly to follow it. But if the road is a mile away, a car with the same speed seems to move much more slowly across your field of vision.

It was this, in fact, that led Barnard to discover the star that is known by his name. In comparing photographs taken some time apart, he found a faint star that had shifted its position considerably, and this led him to suppose that it must be very close. It was. The movement of this particular star across the sky—what astronomers call *proper motion*—is 10.25 seconds per year. It would take about 180 years for this star to move the apparent diameter of the full Moon. This may not seem very rapid, but it is the fastest proper motion yet found.

Astronomers turn to the spectroscope to measure movement in the line of sight, what they call *radial velocity*. They make use of the Doppler effect, which causes an automobile horn to sound higher in pitch when it is approaching than when it is going away. Similarly, as mentioned in Chapter 2, light waves are shortened or lengthened, with movement towards or away from the observer. The dark Fraunhofer lines in a star's spectrum are also shifted, toward the blue end of the spectrum if it is approaching; toward the red if it is receding.

When such a *spectrogram* is taken, with a spectroscope attached to a large telescope, the spectrum of light from an arc, alongside the instrument, is recorded, on the same plate, beside the stellar spectrum. There is no relative motion of the arc, so its lines are in the normal position; they provide a standard with which to compare the stellar lines.

From a single measurement of its radial velocity, one cannot tell whether a star is moving with respect to us or we in respect to the star. But if, in one direction, there is a predominance of approaching stars and most are receding in the opposite direction, we can assume that the Sun, and the rest of the solar system with it, is moving toward the approaching stars. This indeed is the case, for we are moving toward the direction of the constellation of Hercules, at a speed of about 12 miles per second. In figuring radial velocity of a star, this movement must be allowed for.

DOUBLE STARS

Look toward the great dipper in the northern sky some dark night, especially at the star called Mizar, the one next to the end of the handle. If your eyesight is good you will see a fainter star a short distance away. It is called Alcor. The Arabs used to call it the rider, Mizar being the horse. If you cannot see Alcor with the naked eye, try a pair of binoculars, or even opera glasses, and it will be readily apparent. With even a relatively small telescope it is quite prominent, and then, in addition, Mizar itself is seen to be two separate stars. Thus there are really three stars.

Mizar is a good example of a double or binary star, and was the first of its kind to be located. An Italian astronomer named Riccioli discovered it in 1650, and later many others were found.

At first, it was supposed, these were simply cases where two stars, at considerably different distances, happened to be nearly in the same line. Believing this, toward the end of the eighteenth century the English astronomer, Sir William Herschel, with the largest telescope that had been made up to then, began to search for such pairs. He intended to determine the parallax of the nearer. As the Earth moved in its orbit the apparent distance between the pair would seem to change, he thought. The nearer one would oscillate back and forth once a year with respect to the other and more distant body.

His search indeed yielded many double stars, but they did not behave as he anticipated. Most did not show any annual change, but, as he kept on observing them, he found that one would seem to be moving around the other. More accurately, they moved around the center of gravity of the pair. Tie two stones together with a short piece of string and throw them into the air. While the pair of stones is moving forward, they revolve around a point between them, the center of gravity. A great many binary stars have been found. It seems that about half of all the stars that we can see are binaries, while some are multiple systems with three or even more stars held together. It is the force of gravitation, of course, that holds them.

Not all, however, are actually seen as two, even in the largest telescopes, but there are other ways to determine that they are double. Take, for example, the star called Algol, in Perseus, which shines overhead on winter evenings; see Fig. 45. Ordinarily it is of magnitude 2.3, but every 2 days, 20 hours, 48 minutes it starts to dim. After about 4.5 hours it has faded to magnitude 3.5, about a third of its former brightness. It remains this way for about 20 minutes, then starts to brighten. Another 4.5 hours pass; again it is shining with its customary brilliance.

Algol is a binary, and the two bodies are about 6 million miles apart, on the average. But Algol is about 100 light-years away,

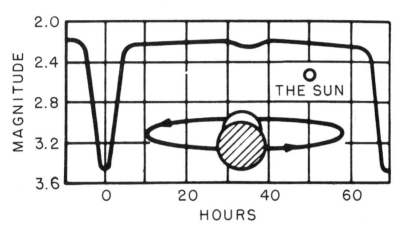

Fig. 45. The light curve of the binary star Algol. The star consists of two bodies, one bright and the other much darker. Every 27 hours, approximately, one of these passes in front of the other. There is a great diminution in brightness when the darker orb thus eclipses the brighter component, and a slight decrease as the fainter one is partly covered. The curve above shows the changes in brightness (in terms of astronomical magnitude). The diagram shows the relative motion of the two components, and the size of the Sun on the same scale is given for comparison. (By permission from *Matter, Earth and Sky*, by George Gamow. Copyright, 1958, Prentice-Hall, Inc., Englewood Cliffs, N.J.)

and at this distance no telescope will show the bodies as two. It happens that one of the stars is considerably fainter than the other. Moreover, the plane in which they revolve is almost in our direction. This means that, on each revolution (which takes 2 days, 20 hours, 48 minutes), the dark one passes in front of the brighter companion, covering more than a quarter of its diameter and causing a partial eclipse. During the 9 hours that it takes to cross the disc of the bright body, the light reaching us goes down, then increases.

Even between eclipses there is a change in light. At the middle of the interval, the brightness drops about a twentieth of a magnitude, or 5 per cent. This happens when the bright star eclipses the fainter one, showing that the latter is not completely dark.

Additional proof that Algol is double is shown by the spectroscope. Before the principal minimum of light, the spectral lines are shifted toward the red end of the spectrum, showing that the bright star is receding, and, after the minimum, it is approaching, as shown by a shift to the blue. This is just what we would expect if the star is revolving as on some celestial merry-go-round, so that it alternates in approach and recession.

SPECTROSCOPIC DOUBLES

The spectroscope also shows that many other stars are double, even though the components are too close—or the system too distant—for any telescope to reveal its members. These are called spectroscopic binaries. If one star is bright, the lines will shift first in one direction, then in the other, as the star approaches and recedes. The fainter companion may not show at all, or only dimly. If both stars are bright, each will contribute its set of lines. When one is toward us, and the other on the far side of its orbit, they will be moving sidewise to the line of sight, and there will be no movement toward or away from us. But after each has made a quarter of a revolution, one will be approaching, and its lines will be shifted toward the blue, while those of the other will be shifted redwards. Thus, there will be two sets of lines. A spectroscopic binary, if both components are about equal in brightness, shows a periodic doubling of its spectral lines. If one is much brighter, its lines will swing back and forth around the mean position.

Sometimes the changes are most complex. There is, for example, a faint star in the constellation of the bull, RW Tauri, an eclipsing binary. One component is a brilliant white, the other is fainter and yellow, about twice the white star's diameter. Every 2.8 days, for 84 minutes, the big yellow star eclipses its brighter but smaller companion. A. H. Joy, at the Mount Wilson Observatory, studied the spectrum of RW Tauri, and found lines due to glowing hydrogen, which were shifted toward the red at the beginning of the eclipse, and toward the blue at the end. But during the middle of the eclipse they disappeared completely.

There is, he concluded, a ring of glowing hydrogen which revolves around the white star and is a little smaller in diameter than the fainter body. At the start of the eclipse, just after the white star is completely covered, one side of this ring is also hidden, while the other is still visible. But because it is revolving, the side of the ring that is still uncovered is rapidly receding—thus giving a red shift. Then the ring, too, is covered, and the hydrogen lines disappear. But presently the other side emerges from behind the

Fig. 46. Two stars, almost in contact. Astronomers believe that, in the beta Lyrae system, material from one star streams toward the other. Each star is revolving around a point between them. Some of the streaming material is lost and spirals outward to form a ring of gas around the system. (Drawing by Felix Cooper. By permission from *The Astronomical Universe*, by W. S. Krogdahl. Copyright, 1952, The Macmillan Co., New York.)

fainter star and approaches, so the lines are shifted toward the blue. Thus the lines of the spectrum of the white star, which had disappeared during the eclipse, reappear.

The star beta Lyrae, in the constellation of the lyre, is another very curious object, as deduced from its variations in light and the complex changes that occur in its spectrum. According to the interpretation by Otto Struve, now director of the National Radio Astronomy Observatory in West Virginia, and Gerard Kuiper, of the Yerkes Observatory, there are two stars, one blue-white, the other yellow, practically in contact. They are so close that atmospheres of the two are combined, and flow from one to the other, as they revolve around the center of gravity in a period of 13 days. But some of these gases are continually ejected into space, forming a ring which spreads out farther and farther, like a celestial pinwheel; see Fig. 46.

According to Struve, the entire pinwheel is about as large as the solar system. Its distance is about 1,600 light years and no telescope can make visible its remarkable structure. Even though it is slowly sending material into space, the loss is small compared to the total mass of the system, about 100 times that of our Sun. Thus Struve believes that it can continue for millions of years.

COLOR AND TEMPERATURE

Not only do stars differ in brightness, they show a great range of color as well. Spica, in the constellation of Virgo, seen in the southwest on evenings of early summer, is bluish-white; Capella, a little higher in Auriga, is more yellowish; while Antares, over to the southeast in Scorpio, is distinctly red.

These differences reflect a difference in temperature. If you heat a piece of iron in a fire, you may get it "red-hot." That is, it glows with a red light. If heated still more, it may become white hot, glowing with white light. At a still higher temperature, the light emitted becomes brighter and bluish in color. The reason is found in one of the laws of radiation—Wien's law—which states that the hotter a body, the more toward the blue (i.e., the shorter the wave length) is its maximum radiation. Even at room temperature, our piece of iron is radiating infrared waves far too long to be seen. Heated to 200 or 300 degrees Fahrenheit, it gives off more radiation, and the waves, while still in the infrared, are shorter. If you hold the iron near your face, you can feel the waves; there is a sensation of heat. If it is heated to 900° F., the radiations are still shorter. Some of them are now in the visible part of the spectrum, and you can see a dull, red glow.

With a temperature still higher, the maximum shifts nearer to the wave lengths that are visible, and, at the Sun's surface with a temperature of about 10,000° F., the maximum is well in the visible range. The hottest stars, then, are blue. Spica is one of these; its temperature is around 50,000° F. Capella, which resembles the Sun in color, is about 10,000° and Antares about 6,500° F.

A simple way to give the color of a star—and hence its temperature—is by the *color index*. The eye is most sensitive to yellow light, and the photographic plate is affected mainly by blue rays. A cooler star, with light mainly yellow or red, will therefore look brighter to the eye than to a photograph. A hot blue star, on the other hand, will be brighter on the plate than to the eye. Thus astronomers compare the magnitude of a star as determined by the eye, using a light-measuring device called a photometer attached to the telescope, with that determined photographically. Or perhaps they use a photoelectric photometer. An "electric eye" or *photocell*, which converts light energy into electricity, is attached to the telescope. By the strength of the current that results, they find the amount of light that comes from the star. Then, by making two sets of measurements, one with a piece of blue glass over the photocell, the other through one of yellow glass, visual and photographic magnitudes are determined.

The difference between the two magnitudes gives the color index. With the star's temperature about 20,000° F., the index is zero, for the magnitude in each color is the same. A cool red star may be a full magnitude brighter in yellow light, and its color index will be 1; a hot blue body will be brighter in blue light and the index will be a negative quantity—perhaps −0.1. Even the hottest stars cannot be more than about half a magnitude brighter in blue than in yellow light.

The color index gives the astronomer his first clue to conditions prevailing on a star. To determine the conditions in greater detail, he must turn to more sophisticated techniques, and study of the spectrum is such a method. With the application of the spectroscope to astronomy in the past century, he has found many facts about the stars.

At the great observatories, big telescopes are used for much of the time to take direct photographs of planets, nebulae, and other objects. The telescope is simply a huge camera; the lens (or mirror, if it is a reflecting telescope) forms a picture of the object on a photographic plate, which is developed and studied. But for the rest of the observational time, a spectroscope is attached to the instrument. The lens or mirror focuses the light of the star—or whatever object is being examined—on the spectroscope. Its light is broken up and spread out, and the photographic plate then records the spectrum, crossed by the dark lines that show the presence of various elements.

The great 200-inch Hale telescope at Mount Palomar is generally used for direct photography during the period the Moon is out of the sky, i.e., around new Moon, between last quarter and first. Around the time the Moon is full and the sky is so bright at night that photography is difficult, the instrument is used with a spectroscope. Then, even though the sky is bright, the image of a star may be placed right on the narrow slit through which its light must pass first, before it goes through the lenses and prisms that form the spectrum. General sky light has little effect.

What we learn about stars in this way applies mainly to their outer layers, their atmospheres, although it may give data which lead toward a better understanding of their interiors. It tells what elements are in them. Hydrogen is prominent in some; others show lines due to heavier elements, such as metals, and some even show compounds, where the atoms have actually combined to form molecules such as those of metallic oxides.

ARRANGING THE SPECTRA

Around the beginning of the twentieth century, one of the pioneers in stellar spectroscopy, Norman Lockyer, in England, was among those who began to realize that stars can be arranged, by spectra, in some sort of sequence, and suggested that there was a gradual evolution of heavier elements from hydrogen. Thus the widely different spectra found among the stars were, he thought, actually due to the presence of different elements.

A great advance was made in 1922 when an Indian astrophysicist, Megh Nad Saha, showed that the many kinds of spectra result from differences in temperature rather than composition. In a relatively cool star, each atom will be in the normal un-ionized state, with its full complement of electrons. But if the star gets hotter, ionization occurs, electrons are lost from some of the atoms, and the atoms no longer absorb, from the light from the deeper parts of the star, the wave lengths they formerly soaked up. As a result they no longer cause dark lines as they did while at a lower temper-

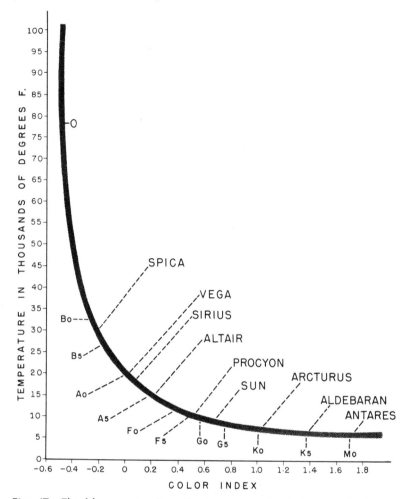

Fig. 47. The bluer a star (i.e., the lower its color index) the higher is its temperature.

ature. Instead, they may absorb quite different wave lengths—and cause a different set of lines, those of the ionized element.

When astronomers first began to classify stellar spectra, they used letters to designate different types. Later they found that the best arrangement of these classes was not in alphabetical order, but that class O should be first, then B, A, F, G, K, M, and N. (A mnemonic sometimes used to remember this order is: "Oh be a fine girl, kiss me now!") The six main classes are B, A, F, G, K, and M.

Rigel and Spica are typical B stars, blue-white in color, with strong helium and hydrogen lines in their spectra. Their temperatures range from 20,000° to 45,000° F. A stars are typified by Sirius and Vega. They are white in color, and the hydrogen lines are stronger than in any other type. Temperatures range from about 13,500° to 20,000° F. (See Fig. 47.)

Type F stars are yellow-white; Canopus (a star best seen from the southern hemisphere) and Procyon are examples. The hydrogen lines are weaker, while those of metals are stronger. Temperatures are from 10,000° to 13,500° F.

Class G is of particular interest to us, because the Sun is included, as is Capella. These are yellow, with surface temperatures from 9,000° to 10,000° F. The spectra show prominent metallic lines, particularly of calcium. Still cooler, with temperatures from 6,300° to 9,000° F., are the reddish stars of type K, such as Arcturus and Aldebaran. In these the metal lines are most prominent, and some bands due to molecules also appear.

Antares and Betelgeuse (the bright star in the shoulder of Orion, prominent in the winter evening skies) are examples of type M. They are definitely red in color with temperatures as low as 3,500°, ranging up to 6,000° F. or so. Many molecular bands appear in their spectra.

These six classes include most stars in our neighborhood at least, but there are some rarer and cooler ones belonging to type N that are known as carbon stars, because that element and its compounds are very prominent. They are the reddest stars known. No very prominent star is in this class.

Stars of type O are even hotter than those of type B, as their temperatures go up as far as 90,000° F. Bluish-white in color, they may show bright bands as well as the dark lines of the other types.

THE HERTZSPRUNG-RUSSELL DIAGRAM

A method of classifying stars by spectral types, i.e., by their temperatures as well as their (actual) brightnesses, has been very helpful to astronomers; see the diagram shown in Fig. 48. This is called a Hertzsprung-Russell diagram. It is named after the Danish astronomer Ejnar Hertzsprung and after Henry Norris Russell of Princeton University. Hertzsprung, in 1906, showed that, among the nearby stars, the brightest are blue and the faintest are red. Russell first prepared this sort of arrangement in 1914; see Fig. 48.

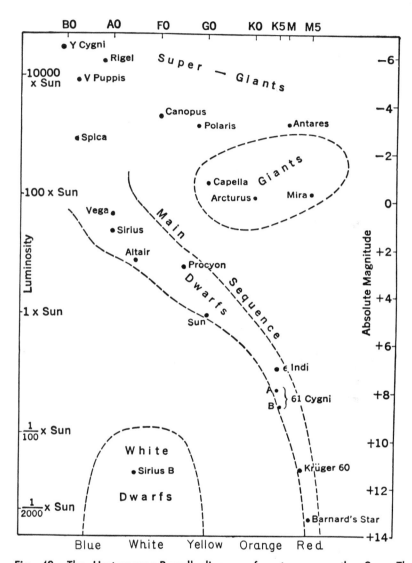

Fig. 48. The Hertzsprung-Russell diagram for stars near the Sun. The broken lines roughly define the regions in which these stars occur most abundantly. The positions of a few representative stars are shown. (By permission from *Astronomy,* by W. T. Skilling and R. S. Richardson. Copyright, 1947, Henry Holt & Co., Inc., New York.)

In his original diagram, Russell put a dot for each of about 300 stars of known distances (without these, of course, their absolute magnitudes could not be determined). The spacing from left to right represented the spectral class, from O to M, and that up and down indicated the luminosity. Most of the stars thus plotted formed a band from the upper left (O-type stars a thousand or more times as bright as the Sun) down to the lower right with M-type stars a hundredth of the Sun's brightness. This is called the *main sequence*. The Sun is about in the middle.

But toward the upper right corner there was a considerable cluster of relatively cool stars (types G, K, and M) that were very bright —a hundred or more times as much as the Sun. In the opposite corner (lower left) there were also a few dots, representing hot type A stars that were very faint—a hundredth as bright as the Sun.

The stars in the upper right-hand corner, being relatively cool, are not nearly as bright per square foot of surface as the hot ones farther to the left. With such a handicap, to be so brilliant, there must be a lot of surface; therefore they must be very large. These are called the giant stars, and Antares is one. Its large diameter was confirmed with an instrument called the interferometer, attached to the 100-inch telescope at Mount Wilson. With it the diameter of Antares (which is about 170 light-years away) was determined to be about 400 million miles—bigger even than the orbit of Mars around the Sun.

The stars in the lower left are dwarfs. Being so hot, they are very bright per square foot, yet so faint that they must be small, with relatively little surface. One of these is the companion to Sirius, which is another binary. Astronomers can calculate, from the relative orbits of such a pair, the mass of each, and they found that Sirius *B*, as the companion is called, contains a little less matter than our Sun, while Sirius *A*, the bright component, is about 2.4 times the solar mass. This difference is less than three to one. Both are type A, so they have about the same temperature and the same unit surface brightness. The absolute magnitude of Sirius *A* is 1.8, while that of *B* is 11.2. This difference, of about 10 magnitudes, corresponds to one of actual luminosity of approximately ten thousand times, so it shows that *B* must be vastly smaller than *A*. It is about a thirtieth of the Sun's diameter, or 29,000 miles, a little smaller than Uranus. But it contains more than a third as much material as *A*, or nearly as much as the Sun!

NINE TONS TO THE CUP

This shows that B must be extraordinarily dense—about 35,000 times the density of water. A cupful of the stuff it is made of would weigh 9 tons on Earth! Moreover, it is not a solid—but a gas!

How can any kind of matter be so dense? The answer is found when we recall that an ordinary atom, constructed of a nucleus with a number of electrons moving around it, is mostly empty space. If you try to compress a substance, no matter whether it is gaseous, liquid, or solid, there is a limit. The electrons of one atom cannot penetrate into the region occupied by those of a neighboring atom. If the atomic structures could be completely ionized, removing all the electrons from each atom, so that there remained only a conglomerate mixture of loose nuclei and electrons, they could be squeezed far closer together.

Such a mixture is called a *degenerate* gas, and that is what exists in Sirius B and other white dwarfs, of which there seem to be a great many. Being so faint, however, they are hard to find. One of them, van Maanen's star, is about 6,000 miles in diameter, even smaller than the Earth. It is about 284,000 times as dense as water. And another, known by its catalog number of A.C.+70°2847, seems smaller than Mars, with a density 36 million times that of water.

But how did the white dwarfs get that way? Apparently, they represent the next to the last stage of stellar evolution. If a star is not too massive, not more than about half again as much as the Sun, it seems that it will turn into a white dwarf after it has used up all its hydrogen fuel. Now the Helmholtz process of contraction will provide energy and the star is so faint that it is able to keep on radiating a long, long time. But finally, even this process comes to an end; the star stops radiating entirely. This may be the ultimate fate of the Sun, but it is one that we hardly need worry about. It will be in the inconceivably distant future. Long before that all life may have vanished from the Earth.

Theories of the course of a star's evolution have altered greatly since 1913 when the H-R diagram was first developed. At that time the Helmholtz contraction process seemed the most likely source of stellar energy. Russell's idea was that the evolutionary sequence would start at the top, with giant stars of enormous diameter. Somehow, they would get on to the main sequence, then slide down it to become cooler, smaller, and fainter, finally ending as white dwarfs. For a star like the Sun this allowed a life of some 50 million years.

With the development of nuclear physics, and the notion that matter could be converted into energy, some astronomers thought that a star could utilize all of its matter in this way. This would allow a lifetime of more than a trillion years, which was somewhat embarrassing, because it gave much more time than they needed. Many other considerations indicated a much shorter life period.

About 1936, the development of nuclear physics had advanced far enough to show that most stars use hydrogen as fuel, either the carbon cycle or the proton-proton reaction, as described in Chapter 4. Less than 1 per cent of a star's substance would thus be used. This shortened the star's lifetime to a more reasonable figure.

However, actual lifetimes vary. The Sun has been shining for billions of years and probably will continue at least as long in the future. But stars of different mass have quite different life expectancies.

THE MORE MASSIVE THE BRIGHTER

Except among the white dwarfs, there seems to be a close correlation between the mass of a star and its real brightness. A star of small mass, say a tenth of the solar value, would not have a great deal of overlying matter to press down on the center and so produce the conditions of high pressure and temperature needed for the nuclear processes that yield energy. The power plant would be small; its output would be no more than enough to permit the star to shine at about a ten thousandth the brightness of the Sun.

On the other hand, a star with ten times the Sun's mass would be able to operate a very large power station at the core. Its rate of energy production would be high enough to allow the star to shine with a brightness a thousand or more times that of the Sun. Using up fuel in such a prodigal manner, the star would have a life time of perhaps a hundredth of the Sun's. This leads to the interesting conclusion that some of these more massive stars, of which there are a number in the sky, may have been formed after life developed on Earth. Stars of small mass, on the other hand, may go back considerably farther into the past and may have life expectancies of many trillions of years.

Bart J. Bok, formerly of Harvard University and now director of the Mount Stromlo Observatory in Australia, has suggested that the evolution of a star a little more massive than the Sun would follow a special course. This is based on calculations made by Fred Hoyle, of Cambridge University, and Martin Schwarzschild, of Princeton. First there is a huge cloud of gas spread out thinly through its great volume. Its own gravitational contraction causes it to collapse, and it gets hotter and hotter. This might take something like 50 million years. Here again there is a difference, depending on total mass. With a mass two or three times that of the Sun, it might go through its infancy in a few million years, while a star with much smaller mass than the Sun might linger there for hundreds of millions of years. This brings it to the main sequence. It remains there a long, long time, converting its supply of hydrogen into helium.

At first hydrogen burns only at the center where the temperature is highest and convection currents stir up the gases. But, after the supply of hydrogen at the core is exhausted and helium takes its place, an *isothermal* core develops, with a high constant temperature. But there is still hydrogen in the outer layers, so the core grows, using up hydrogen as it does so. The outer shells expand, and the star becomes much larger. In this stage it has left the main sequence, and becomes a red giant. With the great expansion, the star has cooled considerably, at least in the outer layers.

Now comes a turning point. Some 5 billion years after the process started, hydrogen is no longer converted to helium; rather helium itself is "burned." Perhaps the process is the one mentioned earlier, where three helium nuclei combine to form carbon 12. But these processes are inefficient producers of energy, so the star rather quickly passes through this stage. It crosses the main sequence again, as a bluish-white type A star. Then it collapses into the white dwarf stage, which Bok calls the cosmic graveyard and where it can remain almost indefinitely. It has taken a total of about 6 billion years to reach this final state.

VARIABLE STARS

The Algol-type stars that we met earlier are but one of many types of variable star. Actually, of course, eclipsing binaries are not truly variable, for there is no actual change in the total light they emit. But many kinds of stars are variable intrinsically. There is one in Cetus, the whale (seen low in the south on late autumn evenings), called Mira, which sometimes is brighter than second magnitude, and quite prominent. From such brilliance, it may gradually fade to about tenth magnitude. This diminution, of about 1,500 times, takes it far below the limit of naked-eye visibility. Then it brightens again and may remain at the maximum for about 10 days before it starts its next decline. The average period, between successive maxima or minima, is 331 days, but this varies considerably, as does the range of variation. Astronomers do not know just what is going on.

In the constellation of Cepheus (best seen in the evenings in October when it is directly north, a little above the Pole Star) is a star known as delta Cephei. This happens to be double, but we are not in the plane in which the two bodies revolve around each other, so there is no eclipse. But it does vary in brightness, in a characteristic way. From maximum magnitude of 3.8, it drops in about four days to 4.3. Then, in about a day and a half, it returns to its former brightness; the period is 5.4 days.

Many stars that show this sort of variation are known; they are called *Cepheids* after the first one discovered. Studies with the spectroscope revealed that the positions of the lines shifted first toward the red, then the blue, indicating alternate recession and approach, just as with eclipsing binaries. Indeed, it was formerly thought that the Cepheids were eclipsing stars. However, when one is at minimum brightness, it shows the most rapid speed of recession. In Algol, as we saw, the minimum occurs when neither star is approaching or receding, and the lines are not shifted at all.

Apparently the Cepheids are pulsating, alternately swelling and shrinking. During the expansion, the part of the star's surface toward us approaches rapidly, and during the shrinkage, this same part recedes. The star is faintest when most rapidly contracting, and brightest when the rate of expansion is greatest. Thus it is not the increased size, with its largest surface area, that makes it brighter; it really does increase in brilliance. At the same time it changes color, to become more bluish at maximum, which means an increase in temperature of about 3,600 degrees.

Apparently the change in size of the star causes an alteration in the production of nuclear energy inside, while that change tends to maintain the pulsations, so if they once start, for some unknown reason, the process would be self-perpetuating. According to one theory, the star contracts, producing higher pressures and temperatures at the core; the output of energy from the hydrogen-to-helium conversion process increases with the temperature. Thus there comes a point where the gravitational pull equals the outward pressure of the gases and of the radiations being emitted from the core.

If the contraction stopped then, the star would be maintained at the smaller diameter; but it doesn't stop. The inertia of the material moving inward carries it past the equilibrium point, just as a pendulum swings past the bottom of its arc, at which it could come to rest. This further increases the output of energy, which finally becomes so great that it does stop the contraction and starts expansion. Inertia again carries it past the equilibrium point. Now the star gets so large that pressure and temperature are considerably reduced. Expansion ceases, contraction starts again, and so the cycle continues indefinitely.

With such a process we might well expect that the Cepheids with lower average brightness, being smaller, would have less mass and could respond most rapidly. The brighter ones, on the other hand, would be much larger and the responses would be delayed. Consequently they would oscillate more slowly and take longer to go through the cycle.

CELESTIAL YARDSTICKS

This, indeed, has been observed to happen, and there is a definite *period-luminosity* relationship among Cepheids. Among the so-called classical Cepheids, a period of a day corresponds to an average absolute magnitude of about −0.5. One with a period of 20 days is about ten times as bright, of about −4 absolute magnitude. This relationship has made the Cepheids valuable yardsticks to the astronomer.

Cepheids usually can be readily recognized because of the way their light varies, brightening rapidly, dimming more slowly. Astronomers have curves showing the relation between period and luminosity; when you once recognize a Cepheid and time its cycle, in days and fractions of a day, you look for this period on the curve and read off the luminosity. The brightness that the star appears to have in the sky can be easily found—with a photometer, for example. The effect of distance on apparent brightness is well known: A star that is of the same luminosity as another but ten times as far away will look a hundredth as bright. (Apparent brightness decreases with the square of the distance.) Therefore, if you know how bright a star actually is, and how bright it looks, you can calculate its distance. This assumes that the diminution in light is due solely to increasing distance, and that there is no light-absorbing material in the way to produce additional dimming. If there is, we would tend to make the distances too great. Actually, in our Milky Way system of stars there is such absorbing material, but astronomers know of its presence and can make due allowance for its effect, but it does cause some complications.

In addition to the Cepheids and long-period variables, like Mira, there are many other types, and amateur astronomers are active keeping track of their changes. Much of this work can be done with relatively small telescopes and simple equipment. The American Association of Variable Star Observers include amateurs in the United States as well as other countries. At the headquarters, in Cambridge, Massachusetts, their observations are collected, correlated, and published regularly for the information of astronomers who wish to use them. The Variable Star Section of the British Astronomical Association is another important group in the same field.

STELLAR EXPLOSIONS

Most spectacular of all kinds of variable stars are the *novae* which occasionally flash out in various parts of the sky. These are also called "new stars," but they are not really new. A nova is a star that suddenly explodes to become a hundred thousand or more times brighter than before, then it gradually returns to its former condition.

A good example is one that appeared in 1918 in the constellation of Aquila (the eagle). Astronomers had not noticed it until the outburst, but as they examined photographs made previously of that part of the sky, they located the star and could tell something of its previous state. It had been of magnitude 11.8 and had been flickering in brightness in an irregular way, which may have indicated some sort of internal disturbance. Then, in a few hours, it increased in brightness about 160,000 times, which brought it to magnitude −1.4, or nearly equal to Sirius. Almost immediately it began to get fainter again. For a while it showed fluctuations, something like those of a Cepheid, so it may have been pulsating.

This did not continue, however, and now it has returned to the eleventh magnitude—and still flickers.

At maximum, its spectrum showed the usual dark absorption lines, all displaced the same amount, due to its radial velocity. But right after maximum there appeared a great many additional lines of absorption, displaced by varying amounts, so there were really several spectra, all superimposed. Then a few bright lines appeared and soon they dominated the entire spectrum. Apparently, the explosion inside burst through the surface, shooting out material in a number of streams, some coming in our direction, some more to the side, some toward the rear. Each showed its own spectrum, with a different shift. Those coming our way were moving from the star at more than a thousand miles per second, evidently the full speed with which the explosion ejected material from the star. Then bright lines appeared, some of them in the same positions as the dark absorption lines. These were evidently caused by glowing gases which produced the absorption, when they were in front of the stars, but shone by their own light when off to the side.

After a few years the star had faded to its former brightness, but astronomical photographs showed around it a nebulous cloud rapidly expanding. Year after year since then, astronomers have taken more pictures, and the cloud is still growing, at the same speed it had at the beginning. Out in the emptiness of space there is nothing to stop it or slow it, so it keeps on extending. Finally it will be so huge, and spread so thin, that it will no longer be observable.

Some novae go through their changes more slowly than this one, and there are many differences in their behavior. And while most of them seem to explode only once, then settle back to their former uneventful existence, there are some that do it over and over, in a period of some tens of years.

Apparently a nova outburst is rather superficial and the amount of stuff thrown out is only about a ten thousandth of the original mass of the star—not more than that of one of the larger planets. A number of years may pass between novae that shine in our skies as brightly as a first-magnitude star. However, some twenty or thirty occur each year in our own stellar system—the Galaxy. But most of these are so distant that an increase of even 10 or more magnitudes does not make the nova bright enough to be seen without a telescope. Although stars that become novae are generally about as massive as the Sun, it seems that the Sun is not likely to become

one. This is most fortunate, for, if the Sun's radiation were to increase by that amount, life would be wiped out completely on the
Earth.

SUPERNOVAE

Much rarer than the ordinary novae, and far more spectacular, are the supernovae that may appear in our Galaxy at average
intervals of centuries. The last to appear (unless one should occur
while this book is in press!) was seen in 1604 in the constellation
of Ophiuchus. Only 32 years prior to that, in 1572, one appeared
in Cassiopeia, and reached magnitude −4. It was as bright as Venus
when most brilliant, and could be seen in the daytime. This played
an important role in the history of astronomy, for it was well observed by the famous Danish astronomer Tycho Brahe—indeed it
is generally known as Tycho's nova. Up to that time it was believed that the heavens were changeless; the appearance of a bright
star where none had been seen before showed Tycho that changes
did occur. Thus it was largely responsible for starting him on a
career which contributed importantly to the development of modern astronomy.

Another (in Taurus) was seen in 1054. This was observed in
China, and it was recorded in the Chinese annals. The material
thrown off is still visible, as a huge cloud of nebulosity or glowing
matter, called the Crab Nebula because its shape somewhat resembles that animal. It is also a prominent source of radio waves,
and some of its radiation may be similar to the cosmic rays that
continually bombard the Earth from space. Indeed, some suggest
that a major portion of these rays come from the crab and similar
nebulae, in other parts of the sky, nebulae that originated in other
outbursts of supernovae.

Outside our Galaxy are many other galaxies that we can observe
through great telescopes; these will form the principal topic of
Chapter 14. There are millions of them, and, as a supernova seems
to occur in an average galaxy about once in four centuries, many
such distant supernovae have been studied. The exploding object
is often brighter than all the rest of the billion or so stars in that
stellar system.

Astronomers distinguish two types of supernova. Those of the
second group are more numerous and reach an absolute magnitude
of about −14, or about 40 million times brighter than the Sun. On

the whole, they behave very much like an ordinary nova, except for the scale, and their spectra are basically similar to those of common novae, although they show greater speeds of expansion.

Supernovae of Group I are about a sixth as frequent as those of Group II, and they have absolute magnitudes of about −16. Their spectra are very puzzling, but they indicate that something very violent occurred. Something between a hundredth and a tenth of the mass is thrown off, and afterwards the star does not, as do the ordinary novae, return to its former state. Evidently some violent nuclear process takes place inside. One suggestion is that it represents the process of conversion of a red, supergiant star, into a white dwarf.

Since supernovae seem to reach about the same absolute magnitude—either −14 or −16 depending on their group—they are helpful in measuring distances. As with the Cepheids, knowing both how bright they are and how bright they look, their distance can easily be calculated. Obviously, it is necessary to know whether any particular supernova belongs to group I or II, but this is shown by the spectrum, and the way the light changes.

STAR CLUSTERS

Not only are some stars double, triple, or multiple—they may even cluster together. The Pleiades, the seven sisters in Taurus, are an example of a loose cluster. In Hercules, overhead on summer evenings, there is an object, which can be seen well even through moderate-sized telescopes, known as Messier 13. This name comes from its number in the catalog, of non-stellar objects in the sky, prepared long ago by a French astronomer named Charles Messier.

This object is an example of a globular cluster, of which more than a hundred are known in our Galaxy. Each of these may contain some several hundred thousand stars, in a spherical mass about 40 parsecs in diameter. The stars are considerably more concentrated than they are in our part of the universe.

When astronomers first began to utilize the Hertzsprung-Russell diagram they naturally assumed that all stars followed the same pattern. But then they took the stars in some of the globular clusters, and made such a diagram for them alone. These stars showed quite a different sort of pattern. Then also Walter Baade, of Mount Wilson, studied one of the nearest of outer galaxies—the one in

Andromeda. This has a well-marked spiral structure, as does our own Galaxy. With ours, however, as we are in it and "cannot see the forest for the trees," it is more difficult to determine its structure. Baade found that the spectra of stars in the center of the

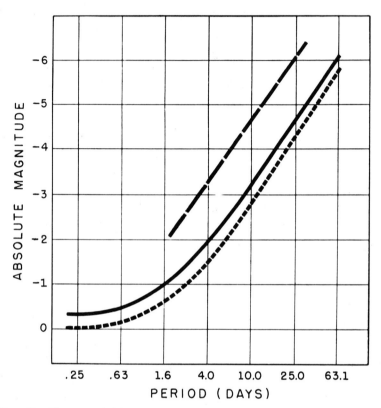

Fig. 49. The period–luminosity relation. The graph shows the relation between the luminosity of a Cepheid variable star and its period of variation. The middle solid line was believed originally to cover all of these objects. More recent work shows that there are two kinds: Population I (upper curve, long dashes) and Population II (lower curve, short dashes). The latter are fainter than Population 1 stars of the same period. (By permission from *Scientific American.* Copyright, 1959, Scientific American, Inc.)

Andromeda galaxy also showed the same sort of arrangement as did those in the clusters. Apparently those in the center of our own Galaxy are similar. The Sun is in the suburbs of this stellar city—in one of the spiral arms, so the conventional H-R diagram represents those in this local region.

Baade suggested that there are two large groups of stars, two *populations,* which he designated I and II. For Population I an important characteristic on the H-R diagram is the *main sequence,* which contains most of the stars. This extends across the diagram, from the very faint red (not white) dwarfs to the supergiants (classes O and B), which are anywhere from 4,000 to 60,000 times as bright as the Sun. The main sequence shows stars of practically every possible characteristic between these extremes. But in Population II, there are few of the brilliant giants and supergiants. Its main sequence extends from red dwarfs to stars that are just a little brighter than our Sun.

Population I stars are found where there is a lot of gas and dust between the stars, which is true where we are. In fact, out of such dust and gas, perhaps stars are still being formed. Where Population II stars are abundant, there is none of this interstellar material; these are the old stars, formed long ago. Some astronomers have proposed that there are really more than two populations. Perhaps there is even a gradual gradation, without any very sharp boundaries, and the two that we recognize today are merely the extremes. The problem is one that astronomers in recent years have been very actively considering, and future work will doubtless make it all much clearer.

The Cepheids, too, are of both populations. Earlier this had not been realized, and it was assumed, for example, that those in other galaxies were just like Cepheids nearer home. Measurements of distance were made on this basis. Now it turns out that there are two kinds; see Fig. 49. Those of the second type run about a magnitude and a half fainter than those of the classical type. It is type II that is found in outer galaxies, and with the change in estimates of brightness, the measuring stick has been altered. It has been shortened, which means that these objects are farther away than astronomers thought a few years ago.

Thus we see how advances in astronomy, as in any science, may explain matters that formerly puzzled us—but they bring up new problems which in turn have to be solved. That is the way science advances.

13

Empty Space: What's In It?

Suppose the authorities of New York City someday were to find that, in addition to their known population of some eight million, there were three million more people they had overlooked; it would be most sensational news!

Yet something of this sort has happened in astronomy in recent years. Our celestial city—the Galaxy—contains at least 25 per cent more matter than astronomers had estimated not very long ago.

They used to talk about "empty" space between the stars, and thought that generally it really was empty. True, there were some glowing clouds of gas and other clouds that reflected the light of nearby stars. These were called nebulae, and they seemed to be localized in certain regions. But now some striking advances have shown that space between the hundred thousand million or so stars in our Galaxy is not empty after all.

It is a far better vacuum than any that we can produce on Earth. Air, at sea-level pressure of 15 pounds to the square inch, contains about 4.4×10^{20} molecules, of nitrogen, oxygen, carbon dioxide, etc., in each cubic inch. With the most efficient vacuum pumps, scientists can get down to about a trillionth of normal air pressure. This leaves about 5×10^8 molecules to the cubic inch. Out in space the density is about a ten millionth of that, and most of the molecules are divided into individual atoms. There are about 16 of these atoms, mainly of hydrogen, to the cubic inch. Spread so sparsely, one might suppose they wouldn't be of much importance. However, there are so many cubic inches in the space between the stars that, even at 16 to the cubic inch, the Galaxy contains about a third as much matter in such interstellar form as in the stars themselves.

One of the first indications that space is not truly empty came, in 1925, when a Dutch astronomer, J. H. Oort, was studying movements of stars toward or away from the plane of the Milky Way. To do this, he had to calculate the gravitational pull of the Milky Way material, and this depended on its total mass. But, when he counted up all the stars and everything else then known to be there, the mass was not enough. There was something else, he decided, but he didn't know just what it was.

Another clue was found, in 1930, by Robert J. Trumpler, at the Lick Observatory in California. We have already mentioned the Pleiades, the seven sisters, in the constellation of Taurus. These form an example of a loose cluster, and many others are scattered around the sky. There are several types of loose cluster, and the members of each type are similar in size. Thus Trumpler could estimate their relative distances. If one cluster was a tenth the diameter of another of the same type, it would mean that the smaller one was ten times as far. Ten times farther away, it should look a hundredth as bright, or 5 magnitudes fainter. But he found that, under such conditions, the more distant cluster was about 6 magnitudes fainter; evidently something besides mere distance was reducing its light. Something was in the way, absorbing a little of the light.

Then there were still other clues. We are all familiar with the red color of the setting Sun. This is ordinarily due to the fact that, as sunlight passes through the atmosphere, some of its blue rays are scattered. These give the daytime sky its blue color. The light that passes through lacks a part of its normal blue component, so red is predominant. When the Sun is high in the sky, its light doesn't have to go through as much air as when it is setting or rising. At the same time that you see the red Sun close to the horizon in the evening, its blue rays are reaching people to the west, from their blue sky overhead. But, when there is much dust or smoke in the air, the setting Sun looks even redder. These dust particles absorb more of the blue part of the light, and the reddening effect is greatly increased.

Astronomers found that, when they compared stars at different distances but of the same spectral class—and hence of the same color—the more remote ones were reddened. Apparently, scattered through space, there is some sort of cosmic dust which affects the starlight in much the same manner that dust in the atmosphere affects the light from the Sun.

STATIONARY LINES

In the spectra of distant stars, astronomers had found dark lines that didn't belong there. They showed absorption—of calcium and other elements—but not by the stars themselves. This was evident because the stars were often approaching or receding, and corresponding Doppler shifts of the stellar lines appeared in their spectra. But the strange lines showed no such shift, which meant that absorbing elements were not moving with the star. They must, therefore, be due to material in interstellar space.

And also, in a number of places in the sky, there are dark spots. Years ago, in England, Sir William Herschel noticed one of these when looking through his great telescope, and exclaimed: "There is surely a hole in the sky!" But these dark spots couldn't be holes; for with the stars at vastly different distances, any "hole" would have to be a long tube devoid of stars and aimed right toward us. Even in the unlikely event that such a starless tube might form, it would soon be filled by the motions of the stars. No, these dark nebulae, as they were called, must be clouds of obscuring matter.

The extent to which interstellar material hides what is beyond depends on the size of the particles. Robert Wilson, a Scottish astronomer working at the Dominion Astrophysical Observatory at Victoria, B.C., explained in one of the informative leaflets issued by the Astronomical Society of the Pacific:

"The interstellar gas is virtually transparent at ordinary visual wavelengths and this is true in general for any cold gas, as shown by the very great distances we can see on a *clear* day. On other days, however, the visibility can be reduced from several miles to a few feet. This happens when impurities in the form of small particles (dust, fog, smog, etc.) are present in the atmosphere. Small particles (solid or liquid) are extremely efficient blockers of light and have a maximum efficiency when their size is of the order of the wavelength of the incident light. This is best illustrated by an example.

"Suppose we were given a single sphere of water, one inch in diameter or about one-half of a cubic inch in volume, and could subdivide this into as many globules as we wished and place them, in space, in the beam of the 100-inch telescope when it is pointed at a star. What would be the obscuration observed by the telescope?

"In the form of a single globule, it would be impossible to detect, even with present-day photoelectric methods. Only when we had broken down the sphere into many globules, each 1/100th of an inch in diameter, would the obscuration (about 2%) become detectable. If the size of the globules is decreased further, the obscuration would increase more rapidly, until globules of the wavelength of visible light [about 1/50,000th of an inch] would effectively block the view of the telescope and we would have conditions similar to a cloudy night. A *further* decrease in size would cause a rapid *increase* in obscuration until the globules were vaporized [and separated into molecules] when obscuration would again be undetectable."

The obscuring particles do not produce the highly selective absorption that causes the dark lines to appear in the spectrum, so the spectroscope cannot tell us much about their nature. However, other ways of analyzing the light do reveal something about them. For one thing, they are polarized.

Ordinary vibrations of light waves, you will recall from Chapter 2, are up-and-down; side-to-side; in fact, in all possible directions. But light can be *polarized,* and the vibrations made to occur mainly in one plane, which may be oriented vertically, sideways, or diagonally. The easiest way to produce polarized light is by passing it through a Polaroid filter, but there are many other methods.

Two American astronomers, John S. Hall and A. W. Hiltner, found that starlight is often polarized and that there is some correlation between the amount of reddening and the polarization. This makes it quite likely that the same interstellar stuff that makes the light red also polarizes it. Moreover, stars in the same direction tend to show the same orientation of their planes of polarization, which would be expected from an extensive cloud in front that caused the effect.

NEEDLE-SHAPED DUST

Spherical dust particles, or those of random, irregular shape, could not polarize light passing by them. Needle-shaped particles could do it, if they were predominantly lined up in parallel directions, but what would line them up? The most reasonable explanation is a magnetic field. There is a familiar experiment, performed in physics classes, to show the magnetic field around a magnet. A glass plate is laid on top of the magnet and iron filings are sprinkled over it. When the plate is tapped, the filings line up along the magnetic lines of force. Similarly, magnetic lines of force in the galaxy might line up these interstellar particles.

This would require that they be of iron or some other metal affected by a magnet. However, they may not be entirely metallic. There is considerable evidence that they are made of non-metallic ices—even ordinary ice or frozen water—but they might have metallic cores.

Now that we have become acquainted with the stuff between the stars, we can see what it has to do with the nebulae that have been recorded in the Galaxy.

Several times we have referred to the Pleiades in Taurus. Six of these stars are ordinarily visible with the naked eye. Through a small telescope you can see more than a hundred, and a photograph taken with a large telescope shows thousands. But a long exposure, through a big instrument, brings out something else: nebulous clouds around many of the stars. Spectral analysis of the light from the clouds shows that it is just the same as that from the stars themselves. In other words, it is reflected starlight. There is a lot of cosmic dust around the Pleiades, which reflects their light, making a good example of a reflection nebula.

A short distance from Taurus is the figure of Orion, the warrior, so familiar in the winter sky. Three stars in a row form his belt, bright Betelgeuse is above, in one shoulder, and Rigel below, in one of his legs. Hanging from his belt is his sword, according to the way he was pictured on the old star maps. And in the sword is the star known as theta Orionis.

On a dark clear night theta looks a little hazy, and through a telescope you can see a beautiful lake of light. Photographs bring out even greater detail. This *Great Nebula in Orion* has been observed since the earliest days of telescopic astronomy. Its spectrum, too, has been recorded, but it turns out to be quite different from that of the nearby stars. There are bright lines, showing emission of light from hydrogen, helium, nitrogen, and oxygen, which have been ionized to varying degrees. This is a good example of an emission nebula. But there still is dust associated with it. Part of the Orion nebula itself is hidden by obscuring clouds, and a short distance away, near the star. Alnitak, the easternmost of the stars in the belt, is one of the most familiar of dark nebulae, with the shape of a horse's head.

What, then, determines whether a nebula is of the emission type, or shines by simple reflection? It is mainly the temperature of the nearby stars. The Pleiades are relatively cool, of type A or among the cooler of type B, with temperatures around 20,000° F. Theta Orionis, however, is much hotter, around 60,000° F., as it is of type O.

FLUORESCENT NEBULAE

Being so hot, much of its radiation is in the ultraviolet, and as these rays shine on the hydrogen and other gases nearby, they ionize them. When the electrons return toward their normal places, light is given off by the process of fluorescence. But the cooler Pleiades yield radiation of much lower energy which is incapable of causing such ionization. All that can be seen nearby is the reflection from the dust. Even in the emission nebulae there is some reflected starlight, although it is overpowered by the fluorescence.

Nebulae like the one in Orion are called *diffuse*. But in addition to these, there is another type of emission nebula. A good example is the Ring Nebula in Lyra, which appears through a telescope like a huge smoke ring. Actually it is not a ring, but a globe of glowing gases. Another, in Ursa Major, called the Owl Nebula, appears as a glowing disc. Two dark spots form the eyes and so make it resemble an owl's face—hence the name.

Since these nebulae present the appearance of a disc, rather than a point, when seen through a telescope, they are quite different from the images of the stars. They resemble somewhat the discs of planets. Thus they have long been called *planetary* nebulae, although they have nothing to do with planets, aside from appearance. They are far larger, and much farther away.

Compared to stars, planetary nebulae are rather rare. Until the end of the 1940's only about a hundred were known; then Rudolf Minkowski, at the Mount Wilson Observatory, began an intensive search and found many new ones, mostly in the center of the Galaxy. Some 500 are now known, at distances out to about 30,000 light-years. However even within this distance, there are undoubtedly many more hidden behind the dust clouds. The total number in our Galaxy may be as great as 50,000, a minute fraction of the number of stars that it contains. Individually, their diameters range from 20,000 to 200,000 times the distance of the Earth from the Sun.

The photograph of the Ring Nebula shows a star right at the center. When you look at it through a telescope you cannot see this star, because its radiation is mainly in the invisible ultraviolet and that means it is very hot. This is typical of the planetaries—this hot star at the center, one with a surface temperature of perhaps 90,000° F. or more.

The spectrum of a planetary shows that its light comes from emission, and also that the gases are expanding at a speed of 5 to 20 miles a second. This reminds us of the behavior of a nova, as described in the previous chapter. Indeed, it has been suggested that planetary nebulae are former novae, but there are serious objections to this theory. One point is that the stars which form the nuclei of planetary nebulae are cooler, bigger, and less dense than former novae.

Even more telling are the arguments advanced by Minkowski. Whereas the envelopes of the novae expand at speeds of 200 to 1,000 miles per second, the greatest known speed of expansion for a planetary is about 35 miles per second, with the mean around 12 miles per second. The mass of a typical bright planetary is about a tenth of the Sun's mass, while that of the gaseous envelope of a nova has been estimated at 1/10,000 that of the Sun. With its high speed of expansion, and low mass, the nova envelope has a short life—usually not more than 20 years—while the planetary nebulae seem quite permanent, lasting probably tens of thousands of years. Thus novae and planetaries seem quite different breeds of objects, even though in both cases the material has been ejected from the star by some internal instability.

THE BIRTH OF A WHITE DWARF

According to one theory, a planetary nebula represents the conversion of a star into a white dwarf. There is one planetary (NGC 7293) for which a parallax has been found, measured from the central star. This is 85 light-years away, and astronomers have determined that its central star has a density 300,000 times that of water, so it is a white dwarf.

Otto Struve has estimated that there are 60,000 planetaries in our Galaxy and that it takes 20,000 years for one to go through its evolutionary course. Thus each year, three stars would become planetaries and three planetaries would become white dwarfs. In a billion years, three billion white dwarfs would be added to the Galaxy—and this is about the total number it is believed to contain.

But now let us return to the material between the stars, principally the gas. One of the most powerful means for studying it has been the application of radio astronomy, as described in Chapter 3. You will recall that in 1951, Purcell and Ewen, at Harvard, first detected the hydrogen radiation waves predicted a little earlier by van de Hulst, in Holland. These have a wave length of 21 cm. or 7.9 inches. Not only do they show the presence of hydrogen, even when it is cold; they also show its movement. In some cases the signals are received at a slightly longer wave length than 21 cm., due to a Doppler shift, and this indicates that the cloud from which it comes is receding. Others are approaching, for their signals are of slightly shorter wave length. Moreover radio waves pass freely through the obscuring clouds that stop the light from distant parts of the Galaxy. Thus they bring us information about remote regions that cannot be observed with any optical telescope. They have shown that our Galaxy has a spiral structure similar to that of the spiral nebulae observed by the millions. But these are the subject of the next chapter.

14

Our Galaxy—and Others

Why is the sky dark at night?

Such a question, at first glance, may seem foolish. The answer is obvious—the Sun isn't up. But consider the stars. If they continued indefinitely in all directions, no matter where we looked we would finally come to a star. At increasingly greater distances the stars would appear fainter, but these greater distances would take in so many more stars that each increase in distance would add the same amount of light. This would continue until stars completely filled the sky, with no open spaces between; any that are still farther away would then be hidden. The sky everywhere would be as bright as the Sun itself, so we would receive from the whole sky some three billion times as much light and heat as we do from the Sun. If this happened, of course, the Earth, like other planets, would be heated far above temperatures that life can withstand.

A German astronomer, H. W. M. Olbers, pointed this out in 1826, and it is called *Olbers' paradox*. The fact that we don't have such a bright sky is good evidence that our original assumption that the stars extend indefinitely must be wrong. They are limited in their extent.

There is other evidence that our stellar system is limited. In dealing with large numbers of stars, we can neglect differences in luminosity, or candle power, and assume that all are of the same brightness. Neglecting absorption in interstellar space, a star of the third magnitude would be 1.6 times as far as one of the second magnitude; one of the fourth, 1.6 times as far as a third-magnitude star, and so on. Thus, all the stars of the first magnitude are within a certain distance, within a sphere of which the Earth is the center. Stars of first and second magnitudes are within a sphere that has 1.6 times the radius—and also 1.6 times the diameter—of the first-magnitude sphere. The sphere of the first, second, and third magnitude stars is 1.6 times the diameter of that one, and so on.

As we reach out to a sphere of larger diameter, we also include a larger volume of space. A sphere of 1.6 times the diameter of another has 4 times its volume. With the stars uniformly distributed, 4 times the volume of space would mean 4 times as many stars—for each magnitude fainter.

But this is not the case. There are 22 stars of the first magnitude and 40 of the first and second, with the ratio less than two. However, this is hardly enough to make any accurate judgment: our immediate neighborhood may not be typical. Going down to magnitude three, we find 135 stars. Here is an increase of 3.4, not far below four. At the fourth magnitude, which includes a total of 450 stars, the ratio drops slightly, to 3.3. It is the same when we go to the fifth magnitude, with 1,500 stars. Then it drops to 3.2 as we go down to the sixth magnitude with some 4,800 stars. This brings us to the faintest that we can see with the naked eye. Below this a telescope is required, and the stars become so numerous that it is hard to count them all. Instead, astronomers have counted selected typical areas.

With 324,000 stars to the tenth magnitude and 870,000 to the eleventh, the ratio has decreased to 2.7. And from nineteenth to twentieth (stars so faint that a really large telescope is required to show them) the number increases from about 560 million to a billion, a ratio of 1.8. At about magnitude thirty, too faint to be seen even with the 200-inch Hale telescope, the ratio would be one. That is, we would then have reached the limit, and further increase in distance would add no more stars.

CONCENTRATED IN MILKY WAY

It was in 1784 that Sir William Herschel began to make such studies of star distribution. Moreover, he noticed that, while the brighter stars were rather uniformly distributed, the fainter ones were concentrated toward the Milky Way. Therefore, he decided, the stars must extend considerably farther toward that luminous band. In other words, the stellar system of which we are part is shaped like a disc. When we look out toward the edge, we see a great concentration of stars—the Milky Way—but when we look toward the sides we see a smaller number.

This conclusion is confirmed by modern star counts. Toward the Milky Way, even for stars that are quite faint, the ratio for each increase in magnitude is close to 4. In fact, toward the constellation of Sagittarius it becomes even greater than 4; in that direction the concentration actually increases. This is the center of our disc-shaped system, the Galaxy.

This is our celestial city—but are there other such cities, other galaxies, beyond its limits? For many years astronomers asked such questions, and were divided in their answers.

On fall evenings, from parts of the world in the north temperate latitudes, one may look overhead toward the constellation of Andromeda and, with a dark clear sky, see a hazy patch of light that looks about as big as the full Moon. It isn't prominent; a telescope shows it better. A photograph made through a large telescope brings out its structure, which is a spiral. Many such *spiral nebulae* were found by astronomers as bigger telescopes were built and observational methods, especially by photography, were improved.

At first they supposed that spiral nebulae were not greatly different from other nebulae, such as the irregular one in Orion. However, there were some peculiarities. The irregular, gaseous nebulae are most numerous where stars are most numerous—toward the Milky Way. This is true of practically all other objects except the spirals. Spirals seem to avoid other types of objects. There are no spirals in the Milky Way direction, but they are most numerous off toward the sides of the galactic disc. One explanation of such distribution might be that the spirals are other galaxies, out beyond the limits of our own. In the direction of the Milky Way, the concentration of stars—and, as later learned, the obscuring dust—would hide them, but toward the sides spirals could be seen with little interference. The philosopher, Immanuel Kant, suggested this in 1785, although the spiral structure of these nebulae had not then been recognized.

The spectroscope provided additional evidence in favor of this theory when it was applied to the spiral nebulae. It showed that their light was quite different from that of the Orion nebula and others of that sort, with the bright lines from glowing gases. The spectrum of a spiral is more like that of stars with many dark lines, but not like any one star. Instead, spirals combine the characteristics of many, as if they were assemblages of stars of various types.

Despite such evidence, however, many astronomers believed, as late as 1920, that the spiral nebulae were part of our own system. But in 1919, the 100-inch telescope began operation at Mount Wilson. It was the largest in the world, an honor it held until the 200-inch at Mount Palomar was finished.

During the early twenties, Edwin P. Hubble, of Mount Wilson, used the 100-inch to photograph some of the larger and presumably nearer, of the spiral nebulae, particularly the one in Andromeda, the only one visible to the naked eye.

A GALAXY OF STARS

In 1924, he was able to show the individual stars of which it consists. Some, fortunately, are Cepheids, and by measuring their periods, he obtained their brightnesses—and their distances. Thus he estimated that the Andromeda nebula was at a little under a million light-years. Later studies, as we shall find presently, have pushed this distance out to more than 2 million light-years, but at least Hubble showed that it was well beyond the limits of our own system, even if that was 300,000 light-years in diameter, as some astronomers then believed. They had not recognized the effect of the cosmic dust in absorbing light, a factor which has helped to reduce the estimated diameter of our Galaxy to about 80,000 light-years.

Hubble found the distances of a few other spirals also and so proved the *island universe* theory—the idea that these really are other "universes," like our Galaxy. As astronomers studied these in greater detail, with more powerful instruments, they realized that from such research they could form a better idea of the possible nature of our own system.

Other galaxies show a variety of forms, and not all are spirals. Some are masses of stars, with little regular structure. And even the spirals show a variety of appearances, but this depends largely on how they happen to be oriented. Some we see on edge, and many of these show a line of dark material in their central plane, much like the meat in a ham sandwich. Others, such as the one in Andromeda, we see at an angle, and others we see broadside.

With the recognition that our Galaxy was probably also a spiral, astronomers sought to draw a plan of the stars in it and to locate the spiral arms. But this seemed to offer insuperable difficulties. It would be very difficult, for example, to draw a plan of Washington, D.C., from a point out on Connecticut Avenue, say at the National Bureau of Standards. From an airplane flying high above the city, the general layout of streets, parks, etc., would be clear.

But even in such a city, you might be able to trace certain streets, particularly the nearer ones, if they were brightly lighted and had many neon signs to advertise stores and theaters.

In 1951, Walter Baade made photographs of the Andromeda galaxy with the 100-inch and 200-inch telescopes, through filters that passed only the red light of glowing hydrogen, and the arms stood out more prominently than in some other colors. This showed that the arms contained a considerable amount of glowing hydrogen. In addition they found that the arms contain many of the giant hot stars of types O and B.

With O and B stars providing such an excellent means of tracing the spiral arms of other galaxies, it occurred to a Yerkes Observatory astronomer, W. W. Morgan, that they might be used in a similar manner in our own. So, in a cooperative effort by several observatories, a search was made for O and B stars in the Milky Way galaxy, and also for faint areas of glowing hydrogen. If the direction and distance of these objects were found, it seemed, the nearer spiral arms at least might be traced.

Already it was known that there are a number of such stars and nebulae in the direction of Orion, and they found that these continued in one direction toward the constellation of Monoceros (the unicorn) and in the other toward Cassiopeia, Cepheus, and Cygnus. This Orion arm was the first one that Morgan identified. He traced it for about 12,000 light-years, and found that it is about 1,200 light-years wide. The Sun seems to be in this arm, about 150 light-years from the inner edge. In addition he found a second arm that passes through Perseus and is about 7,000 light-years away. There is also a third arm which passes through Sagittarius, but it's mostly out of reach from northern observatories. This was traced from the Harvard Observatory's Boyden Station in South Africa. But none of these observations reached out more than about 15,000 light-years from the Sun; the obscuring clouds hid them at greater distances. They didn't even reach to the center of our galaxy, 27,000 light-years away, much less to the other side. So all they showed was the rough arrangement of some of the principal streets in our immediate neighborhood of the celestial city.

RADIO TO THE RESCUE

Then radio astronomy provided a powerful new tool. Baade had shown that one of the finest means of tracing spiral structure was by the interstellar hydrogen gas. And so, when van de Hulst, Purcell, and Ewen showed that hydrogen in the Galaxy could be traced by 21-cm. radio waves, astronomers quickly realized that they could now trace the spiral arms in a way that would not be affected by obscuring matter.

Probably not more than 10 per cent of the hydrogen between the stars is ionized, allowing it to radiate light. But the non-ionized hydrogen, potentially, is capable of emitting 21-cm. radiation, so astronomers can use it to trace all of the spiral arms. As mentioned earlier, the hydrogen waves show a Doppler shift in proportion to the speeds of approach or recession of the clouds of gas. First the radio astronomer directs his radio telescope toward a particular part of the sky, and tunes the receiver to a slightly shorter wave length. Then he changes it, past 21 cm., to the longer waves. A moving pen records the intensity on a strip of paper; it starts low, goes up to a peak when the hydrogen waves are coming in, then drops again.

But a Doppler shift causes the peak to come a little below the exact wave length, if the emitting gas is approaching us, or above, if it is receding. And very often such a record shows two or more peaks. This means that, in the same direction, there are several clouds of hydrogen, moving at different speeds. They would be clouds in different arms.

Thus, the astronomer can tell that there are several clouds, and several arms, in a particular direction, but he must also find their distances. He cannot do this directly, but he has made a tentative model of the layout of the Galaxy and knows what speeds to expect in different directions at given distances. Just as the outermost planets of the solar system move more slowly, in miles per second, than those nearer the Sun, so do the speeds of rotation around the center of the Galaxy vary. Our Sun and the planets with it, as well as nearby stars, all at about the same distance of 27,000 light-

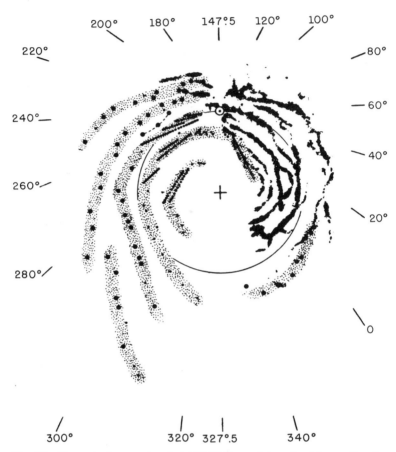

Fig. 50. The spiral structure of the Galaxy as determined by radio observations. The galactic center is marked by the cross, and the Sun's position—27,000 light-years from the center—by the open circle with central dot. The black arms are those whose position is determined from northern hemisphere data (Leiden). Those indicated by stippling have been located with southern hemisphere data from the Sydney observatory. (By permission from *The Astronomer's Universe*, by Bart J. Bok. Copyright, 1958, Melbourne Univ. Press, Victoria, Australia.)

years from the galactic center, revolve around the center at a speed of about 140 miles per second. Stars that are farther out move more slowly, while those nearer the center are more rapid. This was shown by spectroscopic and other observations long before the development of radio astronomy. Thus, even though he didn't know where the various arms were located, the astronomer already had a plan, showing the velocities that would occur at different distances from the center. Thus, when the radio astronomer finds a particular Doppler velocity for a hydrogen cloud, he can give it a definite distance.

The first such radio observations of the spiral arms were made from the Leiden observatory in Holland, but they could only reach the northerly parts of the Milky Way. Astronomers at Sydney, Australia, then observed the other parts. Thus they have plotted a large part of our Galaxy, as shown in Fig. 50. The Orion arm, for which Morgan identified the nearby parts, and the one in which the Sun is located, has been extended far in both directions. The curve of the spiral is taking us in closer to the center, so the arms are moving like a watch spring that is being wound up.

Bart J. Bok has summarized our present knowledge of the Galaxy. While our picture of the spiral pattern is still tentative and subject to further modification and refinement, he says:

". . . there can be little doubt that our Milky Way system is truly a spiral galaxy and that the spiral arms occupy most of the region between 10,000 and 50,000 light-years from the center. We have found that interstellar gas plays a very important role in our Milky Way system and that for our region around the Sun it accounts for approximately one-third of the total density of matter. Cosmic dust is far less prevalent than gas, but it must be reckoned with in all our researches, first, because the dust is a fine tracer for the gas and helps us to find the spiral pattern, and, second, because the cosmic dust is sufficiently dense to hide from large optical telescopes more than half our Milky Way system.

"Radio-astronomical studies supplement our optical studies of the Milky Way in a most satisfactory fashion. The radio rays possess the happy faculty of penetrating without loss of energy through the dense clouds of cosmic dust near the galactic plane, and by means of radio astronomy we seem to have no difficulties in studying the other half of our galactic system. Radio astronomy fails in that it does not as yet give us a well-defined method for fixing the distances of the sources of galactic radio emission, but . . . real headway can be made through coordinated studies by optical and radio-astronomical means." *

* By permission from *The Astronomer's Universe* by Bart J. Bok. Copyright, 1958, Cambridge Univ. Press, Cambridge, and Melbourne Univ. Press, Melbourne.

THE GLOBULAR CLUSTERS

In Chapter 12, in connection with the Cepheids, we mentioned the globular star clusters but did not describe their connection with the Galaxy. The average diameter of such a cluster is about 130 light-years and it may contain several hundred thousand stars. These stars are more concentrated than in the parts of space near us. At the center of such a cluster, where the density is about a hundred times greater than the average throughout its huge volume, the stars may be concentrated about 1,500 times as thickly as they are around the Sun, and the average distance between stars may be but a small fraction of a light-year. From a planet revolving around a star at the center of a globular cluster, the night sky would be dazzling. The brightest stars would be as brilliant as the full Moon, while there would be thousands as bright as Sirius.

The distribution of globular clusters is most significant. Over a hundred are known and perhaps another hundred are hidden. But most of them are in one half of the sky, towards Scorpio and Sagittarius; the other half is almost devoid of them. This was very puzzling when astronomers thought that the Sun was at the center of the Milky Way system, but it is easy to explain when we realize that we are out in the suburbs. The 200 or so globular clusters themselves form a spherical system, grouped around the center of the Galaxy. Those most distant from the galactic center are a little less than our distance: that's why we see them in the half of the sky toward the center.

With the stars in a globular cluster so thickly distributed, there is a considerable gravitational pull on the individual stars by the combined mass of the entire cluster. All the members of a cluster must be revolving rapidly in orbits around the center, otherwise they would fall toward it.

And all the globular clusters themselves seem to be moving in very elongated orbits around the center of the Galaxy, so they dip in close to the center, then swing out to their maximum distances of 20,000 or so light-years. Struve has estimated that the period of revolution of a familiar globular cluster—the one in Hercules, overhead on a summer night—is about 100 million years. With the lifetime of the Galaxy some 6 billion years, each cluster, therefore, may have dipped into the Milky Way nucleus 60 times.

The stars in a globular cluster are mainly of Population II, and as these are believed to be old stars, it seems that such clusters were formed a long time ago. Perhaps they evolved from a compact cloud of dust and gas, but none of this now remains between their stars. Perhaps such vestiges have been swept away on successive passages through the center of the Galaxy. They may have been drawn into the stars themselves, or pushed out into space by the radiation pressure of light from the stars.

THE MAGELLANIC CLOUDS

Visible in Southern Hemisphere skies, in the constellations of Dorado and Hydrus, are two patches of light that resemble detached pieces of the Milky Way. A telescopic view reveals that, like the Milky Way, they are swarms of stars. In them are many of the same kind of object that we see elsewhere in the sky—stars of various types, including Cepheid variables, hot stars of types O and B, star clusters, cosmic dust, and interstellar gas; all these appear. These are called the Magellanic Clouds, after the great Portuguese navigator whose men first circumnavigated the globe and brought back to Europe a description of the objects.

These clouds are the nearest of the other galaxies. The larger cloud, which extends for about 11 degrees in the sky, is at a distance that has been estimated at about 145,000 light-years. This would make its diameter about 30,000 light-years, so it is much smaller than the Milky Way galaxy. The smaller cloud is apparently a little farther—163,000 light-years is one estimate—and its diameter about 23,000 light-years. These clouds are not generally classed as spirals, although some astronomers have thought they detected some trace of spirality in the larger. Generally they are considered irregular galaxies.

In the constellation of Andromeda, however, is a fine spiral. When Hubble first identified the Cepheids in this object, he assumed (as he had every right to assume, on the basis of then current knowledge) that these fitted into the same scale of brightness used for other Cepheids—in the clusters and in our own system. But after Baade discovered the two stellar populations, as noted earlier, astronomers realized that there are two kinds of Cepheids as well as of other stars.

In 1946, a Swedish astronomer, Knut Lundmark, at the University of Lund, called attention to the fact that the distance of the Andromeda galaxy, as determined from the Cepheids, was about half of the value obtained from estimates made by other means. But still most astronomers who worked on the problem thought that the Cepheid method was the most reliable.

In our own Galaxy, Cepheids had been discovered in the globular clusters, with periods of about half a day, as compared with those studied earlier, with periods of the order of 10 days. Nevertheless, it seemed, they all fitted on the same scale of period and brightness. The cluster-type would have an absolute magnitude of about zero, or one-sixth the brightness of the 10-day stars. At the Andromeda galaxy's estimated distance of 800,000 light-years, they would appear of about the 22nd magnitude.

THE CEPHEIDS THAT WEREN'T THERE

The 100-inch telescope can only observe stars as faint as the 20th magnitude, so the cluster-type Cepheids in the Andromeda galaxy were invisible with that instrument. But, as the 200-inch can go down to magnitude 22, it seemed capable of showing this type. It seemed certain that such cluster-type variables were present. However, when Baade hunted for them with the 200-inch, he couldn't find any! Evidently something was wrong. Perhaps Lundmark had been right, perhaps the other criteria of distance— globular clusters, new stars, etc.—were to be trusted, and the Andromeda galaxy was twice as far as they had thought. Then the cluster variables in it would be too faint to be seen even with the 200-inch.

Globular clusters also had been found around the Magellanic clouds, and astronomers had searched these for cluster variables, thinking they would appear about magnitude 17. None had been found. But then J. Wesselink and A. D. Thackeray, at the observatory in Pretoria, South Africa, used a powerful 74-inch telescope, that had recently been installed, to look among the fainter stars. Sure enough, they found cluster-type Cepheids, but about 1.5 magnitude fainter, i.e., about a quarter the luminosity. In most respects, other than brightness, these were like the rest of the Cepheids. Thus it became clear that the Cepheids are of two types, which are known as I and II, corresponding to the two stellar populations.

But still astronomers wondered where the error was. The classical type I Cepheids might be brighter than they had formerly supposed—or those of type II might be fainter. The matter was settled at the Mount Wilson–Palomar Observatory. Using data obtained by Allan R. Sandage in a study of one star cluster, Baade was able to show that its variables, which were of the cluster type (II), had an absolute magnitude of about zero, agreeing with the earlier determinations.

Hence the error had been made in estimating the brightness of the older, classical-type Cepheids. They were about 1.5 magnitude brighter than we used to think. And if they were brighter, they had to be pushed out about twice as far to give the same apparent magnitude. It's something like weighing with weights that you unexpectedly find are twice as heavy as you thought them to be. The weight marked "one pound" really weighs two pounds. Hence all the things you weighed before are twice as heavy as you had supposed.

An even better analogy might be this: Suppose that you are in a big field, at night, where there are a lot of electric lights at different distances. They're all supposed to be 25-watt lamps; so, from the way they look, you can estimate which are near and which are farther away. But now you find that some are 100-watt lamps, four times as bright as you thought them to be. It is easy to see how you would have placed these too close. They would look as bright as a 25-watt bulb half as far away, since the variation corresponds (inversely) with the square of the distance, and doubling the distance reduces the apparent brightness to a quarter.

Such considerations made the distance of the Andromeda galaxy 1.6 million light-years, twice the old value of 800,000 light-years. But even this has had to be modified, and later estimates put the distance at about 2.5 million light-years, a value probably subject to more revision. Moreover, it seems that the Cepheids are not as reliable yardsticks as we once thought, for they do not fit on a neat curve. They occupy a wide band, and even if two Cepheids have the same period, and both are of the same type, they may not be of similar luminosity. Color seems to be another important factor in determining brightness.

One result of the increased distance of the Andromeda galaxy has been to remove an apparent discrepancy in size. When it was placed less than a million light-years away, it seemed considerably smaller than our system. But now we know that it is even bigger than ours, which seems to be average, and astronomers feel better satisfied.

OUR LOCAL GROUP OF GALAXIES

Just as stars group together into clusters and galaxies, so the galaxies themselves gather into groups, and the Milky Way system belongs to one. The Andromeda spiral; another in the constellation of the triangle, less than half the diameter of our own; and the Magellanic clouds: all are members of the local group. So are at least nine other objects, most of which are considerably smaller. Perhaps there are some others that have not been identified. One interesting point is that only three of these are spirals, but they are the biggest. The others include elliptical systems or irregular galaxies, some less than a tenth the diameter of the Milky Way Galaxy. If this region of space is typical, it would seem that spiral nebulae are not the most numerous of the outer galaxies. However, being generally larger and brighter, they are the easiest to see at considerable distances.

Our cluster of galaxies is only one of many in the sky—and it's a rather small one at that. At a distance of about 40 million light-years, in the direction of the constellations of Cassiopeia and Coma Berenices, is a much more spectacular cluster, or *supergalaxy*, with some 500 members. It seems that the universe of galaxies is composed of clusters of different sizes.

The mean distance between galaxies (in the part of the universe that we can observe) is something over 2 million light-years, but in a cluster they are much closer. So close are they, in fact, that perhaps once in a billion years any one of them might collide with one of its neighbors. But even if two galaxies collide, the stars of each are so far apart in proportion to their diameters that one galaxy can pass freely through another without any collisions of stars. However, there would be plenty of collisions between atoms of hydrogen in the interstellar gas. These atoms would quickly become ionized and would be given high speeds—equal to that of a temperature of many millions of degrees. Thus the gas would be moving so fast that it would soon escape from each of the participants in the collision, and they would be left with practically empty space between the stars.

Such highly ionized gas is a good emitter of radio waves. During the earliest days of radio astronomy, a very strong source of radiation was detected in Cygnus. When the 200-inch telescope was directed toward this direction, a rich cluster of galaxies was discovered. Right in the direction of the radio source there was a peculiar object—a galaxy with two condensations close together. This is shown in Plate 16. Apparently this is a collision, and the tidal pull of one galaxy on the other accounts for their peculiar appearance. Moreover, the spectrum of this object shows that more than half of the light is radiation from glowing hydrogen, a fact quite consistent with the collision hypothesis. Even if this object were considerably farther—so distant that it could not be photographed even with the 200-inch telescope—we could still pick up its radio waves. Perhaps many radio sources, most of which have not been identified with observable objects, also represent galaxies in collision.

THE RED SHIFT

When the first spectroscopic observations were made of the spiral nebulae, as they were called at that time, a few were found to be approaching the Solar System, but, as these studies extended to fainter objects, red shifts, indicating recession, seemed to be the rule. In the years between 1929 and 1936, Milton L. Humason, at Mount Wilson, obtained spectra for a great many galaxies, and all showed a shift to the red. As their distances were estimated from various criteria, it proved, as Hubble pointed out, that there is a close relation between their distances and the speeds at which they seem to be receding from us. In fact, this relation is now so well established that it works the other way—the red shift in the spectrum of a galaxy is now used to determine its distance.

One galaxy, NGC 4473, at a distance of 16 million light-years, shows a red shift equivalent to a speed of recession of 1,400 miles per second. Another, a member of a cluster in Ursa Major, apparently at a distance of 170 million light-years, is receding at 9,600 miles per second. Still more distant is one in a cluster in Gemini, 270 million light-years away, and moving from us at a speed of 14,300 miles per second!

But even these records were surpassed in the summer of 1960. Rudolph Minkowski then announced to the American Astronomical

Society that he had photographed, with the 200-inch Hale Telescope, what seems to be a pair of colliding galaxies in the constellation of Boötes. With exposures up to nine hours, he even recorded the spectrum.

Here was no slight shift of the lines. Radiations ordinarily in the invisible ultraviolet registered in the middle green part of the spectrum, while the green itself was shifted into the infrared. This indicates a recession of some 90,000 miles per second—nearly half the velocity of light. And the distance corresponding to this speed is about six billion light-years or some 36 sextillion (3.6×10^{20}) miles!

It was radio astronomy that showed how to locate this remarkable object. About ten years earlier, its radiation had been picked up with a radio telescope at Cambridge University. Minkowski then tried to find it with the 200-inch, but the position was not sufficiently precise.

Then, newer and more accurate radio telescopes were built. From observations made at Cambridge, and also at Owens Valley, California, he was able to draw a close bead on this celestial broadcaster. So now it has set several new records; it is the most distant object ever photographed, and also the most rapidly moving, as shown by the great shift of its spectral lines.

What causes such red shifts? Are they truly the result of increasingly rapid recession—or does something happen to light as it travels over such tremendous distances, causing it to lose energy? If there were such an effect, it would be evident as a shift of the spectral lines toward the red. And, as the loss in energy would be proportionately greater the more distant the object, this might account for the observations. But the trouble is that physicists know of no way by which light can lose energy, merely because it has a long way to go.

On the other hand, it may really be a Doppler shift, due to actual recession. This has led to the expanding universe idea: that originally all the galaxies were close together in one huge cosmic atom, which exploded billions of years ago. Ever since, according to this theory, all the galaxies have been drawing farther and farther apart.

With the galaxies thus pulling away from our part of the universe, you might think that they didn't like us, that they wanted to get far away from us as quickly as possible. But actually, they are not receding from us any more than from any other galaxy.

Imagine a swarm of bees in a hive, closely packed together. Then imagine that the hive suddenly disappears, so that the swarm starts spreading out. The distance from any bee to any other would continually increase, and so it would seem to any insect that the others were all pulling away from him. But each of the others would similarly think that the first bee was pulling away from him.

The interpretation of the red shift is still a fundamental problem of cosmology, which is the study of the origin and development of the universe. In the next, and final, chapter, we shall consider some of the ideas as to how it all came about—and where it is going.

15

How It All Came About

While the discovery that we live in a limited galaxy of stars resolved Olbers' paradox—as far as the stars are concerned—it came up again with regard to the other galaxies. If they extended out, with no limit, it would not matter in what direction we looked; we would come to one eventually. Thus, even between the individual stars in our own Milky Way system, there would be distant galaxies to light up the sky.

Possibly the arrangement of the galaxies might be the explanation. If, instead of being distributed uniformly, they were arranged in groups as we know some of them to be, and if these in turn were parts of higher groups, Olbers' conclusion might not apply. But the final explanation came from the red shift.

This has been detected with the 200-inch telescope to some six billion light years. Moreover, it has also been found in the 21-cm. radiation picked up by radio telescopes. Distant radio sources, far beyond our galaxy, show exactly the same sort of shift of wave length. Thus, there seems no doubt that there is such a shift— apparently the result of actual expansion of the universe. This does not mean that the galaxies themselves are growing, for in such a system the gravitational attraction of the stars and other constituents holds it together. Rather it is the distances between galaxies that are getting larger.

As measured from the nearest galaxies, the speed of recession increases about 35 miles per second for every added million light-years of distance. At this rate, an object about 6 billion light-years away would recede at the speed of light itself. Consequently, one that far away—or farther—would be quite invisible, for its light couldn't reach us. No matter how powerful the telescope, it could only observe things in a sphere 6 billion light-years in radius, with our Galaxy at the center.

Astronomers, however, had suspected that the same ratio of increased speed with distance does not hold for the most remote objects. Instead, they thought, the distance would increase more for the same added speed when you reached out to several billion light years or more. Or, in other words, in the last billion years or so, the rate of recession has been diminishing.

This seems to be the case, and Minkowski's object in Boötes is believed to be about 6 billion light-years away, with an apparent speed of recession a little less than half that of light. Perhaps the velocity of light would be reached at something like 15 billion light-years. That would then be the limiting horizon of our observable universe, so this may be the answer to Olbers' paradox as it concerns the galaxies.

Of course, an observer in some far distant galaxy would also have a horizon 15 billion light-years from him. If he were 5 billion light-years away from us, he could see 5 billion light-years beyond our horizon, in his direction from us. He could view many galaxies that we cannot observe. But, on the other hand, in our direction from him, we could see equally far beyond his horizon and view galaxies invisible to him.

Tracing backward from the observed speeds of recession of the galaxies, we find that, some 5 billion years ago, they were all lumped together. As early as 1927, a Belgian mathematician and astronomer, the Canon Georges Lemaître, concluded, from his studies of Einstein's theory of relativity, that something of this sort might be happening. The work of Hubble and Humason seemed to confirm his theory.

OUT OF THE PRIMEVAL ATOM

The Belgian's idea was that, at the beginning, all the present material in the universe was compressed into an extremely hot and homogeneous "primeval atom," as he called it. This matter began to thin out as the universe expanded. At the same time it cooled off and was differentiated into the galaxies, stars, nebulae, and other parts of the universe we know at present.

When Hubble and Humason first announced their findings, it seemed that the expansion had begun less than 2 billion years ago. Yet geologists had measured the age of some ancient rocks (from the proportion of uranium that had been converted by radioactive processes into lead) and found them to be 3 billion years old! Since the universe could hardly contain rocks older than itself, something seemed wrong. This was cleared up, however, when Baade announced his revision of the galactic distance scale. Now the age is considered to be many billions of years, perhaps ten or more. No very precise figures are yet available.

But just what did happen 10 billion or so years ago? One idea, mainly due to George Gamow, professor of physics at the University of Colorado, is the "big bang theory." Before expansion started, he has suggested, there was another universe which collapsed and squeezed all its material together. The expansion that is now going on is the elastic rebound, which began when the stuff of the previous universe had been squeezed to the greatest possible extent.

The "big squeeze" left a mixture of neutrons, protons, and electrons. For this he revived the old word, *ylem*, which Webster defines as "the first substance from which the elements were supposed to be formed."

As the ylem expanded and cooled, there was a period of "nuclear cooking," lasting about an hour of our time, with conditions very similar to those of an exploding hydrogen bomb. Neutrons and protons began to stick together, forming the prototypes of the nuclei of our present-day atoms. Some hundreds of millions of years passed, and the stars were formed, condensed from turbulent whirls in great gas clouds. Some of the left-over materials around them formed planetary systems.

Not all astronomers agree with this theory of the evolutionary universe. Opposed to it are the advocates of the "steady-state universe," proposed by a group of British cosmologists, particularly Fred Hoyle, Hermann Bondi, and Thomas Gold. While Hoyle's approach is a mathematical one, based on the theory of relativity, that of the other two is built up from the *cosmological principle:* that, except for local irregularities, the universe as a whole looks the same from any place or at any time. Thus it has no beginning or end: it has always existed and always will exist.

IS CREATION STILL GOING ON?

To maintain such uniformity in space, along with the expansion, they assume that matter is continually being created; that it is a fundamental property of space that an occasional hydrogen atom shall appear—formed out of nothing—in the regions between the galaxies. This seems a radical proposal to many astronomers and physicists. It violates one of their most fundamental laws— that of the conservation of matter and energy. Matter can neither be created nor destroyed, they have long believed; it can only be changed in form. This includes changing matter into energy or energy into matter.

The rate at which hydrogen is created does not need to be very great; in fact, it is surprisingly small. As we have seen, the great volume of space between the stars of our own galaxy makes it possible for the exceedingly rarefied interstellar hydrogen to form a considerable fraction of the total mass. Similarly in intergalactic space. If, in a region the size of Grand Central Station, just one hydrogen atom were formed every thousand years, it would be enough to replace the loss of the galaxies that have departed. This would be roughly equivalent to an atom every hundred thousand years in an ordinary room—such as the one in which you may now be reading this. At such a slow rate, by human standards, it would be quite impossible to notice the creation of matter—certainly it would be far too small to affect any of our experimental data.

If hydrogen is thus being formed, it means that even intergalactic space is not completely empty. However, the concentration of hydrogen in those regions would be about a millionth of the amount found between the stars within a galaxy. There would be about one atom in a cube 40 inches on a side. At the proposed rate of creation, all existing matter would move out of any region of space—and be replaced by newly formed matter—every 2 billion years. Our own bodies provide a good analogy to what is happening in the universe, if the steady state theory is true. Our tissues are continually being broken down and replaced by new material so that today there are few—if any—of the same atoms that were in our bodies 20 years ago. Yet a person remains the same individual; he is recognized by his friends.

If we could detect intergalactic hydrogen, some valuable information might be secured, but this is most difficult. These hydrogen atoms, like those between the stars, would occasionally flip over and produce the 21-cm. radiation which proved so helpful in establishing the outlines of our own galaxy. But in outer space, its detection is far more difficult. Not only is the radiation far weaker, because the gas is so much more sparsely distributed, but there is also the effect of the motion and the result of the cosmic red shift.

At increasing distances, the shift would be greater and greater, just as it is with the spectra of light from the galaxies. Thus, the hydrogen emission would not produce a peak on the records as it does when it comes from the arms of our own galaxy, where each such cloud of gas is at roughly the same distance and moving with the same speed. The record of hydrogen from intergalactic space would be not a peak but a broad plateau, extending on the long-wave side of the 21-cm. position. And it would be so weak that it would be hard to detect. Nevertheless, with the building of new radio telescopes, far bigger and more sensitive than any now in use, success may come.

LOOKING BACKWARDS INTO TIME

Because light takes a perceptible time to travel, we never see anything as it is exactly now. If two persons are sitting in a room, chatting, it takes about a two-hundred-millionth of a second for the light from the face of one to reach the other. Such a brief period is not appreciable in our ordinary life, but in many branches of scientific work it would be important. The light from the Moon takes about a second and a half to reach us, still hardly enough time to make any perceptible difference in its appearance. And the same thing is true of the Sun, whose light takes a little over eight minutes to cross the 93 million-mile gap which separates us.

Sirius, the dog-star, which we see in the winter evening sky, sends us its light in 8.7 years, hardly an appreciable time in the development of a star. And even when we reach out to the Andromeda galaxy, some two and a half million light-years away, there is not a great deal of difference. If we could see the galaxy as it is now, instead of as it was when its light left, it would probably look much the same.

But the most distant galaxies that the 200-inch Hale telescope can reach are about 2 billion light-years away. And 2 billion years is about a third of the multi-billion year period since expansion of the universe supposedly began. Two billion years ago the galaxies were much nearer to each other than they are now, according to evolutionary reasoning. But, with the steady-state hypothesis, new matter appears just fast enough to replace old matter that is going

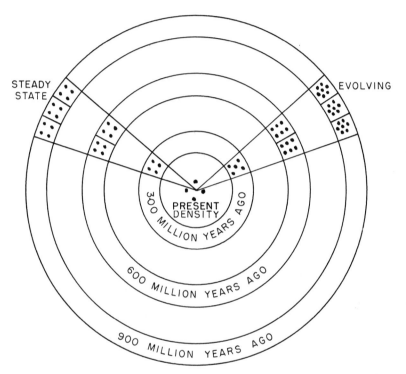

STEADY STATE

EVOLVING

PRESENT DENSITY

300 MILLION YEARS AGO

600 MILLION YEARS AGO

900 MILLION YEARS AGO

Fig. 51. The steady state *vs.* the evolutionary hypothesis. In a steady-state universe, with new material continually added, the density of clusters is the same throughout space (left). If it is evolving, the apparent density would increase with distance (right) as we observe an earlier stage. In this sector, the same volume of space that contains four clusters locally would show seven at a distance of 900 million light-years. (By permission from *The Universe.* Copyright, 1956, 1957, Scientific American, Inc., New York.)

out of sight; 2 billion years ago, then, the galaxies were no more concentrated than they are now. Thus, a good test of which idea is correct would be to measure the distribution of these very distant galaxies and compare them with the distribution of those nearer home; see Fig. 51.

While Minkowski did photograph the colliding galaxies in Boötes, 6 billion light-years away, 2 billion light-years represent the usual limit of the Hale telescope. The brightest galaxies at that distance are just barely seen. To determine their general distribution, they would have to be observed much more clearly, so that the fainter ones could also be counted. This would require a telescope that could reach still farther into space before it reached its horizon.

Radio astronomy may provide the means of doing this, since it can penetrate even farther into space, perhaps to the limits of the observable universe. New radio telescopes are being built, with reflecting dishes hundreds of feet in diameter. Even if they cannot pick up waves from intergalactic hydrogen, they may detect radiation from the distant galaxies themselves, especially if they are colliding. If the galaxies out there are closer together, they collide more often. If these very distant radio sources prove to be more numerous than those in a similar volume of space closer to home, it might be good evidence for the evolutionary hypothesis. But if they are not more numerous, the steady-state hypothesis will gain strong support.

MATTER AND ANTIMATTER

This book began with a discussion of the nature of the atom, and consideration of the possible formation of matter in space brings us back to it. What we consider an "ordinary" atom consists of a positively charged nucleus (of protons and neutrons) with negatively charged electrons moving around it. But physicists have identified electrons with positive charges, called *positrons*, as well as *antiprotons*, which are negatively charged protons. Antimatter, with antiprotons in the nuclei and positrons moving around them, would have exactly the same inertial and gravitational properties as ordinary matter.

Any creation process, it seems, should produce equal amounts of each kind. If matter and antimatter come into contact, there would be a tremendous explosion, as the opposite charges would neutralize each other, and the entire amount of matter of each kind would be converted into energy. Indeed, it has been suggested that some of the very energetic galactic collisions have been between galaxies of opposite compositions. Any one galaxy would have to be mainly of the same kind, although Fred Hoyle and another English astronomer, G. R. Burbidge, showed that one could sustain as much as one part in ten million of the opposite variety.

The formation and evolution of the universe is a big problem—indeed we could hardly have one any bigger! Much smaller, but of more immediate importance to us, is what happened in the universe to produce our own solar system. For centuries, philosophers and astronomers have considered this problem and arrived at various theories, none of which is now fully accepted.

In 1755, Immanuel Kant suggested that originally there was a disc-shaped nebula with a marked central condensation, slowly rotating. This idea was developed further by Pierre Simon Laplace, a French astronomer, who supposed that the nebula was originally very hot. As it cooled off it contracted, and rings of gas split off and later condensed to form the planets, along with their satellites. The central condensation developed into the Sun. Before spiral nebulae were recognized as external galaxies, some thought that these were solar systems in the process of formation. But this theory ran into serious objections, one being that the gaseous rings wouldn't condense, but would disperse out into space.

Then, around 1900, astronomers began to turn to the idea of a catastrophic origin of the solar system—that another star happened to pass close by our planetless Sun. By its gravitational attraction it pulled out, from the Sun, material that condensed to form planets. A modification of this theory had the other star actually hitting the Sun. But this too was discarded, as it was shown again that stuff so torn out of the Sun would not condense into planets. There were other serious objections as well.

About 1944, Carl F. von Weizsäcker, in Germany, proposed a new theory which has some resemblance to the Kant-Laplace nebular hypothesis, although it is founded on quite different considerations. According to him, after the birth of the Sun, formed out of gas clouds in the primitive galaxy, there developed around the Sun a local cloud of dust and gas with about a tenth the solar mass and with a diameter of about 10 billion miles, similar to that of the solar system today.

Such a cloud, von Weizsäcker showed, would tend to form into many turbulent units, and finally into vortices or whirlpools. Finally there would be rings of vortices of similar diameters, their distribution and size dependent on the original distribution of the gas and dust around the Sun.

With the vortices all turning in the same sense, either clockwise or counterclockwise, there would be great differences in velocity at the boundary between one ring and the next. Between these, von Weizsäcker assumed, secondary eddies would appear, like roller bearings between two turning wheels. The sense of rotation of these would be opposite to that of the big whirlpools.

PLANETS FROM ROLLER BEARINGS

It was in these roller bearings, according to this theory, that the planets were born. Condensation of gas into solid matter would start there; when enough had accumulated, it would have sufficient gravitational attraction to draw in more material and grow larger. Thus they would form the *protoplanets* from which our present planets later developed.

This theory does answer one of the fatal objections to the original nebular hypothesis, as well as to later theories, that of *angular momentum*. This effect is demonstrated by a spinning ice-skater. As she starts spinning, her arms are outstretched. Then she pulls her arms in close to her side, and she spins more rapidly.

In a spinning body, angular momentum, which is a product of the mass and the distance from the center around which it is rotating, tends to remain constant. With the skater, at the start of the spin, the arms are relatively far from the body, and the rotation is relatively slow. But when she pulls in her arms, the distance is reduced. Therefore, the speed of rotation increases, to maintain the same angular momentum. Then if she stretches her arms, the rotational speed goes down once more.

Jupiter, with its large mass and considerable distance from the Sun, has about two-thirds of the total angular momentum of the whole Solar System although it has only .1 per cent of the total mass. It would seem that the Sun, with the bulk of the mass, should also have most of the angular momentum. To do so, with its present size, it would have to rotate once in 12 hours instead of its actual period of 27 days. The theory of Kant and Laplace provides no mechanism by which it could have been transferred out to Jupiter.

But the theory of von Weizsäcker does. Friction between rings of vortices would tend to slow down the faster-moving inner parts, and to speed up the outer parts of the gas cloud, which had been moving more slowly. There would be a transfer of angular momentum outwards; Jupiter, as the largest planet, might well end up with most of it.

Gerard P. Kuiper, of the University of Chicago's Yerkes Observatory, developed von Weizsäcker's original ideas into a hypothesis that many astronomers look upon with considerable favor. This puts the formation of the planets and the Sun itself at about the same time. Out of original hydrogen (which may either have been formed at the time of the "big bang" or by later creation, as the steady-state theory would have it) would be constructed the great cloud of gas that was the embryo Galaxy. No doubt there would have been great turbulence, with many eddies and local compressions of the gas. But then gas pressure would cause most of these to expand again and dissipate. Once in a while, however, a condensation would be so large that its own gravitational attraction would hold it together. Under this pull the mass would start to contract. The process proposed by Helmholtz for the source of the Sun's energy would then come into play, so it would increase in temperature as it decreased in volume. It would begin to emit heat rays, and later visible light and ultraviolet. Eventually the interior would become so hot that the thermonuclear process would be switched on, and there would be a star much like those we see today. Some of the lighter elements would probably be formed from hydrogen earlier as the clouds formed and condensed, and many heavier atoms would be created in the hot interior of the star.

According to Kuiper, planets began to develop as the original huge cloud was beginning to warm up. In each planetary condensation, the heavier materials would be pulled to the center, leaving extensive atmospheres of lighter gases around them. Their masses would be many times that of the present planets. The Earth, at that stage, may have contained 1,000 times as much matter as it does today; proto-Jupiter perhaps 10 or 20 times its present mass, Saturn about 50, and Uranus and Neptune about 100 times the masses they have now.

As the Sun came to something like its present temperature, heated by the thermonuclear fires at its heart, it began to pour out radiant energy, whose radiation pressure blew away the hydrogen-helium atmospheres of the protoplanets. Mercury, Venus, Earth, and Mars, close to the Sun, lost practically all of their early layers of gas. The Earth's present atmosphere was formed later, from processes in the planet itself. Jupiter and the other giant planets were farther away, so radiation pressure was lower. This, combined with their greater mass—and great gravitational attraction—enabled them to hold on to much of their original atmospheres, which they still possess.

ORIGIN OF THE ASTEROIDS

According to this hypothesis, asteroids are not the remains of an exploded planet. It assumes that, at a distance of about three times that of Earth from the Sun, there was a region of lower density, insufficient for the formation of a full-scale protoplanet. A number of smaller planets, of the order of a few hundred miles in diameter, were formed instead. The four largest asteroids are now of such a size; they may have survived intact. Others, however, might have collided, and broken into bits, supplying the smaller asteroids as well as the meteorites that move through the solar system and occasionally land on Earth.

The larger protoplanets, it is presumed, themselves formed small-scale models of the solar nebula, and parts of these gas clouds became satellites by a mechanism similar to that by which the protoplanets themselves were made. Some of these satellites were probably retained until the present time, their originally highly elongated orbits becoming more and more circular through the ages. Others, perhaps, escaped their parents, to move for a time in their own orbits around the Sun or even to leave the Solar System entirely. But, eventually, the large planets might have recaptured some of these lost satellites as they happened to come near them again. These would hardly return to nice regular orbits like those which had remained at home. This theory would explain bodies like the four outer satellites of Jupiter, which move backward around the planet, in orbits of great eccentricity, and in planes very different from that of the four innermost satellites.

In the outermost reaches of the solar nebula, the density was too low for protoplanets to form and finally it became so cold that the gases—water vapor, ammonia, and methane—along with some of the gases forced out from the protoplanets by the Sun's pressure, formed frozen porous masses which became comets. This process, perhaps, created the cloud of comets which, Oort has suggested, surround the solar system out to great distances. Out there the comets would be permanent, and they would provide the reservoir from which one is occasionally drawn in toward the Sun, to begin a career which will end in its destruction after a relatively short time on the cosmic calendar. It would end, as we have seen, as a meteor swarm; thus we might explain the apparent differences between the meteors of a shower like the Perseids, and the stray meteors and meteorites that come in all the time.

Undoubtedly we are still far from the final answer to our question of how the solar system was formed. The theories of von Weizsäcker, Kuiper, and all the other astronomers who have contributed to this field, will be modified in many respects, perhaps even rejected entirely. But it does seem that we are getting closer to the truth than ever before.

One interesting point is that such theories make it seem much more likely that there are many other inhabitable worlds. For the process just described would not have taken place only with the nebula that formed the Sun. Other stars would have followed a similar process. We used to think that it took a collision, or at least a near approach, of one star to another to form a system of planets, and it seemed that such an event would be extremely rare. There is so much space between the stars, as we have pointed out several times, that there is plenty of room for stars to move about without even a near collision. There could be no more than a very few planetary systems in the entire Milky Way galaxy, according to such ideas.

But, on the modern view, it seems that planetary formation is not unusual in the development of a star. Many of the stars we see in the night sky may thus have planets revolving around them. And if they are so numerous, there is a good chance that many will have conditions suitable for life, and even life itself. Living organisms, and even intelligent creatures, may well exist in many systems.

But what of the future? Soon, it seems, man will get to other planets in our solar system; at a much later date, perhaps, he will even travel to other stars, and possibly visit planets revolving around them. But it seems most unlikely that, in any foreseeable time, any large number of the Earth's inhabitants will be able to migrate to other systems. If the Sun were to become a supernova, or even a nova of the ordinary kind, the human race would be doomed.

THE SUN'S LONG FUTURE

Fortunately for our species, and for even higher forms that may evolve from it, we seem to have a long future, unless we commit suicide in a succession of atomic wars. Subrahmanyan Chandrasekhar, Indian-born astrophysicist at the University of Chicago, has found that, in its normal evolution, a star with a helium core greater than 1.44 times the Sun's mass has to get rid of the excess material

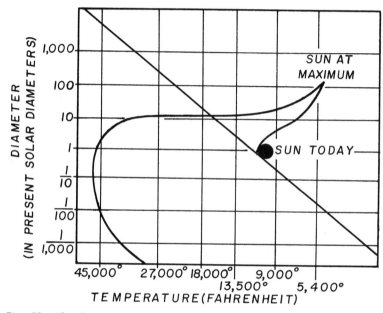

Fig. 52. The future of the Sun, according to Allan Sandage. First it will become larger and cooler; then it will become much smaller and considerably hotter than it is today.

before it can settle down as a stable white dwarf. Many prominent stars, even of those in the main sequence of the Hertzsprung-Russell diagram, where the Sun is also located, are more massive than the Sun. Vega, for example, has 3 times, and Sirius 2.4 times, the solar mass. Probably their helium content is above the Chandrasekhar limit, and they might turn into supernovae. But for the Sun that seems impossible.

Some indication of what the future evolution of the Sun may be is given by the researches of Allan R. Sandage and Harold L.

Johnson. The former is at the Mount Wilson and Palomar Observatories, the latter at Lowell Observatory, Flagstaff, Arizona.

They studied an open star cluster, Messier 67, in the constellation of Cancer. The several thousand members seem to be about the same age. Some are in the main sequence and even belong to the same spectral class as the Sun. But also there are red giants—and white dwarfs. Some are as massive as the Sun, some less, and some are heavier. Sandage thinks that the Sun's evolution can be foretold from his studies of these stars; see Fig. 52.

He concluded that we have another 5 billion years before anything drastic happens to the Sun. But then it will leave the main sequence, expanding to something like thirty times its present diameter. As it does so it will cool down to a surface temperature of about 6,000° F. But, with its larger area, it will radiate more and more heat to the Earth. Even with the Sun only four times its present diameter, the Earth's average temperature will be about 158° F., and that would be enough to end most forms of life. With continued solar expansion, it would rise finally to some 1,400° F.

But with the Sun at maximum diameter, it will rapidly burn up its hydrogen fuel and, when the supply is close to exhaustion, it will shrink again, crossing the main sequence as it gets hotter, and finally ending as a white dwarf at a temperature of 30,000° F. But it will be so small—less than a thousandth of what it is now —that it will radiate very little heat. The Earth by then will have cooled off to a frozen world.

In the 5 billion years before the Sun begins to change, man or his successors, if they have survived other perils, would seem to have ample time to find some means of adaptation to the coming conditions, perhaps even emigrating elsewhere in the universe. As Sandage has pointed out, it is most fortunate that the Sun didn't happen to reach a mass 10 per cent larger than it is. In that case, it would now be approaching the end of its life instead of being at its prime, in middle age!

Index